Basic Statistics

INTERNATIONAL HANDBOOKS OF QUANTITATIVE APPLICATIONS IN THE SOCIAL SCIENCES

Including selected volumes originally published as Quantitative Applications in the Social Sciences (QASS)—a Sage University Papers series

Series Editor: **Michael S. Lewis-Beck,** *University of Iowa*

Publisher
Sara Miller McCune, Sage Publications, Inc.

Acquisitions Editor: C. Deborah Laughton

Basic Statistics

Michael S. Lewis-Beck
editor

International Handbooks of Quantitative Applications
in the Social Sciences
Volume 1

SAGE Publications
Toppan Publishing

For information address:

SAGE Publications Ltd
6 Bonhill Street
London EC2A 4PU
United Kingdom

SAGE Publications, Inc.
2455 Teller Road
Thousand Oaks, California 91320
United States

SAGE Publications India Pvt. Ltd.
M-32 Market
Greater Kailash I
New Delhi 110 048 India

Printed in Singapore

British Library Cataloguing in Publication Data

Main entry under title:

Basic Statistics.—(International
Handbooks of Quantitative Applications in
the Social Sciences; Vol. 1)
I. Lewis-Beck, Michael S. II. Series
519.5

ISBN 0-8039-5427-1

93 94 95 96 97   10 9 8 7 6 5 4 3 2 1

Sage Production Editor: Astrid Virding

iv

CONTENTS

EDITOR'S INTRODUCTION

The inaugural volume of our **International Handbooks of Quantitative Applications in the Social Sciences** series begins, as it should, at the beginning. The five chapters here, each well-received publications in our long-established green monograph QASS series, provide the foundation in basic statistical concepts and methods that every quantitative social scientist must have.

I assume the modal reader comes to the volume with a professional interest in data analysis, but has had little, if any, serious experience. Arranged logically, the chapters move from simple univariate statistics to more complicated bivariate statistics. Their reading should be sequential, for an early chapter prepares the student for a later one. Although the topics are introductory, the presentation is neither simple-minded nor cookbook. The authors are recognized experts and, while aiming to make the material accessible to beginners, are mindful of technical nuances. At appropriate points, treatment becomes quite sophisticated, thereby offering valuable insight even to advanced researchers or teachers of statistical method. Below, to give a flavor of the research questions this material addresses, I work through an example.

Imagine that an educational sociologist, Professor Linda Blue, has the task of assessing schooling needs in the town of Riverview. According to local newspaper editorials, and certain conversations she has overheard in a coffee shop, the people of the town are poorly educated. But, as a social scientist, she realizes such spotty evidence may be inaccurate. Therefore, she designs a scientific survey, to be administered to a random sample of 500 of the town's 20,000 residents.

Among the survey items, one asks about years of schooling, and she uses responses to it to help answer the initial research question: Are the people of Riverview poorly educated? In the sample, *mean* years of schooling = 11.6, suggesting that the typical citizen is not, after all, poorly educated. But are no citizens poorly educated? In the sample, several respondents had less than 6 years of education. Indeed, the *standard deviation* of the education scores was 2.9 implying that, while a fair number are relatively highly educated, a fair number are not.

These elementary univariate statistics appear to tell a good deal about the educational attainment variable in Riverview. Moreover, the mean is the preferred measure of *central tendency,* the standard deviation the preferred measure of *spread,* because the variable is measured at the *interval level* (e.g., it is a meaningful count—years).

But suppose educational attainment had been measured at the *ordinal level* (e.g., a ranking from less to more). Let us say the variable ranked respondents in three categories, from "no high school" to "some high school" to "finished high school." Alternatively, suppose educational attainment were measured at the *nominal level* (e.g., simple presence or absence of an attribute). Let us say the variable simply placed respondents in one of three categories, according to the type of school they attended: "Catholic," "Protestant," "Secular." In either case, nominal or ordinal, summary statistics other than the mean and the standard deviation are preferred. Thus, level of measurement issues shape the choice of central tendency and spread measures, choices fully and clearly explicated in the first chapter, by Weisberg.

Another fundamental distinction concerns the *sample* and the *population.* Social researchers are seldom able, because of time, money, and other practical considerations, to study the whole population of interest. Hence, they draw *scientific probability samples,* such as a *simple random sample,* which permit *inferences* (accurate within known limits) to be made about the population. Suppose Professor Blue finds that, among the males in her random sample, mean years of education = 12.5, in contrast to a mean score for females = 10.9. These results support her *hypothesis*: males in the town have more schooling than females. However, she is dealing with a sample rather than the whole town population, and cannot be completely sure.

Possibly, the mean difference in the sample occurred by "luck of the draw," and would disappear if all males and females in the town were interviewed, something she cannot afford to do. Therefore, she conducts a *significance test*—in this case, a *difference-of-means test*—to see how likely it is that these mean differences in the sample occurred merely by chance. She finds the difference *statistically significant at .05*. Thus, she rejects the *null hypothesis* of no relationship between gender and education (and accepts that there are five chances in one hundred that this rejection is in error).

Generally, significance testing is a powerful tool of inference, providing the researcher with indispensable evidence in judging whether a relationship between two variables exists. The second chapter in this volume, by Mohr, carefully unfolds the overall logic and method of significance testing, concluding with an assessment of its functions. Reynolds, in the third chapter, specifically expands on significance testing for nominal data, through his explication of the *chi-square test*. He goes on to treat *measures of association* for nominal data, with particular attention to *lambda,* a proportional reduction in error measure. Lambda is perhaps the leading measure for assessing the strength of relationship between two nominal variables.

Ordinal measurement is a move up the precision ladder from nominal measurement. Ordinal social science variables, of which there are many, demand ordinal measures of association. Several varieties are explicated in the chapter by Hildebrand, Laing, and Rosenthal. Among them are Somer's *d*, gamma, tau, and Spearman's rho. These are just four options, but the choice of one over the other can spell differences in the substantive interpretation of results.

Suppose the following two ordinal variables from Professor Blue's survey: X_1 = satisfaction with own educational experience (scored 1 = not satisfied, 2 = fairly satisfied, 3 = very satisfied); and, X_2 = support for public spending on education (scored 1 = lower spending, 2 = keep spending at same level, 3 = increase spending). Her hypothesis—as X_1 increases, X_2 increases—receives support from a gamma = .56 and a tau-*b* = .34. Which is the preferred measure of association? While both are in common use, tau-*b* is generally preferred because it adjusts downward for *ties* (e.g., two cases that have the same X_1 score but a different X_2 score), but gamma does not. Hence, gamma will almost always inflate a relationship, making it appear "too big." (At least too big compared to tau-*b*, for both have a theoretical upper bound value of 1.0.)

The issue of ties in ordinal measures of association is carefully considered in the last chapter, by Liebetrau. Moreover, he provides a summary review of measures of association for all levels of data, including interval. With interval data, there is consensus on the preferred measure: *Pearson's product-moment correlation coefficient*, symbolized with the letter, *r.* Imagine Professor Blue finds that for two interval variables, income (measured in dollars) and schooling (measured in years), $r = .71$. Then, she could claim that there exists a strong linear bivariate relationship between schooling and income. Of course, the correlation, in itself, does not establish causation.

This volume gives budding social science researchers the basics they require. It speaks to fundamental questions. What is the level of measurement for the variable of interest? What is a typical value? Are the values spread out? What is its relationship to another variable? How best to describe that relationship? What to say about the association in the population? After the analyst has absorbed these chapters, the answers to these questions will tend to come easily, regardless of the data-set at hand. From that point, he or she can usefully go on to multivariate research. An appropriate start there would come from the exposition of regression analysis, in Volume 2 of the **International Handbooks**.

—Michael S. Lewis-Beck
Series Editor

PART I

CENTRAL TENDENCY AND VARIABILITY

HERBERT F. WEISBERG

1. INTRODUCTION

"Variety is the spice of life," or, as the French say, "vive la différence." Statisticians agree—the study of variety and differences is what statistics is about. The statistical term for this is *variation*. Indeed, statistics is sometimes called the "science of variation." The concept of variation emphasizes that an interesting variable is one that varies, such that not every observation has the same score for the variable.

If the French seem captivated by "la différence," Americans seem more fascinated with "the typical." We want to know what typical people do and think, perhaps so that we can be sure that we ourselves are not unusual in our actions and attitudes. Statisticians also focus on measuring what is typical. The statistical term for this is *central tendency*, or, more simply, *center*. Variation emphasizes differences, whereas center emphasizes the typical.

This monograph explains how to measure the center and variation on a single variable, as a prelude to being able to study more complex interrelationships between variables. Pairing center and variation together in these pages emphasizes that neither is sufficient in itself—it is necessary to understand both.

Measuring Center and Spread

There are actually several statistical questions that can be asked when analyzing a variable. The first is how the variable was measured. Variables can be measured with different numeric or nonnumeric properties, and this must be understood before statistical analysis is

AUTHOR'S NOTE: *I would like to thank William Jacoby, two anonymous reviewers, and Michael Lewis-Beck for their suggestions and comments on this monograph.*

1

begun. This concern is discussed in terms of *levels of measurement,* and is explained in Chapter 2.

The next statistical question about a variable is what kind of distribution its values have. The statistical summarization of a variable should include examining its distribution, especially graphically. Chapter 2 also shows some ways to examine distributions of variables.

The third statistical question about a variable is what a typical result is on it. That is what we shall call the *center* or *central tendency* of the variable. Averages are the most familiar example of central-tendency statistics. Measures of center also are termed *measures of location* or *representative values.* No single number can do justice to describing a variable on which different cases have different values, but a measure of center is a useful beginning point for summarizing variables. Chapter 3 explains several measures of center.

Thinking in terms of a typical value of a variable calls attention immediately to the fourth question: How typical is that typical value? That leads to measuring the *spread* of a variable in order to see how much the cases differ on the variable. This is also termed the *variation* on a variable, its *dispersion,* or its *scale.* Chapter 4 explains measures of spread.

A fifth question arises when a *sample* is studied but the researcher desires to describe a broader *population*: How do sample results generalize to the population? The applicability of the distinction between samples and populations to measuring center and spread will be presented in Chapter 5.

Once the amount of variation on a variable is measured, further statistical questions can be asked about it. Groups can be compared to find which vary most; variables can be compared to check how similar their values are; differences on a variable can be analyzed to see if they correspond to the differences on possible explanatory variables. Chapters 4 and 5 introduce these topics, showing ways in which the variation concept is used in practice.

Levels of measurement, distributions of variables, measures of center, and measures of spread are closely linked topics. A variable's level of measurement helps determine the appropriate ways of summarizing distributions and the appropriate measures of center and spread. Variation measures dispersion around the typical value of a variable, and generalizing from samples to populations is based on the variation of the variable. In these senses, Chapters 2 through 5 are tightly related.

The topics treated in this monograph are among the oldest in statistics. In addition to the classical ways of looking at them, there are also some newer ways. In particular, there has been a movement in applied statistics toward *exploratory data analysis*, usually abbreviated as EDA (Hartwig & Dearing, 1979). EDA emphasizes the virtue of becoming familiar with the data, rather than just computing one or two summary statistics. In part, the differences are stylistic; the EDA style has caught on with such new phrases as *measures of center* and *measures of spread*. Additionally, the EDA school has devised new measures of center and spread. This monograph introduces both the classical and EDA perspectives.

Evaluating Measures of Center and Spread

In looking at measures of center and spread, we will find that there are several alternative measures. What considerations affect this choice between possible measures? The first criterion is that the measure be

1. appropriate for the measurement level of the variable.

This criterion is explained further in Chapter 2. However, there are often several measures that can be used at the same level, so choices must be made among these measures.

Another way of asking this is to ask what makes a good descriptive statistic. Many desirable properties for summary statistics have been proposed over the years. Yule and Kendall (1968: 103-104) state that an average should be

2. "rigidly defined" rather than just approximated,
3. based on all the observations,
4. simple and comprehensible,
5. calculated with ease,
6. expressed in algebraic terms, and
7. robust (little affected by fluctuations between samples).

Although none of these are absolutes, they are useful criteria for choosing and evaluating measures of center and spread.

Six additional desirable properties of such statistics are that they be

8. unique, rather than multivalued;
9. generalizable to two or more variables;
10. resistant to outliers (not overly affected by extreme cases);
11. not overly affected by combining categories;
12. defined even when a variable has open-ended categories; and
13. equal to actual data values, or at least in their metric.

As measures are described in Chapters 3 and 4, mention will be made when a statistic excels on any of these criteria or is weak on a criterion. The distinction between populations and samples leads to three more formal criteria used to evaluate sample estimates: that they be

14. consistent for large samples,
15. unbiased for small samples, and
16. efficient when compared to other possible estimators.

These final criteria are too technical to consider until the end of this monograph.

No statistic is ideal on all 16 criteria, so it is necessary to decide which criteria are most important in actual data analysis situations. Furthermore, multiple measures often will prove useful for the same data, because each can be effective in portraying different aspects of the data.

2. LEVELS OF MEASUREMENT

A necessary beginning point in statistical analysis is to understand the measurement properties of the data (Jacoby, 1991: chap. 2; Weisberg, Krosnick, & Bowen, 1989: chap. 8). This is usually discussed in terms of each variable's *level of measurement*. Measurement itself can be defined as the process of assigning labels or values to observations. There are different types of assignment processes, resulting in variables with different mathematical properties.

Several levels of measurement are sometimes distinguished, but we shall find it useful to divide variables into three basic types: nominal, ordinal, and metric. Nominal variables consist of a series of unordered categories, as when categorizing a person's religion as Protestant, Catholic, Jewish, and so on. The variable is ordinal when there is an order to the categories, but no real unit of measurement. Metric variables are ones for which the categories are intrinsically numeric, like a person's age.[1]

We also shall distinguish a further measurement situation: dichotomous data. A dichotomous variable has only two categories, as when dealing with a person's gender. As we shall see, the usual level of measurement considerations do not apply fully for such variables.

The level of measurement of a variable is important because it limits the statistics that can appropriately be used on the variable. For example, values can be summed and averaged meaningfully only for strictly metric data. Nominal variables cannot be summed and averaged, and it is usually best not to sum and average ordinal variables. Similarly, the value of the middle case cannot be examined for nominal variables whose categories are unordered.

Metric analysis of ordinal variables should be precluded because they are nonnumeric. However, their ordered categories are presumed to reflect a continuous underlying concept, and that leads to a temptation to move ordinal variables up to the metric level. This tension will be returned to at several points in this monograph.

The level of measurement of a variable should be considered before performing statistical analysis on it, and even before collecting data. At the analysis stage, applying statistical techniques that require metric data to nominal variables would be fallacious. At the data-collection stage, metric versions of variables should be obtained, when possible, rather than nonmetric versions if metric-level analysis is planned. These implications can best be understood by explaining each basic level of measurement in greater detail.

Nominal Scales

The lowest level of measurement involves just categories, without order to these categories. Variables measured in this way are termed *nominal* variables. For example, the region of the country in which a person lives—either north, south, east, or west—is a nominal variable. These regions are just categories, with no particular order and no real numeric properties.

Numbers can be assigned to nominal variables, particularly to facilitate their analysis on the computer. Thus, regions might be coded as 1 for north, 2 for south, 3 for east, and 4 for west. However, these are just arbitrary numbers. We could as well code them 300 for north, 20 for south, 4,000 for east, and 1 for west, as there is no meaningful order to the categories.

Some nominal variables have numbered categories. If the numbers are assigned to label categories but the numerical order does not correspond to a property of the objects, then the variable is still nominal. Social security numbers are an example of numbers being used to label categories. There may be some system to how they are assigned, but they are not based on a single ordering principle. No one cares if their social security number is lower than another person's, because these numbers do not measure how much of an ordered property the objects have.[2]

As will be seen in Chapters 3 and 4, measures of center and spread have been developed for nominal variables based on the relative frequencies of observations in each category.

Before computing statistical summaries of variables, it is important to examine their distributions. One way to do so is to display the variable's *frequency distribution.* Each category is listed with its corresponding frequency—the number of observations falling into that category. The notation that will be used for the frequency of category k will be f_k. The total number of cases will be denoted as N. Note that the sum of the frequencies of each separate category should equal the total number of observations. The symbol Σ (the Greek letter *sigma*) is commonly used to represent a sum (with a subscript to show that the summation is over all possible different values of k—that is, over all categories). Using this notation (explained further in the appendix to this chapter),

$$N = \sum_k f_k.$$

Sometimes it is useful to show the proportion of cases falling into the particular category k. This proportion will be denoted as p_k. A proportion is the number of cases in the category divided by the total number of cases:

$$p_k = f_k/N.$$

Note that the proportions of the different categories on a variable will always add up to one. After all,

TABLE 2.1
Distribution of Crimes

Crime	Frequency	Percentage
Homicide	10,000	5
Rape	20,000	10
Robbery	40,000	20
Assault	60,000	30
Burglary	70,000	35
Major	30,000	15
Minor	40,000	20
Total	200,000	100

Mode:	Five Major Categories Burglary	Burglaries Subdivided Assault
Variation ratio	.650	.700
Index of diversity	.735	.795
Index of qualitative variation	.919	.954
Entropy	2.064	2.409
Standardized entropy	.889	.932

$$\sum_k p_k = \sum_k (f_k / N) = (1/N) \times \sum_k f_k = (1/N) \times N = 1.00.$$

Finally, the distribution on a variable can be represented by a *percentage distribution*, which shows the percentage of cases falling into each category. Percentages are just the proportions multiplied by 100. A percentage distribution should always sum to 100 percent.

As an example, consider the data in Table 2.1 showing the frequencies of different crimes in a city in which 200,000 crimes were reported in 1 year. The frequencies are shown in the second column and the corresponding percentages in the third column. According to these data, 35% of the crimes were burglaries, 30% assaults, 20% robberies, 10% rapes, and 5% homicides.

Frequency distributions can be portrayed effectively in graphs. The most common graph is the *bar chart*, as in Figure 2.1, section a. Each category is represented by a separate vertical bar whose height shows the category's frequency. A related diagram is a *pie chart*, as in Figure 2.1, section b. The unit circle is divided into a series of pieces standing for each category, with the size of a slice of the pie representing the proportion of cases falling into that category. Because the

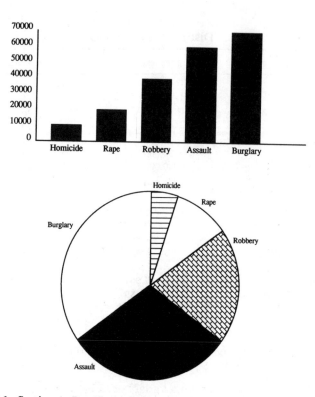

Figure 2.1. Section A. Bar Chart of Crime Reports
Section B. Pie Chart of Crime Reports

variable is nominal, the category order for these charts is arbitrary
and should not be overinterpreted.

Ordinal Scales

Some nonnumeric variables have an order to their categories. These
are called *ordinal variables*. For example, hospitals describe the condition of patients as "resting and comfortable," "stable," "guarded,"
or "critical." These categories are ordered but are not numeric. Note
especially that the intervals between these categories are not necessarily equal—there might be only a slight difference between describing the
patient's condition as "comfortable" versus "stable," in contrast to a

large difference between describing it as "guarded" versus "critical." Because the intervals between categories are not necessarily equal, this is only ordinal measurement.

Numbers are often assigned to ordinal data to facilitate storage and analysis on a computer, but that does not make them into true numeric data. The numbers assigned to ordinal variables can be termed *order numbers,* because only the order matters. As a result, adding them together or performing most other arithmetic operations on them would be inappropriate.

A common system for scoring ordinal variables is called *integer scoring:* the number 1 is assigned to the first category, the number 2 to the second, and so on. But even after integer scoring, the variable is ordinal because the categories are not necessarily equal steps apart on the continuum.

A prevalent type of ordinal data is ranked data. For example, it is customary to refer to the standings of sports teams in their league. These standings are numeric, like third or fourth in the league, but they are just order numbers. After all, the second-place team might have a winning percentage very close to that of the third-place team, but the third-place team might have a much higher winning percentage than the fourth-place team. Indeed, by examining the standings of the teams, we have converted numeric winning percentages into ordinal data.

Special measures of center and spread have been developed for ordinal data, and these will be presented in Chapters 3 and 4.

In dealing with ordinal data, it is important to understand the notion of a *percentile.* A percentile is a category of the variable below which a particular percentage of the observations fall. For example, the 50th percentile is the value below which 50% of the observations fall; the 25th percentile (also called the bottom *quartile*) is the value below which 25% of the observations fall; the 75th percentile (the top quartile) is the value below which 75% of the cases fall; and so on.

The distributions of ordinal variables are portrayed with the same type of frequency distributions and bar charts used for nominal variables.

Metric Scales

A metric variable is one that has a unit of measurement, such as dollars or inches. Typically, numeric variables answer questions of how much or how many. For example, the price of objects is a metric variable, because it is an answer to the question "how much do the objects cost?"

Actually, there are two major types of metric variables—ratio and interval variables. The highest level of measurement is the *ratio scale*. Ratio variables are numeric, with a defined unit of measurement and a real zero point. For example, length is a ratio variable. It is intrinsically numeric, there is a defined unit of measurement (such as the inch), and it has a real zero point (zero inches).

The zero point is essential here. Because there is a zero point, *ratio statements* can be made, such as the statement that one person is twice as tall as another person. If it makes sense to consider one value twice as large as another, then the variable is ratio. Multiplication of a ratio variable by a constant does not destroy its ratio character, but addition of a constant to a ratio variable does. (For example, if an older sister is exactly twice as tall as a younger brother and both grow two inches, the ratio of their heights is no longer 2:1.) As a result, ratio variables can legitimately be transformed by multiplication, but not by addition.

Other numeric variables have a defined unit of measurement but lack a real zero point. These are termed *interval-level variables,* as their most important characteristic is the equal intervals between successive values. The usual example of an interval variable is temperature as measured on a Fahrenheit scale. Temperature is intrinsically numeric and there is a defined unit of measurement (the degree), but the zero point is not real because zero Fahrenheit does not mean the absence of temperature. (Temperature also can be measured on a ratio scale—the Kelvin scale, which is based on an absolute zero.) Because zero degrees Fahrenheit does not mean the absence of temperature, a 20-degree temperature is not twice as hot as a 10-degree temperature. (Adult shoe sizes are another example of an interval-level measurement.)

The units are fully meaningful for interval scales. There are equal intervals between, say, 20 and 21 degrees Fahrenheit and between 10 and 11 degrees. The amount of the property being measured, here heat, differs in each case by the same amount, so the intervals are real. Multiplication of an interval variable by a constant does not destroy its interval character, nor does addition of a constant injure its interval characteristics; as a result, interval variables are said to be transformable by linear rules.[3]

A further complication for metric data involves *grouping*. If a variable is continuous, then its values can take on any fractional value, such as a daily high temperature of 85.3235 degrees. Rather than give overly precise values, it is common to group the results into *classes* or *intervals* when preparing statistical presentations and analyses, as when saying that a daily high temperature was in the 80s.

Grouping the data draws attention to the *limits* of each interval. Say, for example, the classes are stated as 70-79, 80-89, and so on. How is a value such as 79.7 handled under such grouping? The *true limits* of an interval show its exact lower and upper limits. Thus, if values above 0.5 are routinely rounded up, then the true limits of the 80-89 interval are 79.5 and 89.5, so 79.7 is part of this interval. Note that this interval has a *width* of 10, because its true limits are 10 units apart. Its *midpoint* is 84.5 (the sum of the lower true limit and the upper true limit divided by 2).

If the analyst instead rounded all fractional values down to the next lowest integer (as is usually done with human ages), then the true limits of the 70-79 interval would be 70.0 and 80.0, so 79.7 would be part of this interval. The interval width is still 10, but the midpoint is 75.0. Either rounding system can be used, so long as the true limits are determined properly.

Graphs are effective for displaying distributions for metric variables. One type of graph is the *histogram*, as shown in the display of daily high temperatures in Figure 2.2, section a. Areas over categories (rather than heights of bars) represent relative frequencies. The total area under the histogram is 1.0, so the proportion of the area over a range of values shows the proportion of cases falling into that range. A related form of display is the *frequency polygon*, which is obtained by connecting the frequencies of each category with a line, as shown in Figure 2.2, section b. It is smoother than the histogram.

A more modern type of display is the *stem-and-leaf plot* (shown in Figure 2.2, section c), which lists the actual data values while showing the distribution's shape. The first digit is given on the left of the line; the values on the right show the last digits that occur. The top row shows that 65° occurs twice; the next row that 70°, 72°, and 73° occur once each. The 70° range has been divided into two categories, with separate rows for 70°-74° and 75°-79° (the same for the 80° range). Note from Figure 2.2 that it is common to use grouping for histograms, frequency polygons, and stem-and-leaf plots of metric variables.

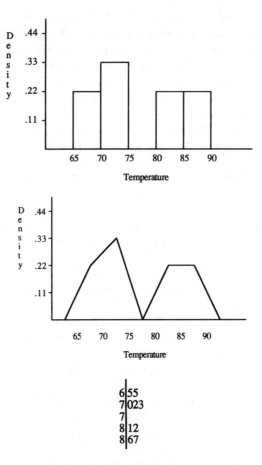

Figure 2.2. Section A. Histogram of Temperatures
Section B. Frequency Polygon of Temperatures
Section C. Stem-and-Leaf Plot of Temperatures

Dichotomous Variables

Many social science variables are binary, such as whether or not a nation goes to war and whether a rat turns left or right in a maze. The usual level of measurement distinction matters less for measuring the center and spread of such dichotomous variables than for other data.

The dichotomous variable can be thought of as nominal, just two un-ordered categories. Or, the variable can be thought of as two ends of an ordinal variable. For example, whether or not a nation goes to war in a sense measures an underlying ordinal variable about the nation's propensity to engage in war.

Dichotomous variables are also often treated as metric by assigning the value of 1 to one category (usually to mark the presence of some attribute) and 0 to the other category (to mark its absence). This is called *dummy-variable* scoring. As an example, whether or not the country went to war can be scored 1/0, 1 for the country going to war and 0 for it not going to war. This scoring may seem arbitrary, but there is no loss of generality.

The distribution for a dichotomous variable can be shown by giving the likelihood of a "success" for a single observation. This is the proportion of 1 scores (as opposed to 0 scores). This proportion, or probability, is f_1 (the frequency of 1s) divided by the total number of cases:

$$p = f_1/N = 1 - (f_0/N).$$

Categorization Rules

There are two constraints on categorizations that hold at every measurement level: A proper categorization should be *mutually exclusive* and *exhaustive*. Requiring categories to be mutually exclusive means that each case should fall into only one category. Requiring categories to be exhaustive means that each case should fit into some category; no case can be left out of the classification. A variable consisting of categories that are not mutually exclusive or exhaustive should be revised to make its categorization more consistent prior to statistical analysis.

Making a categorization exhaustive often requires including one or more categories to represent *missing data*. For example, when collecting data on the illness of people in hospital beds, some hospitals might not provide full information. Missing data categories are generally omitted from statistical analysis when they are irrelevant.[4]

Appendix: Summation Notation

In several places in the text it is necessary to examine summations of a series of values. The usual convention is to represent the separate values with a letter to denote the variable (such as X) and a subscript to show the case number: 1 for the first case, 2 for the second, and so on, up to N, where N is the total number of cases. The summation of the X values is denoted by using a capital Greek letter sigma (Σ). The full notation to represent the sum of all the Xs, from X_1 through X_N, is

$$\sum_{i=1}^{N} X_i = X_1 + X_2 + \ldots + X_N.$$

This is read as "the summation of X-sub-i, from i to 1 to N." It is often written in an abbreviated style as $\Sigma_i X_i$, or even more simply as ΣX.

Some rules about summations must be understood in order to follow the derivations in the text. For example, say that each value of X is multiplied separately by the same constant c (c could be the number 2 or any other number). Summing a series of numbers that have been multiplied by the same constant is the same as multiplying the sum of the numbers by that constant:

$$\sum cX_i = cX_1 + cX_2 + \ldots + cX_N = c(X_1 + X_2 + \ldots + X_N) = c \times \sum X_i.$$

The summation of a constant N times is the same as N times that constant:

$$\sum_{i=1}^{N} c = c + c + \ldots + c = N \times c.$$

Summing a series of numbers that have a constant subtracted from them is the same as subtracting N times that constant from the sum of the numbers:

$$\sum (X_i - c) = X_1 - c + X_2 - c + \ldots + X_N - c = \sum X_i - (N \times c).$$

In some proofs in the text, variables are multiplied by their means or the mean is subtracted from each value of the variable. In these equations, the mean can be treated as the constant following the rules above. Thus, summing the values of X multiplied by their mean, $\overline{X}$ (called "X-bar"), is the same as multiplying the sum of the original numbers by the mean:

$$\sum \overline{X}X_i = \overline{X}X_1 + \overline{X}X_2 + \ldots + \overline{X}X_N = \overline{X}(X_1 + X_2 + \ldots + X_N) = \overline{X}\sum X_i.$$

Similarly, summing the difference between the values of X and their mean is the same as subtracting N times the mean from the sum of the original numbers:

$$\sum (X_i - \overline{X}) = X_1 - \overline{X} + X_2 - \overline{X} + \ldots + X_N - \overline{X} = \sum X_i - (N \times \overline{X}).$$

It is also sometimes necessary to work with a sum of squared values. The sum of squares of the values of X is denoted as

$$\sum_{i=1}^{N} X_i^2 = X_1^2 + X_2^2 + \ldots + X_N^2.$$

This is not equivalent to squaring the sum of the variable X:

$$(\sum_{i=1}^{N} X_i)^2 = (X_1 + X_2 + \ldots + X_N)^2 = X_1^2 + 2X_1X_2 + X_2^2 + \ldots \neq \sum_{i=1}^{N} X_i^2.$$

3. MEASURES OF CENTER

Measures of center summarize the typical value of a variable. They are often thought of as averages, though the familiar average is not always the most appropriate way to summarize *center*. There are three major statistics that are used to gauge different aspects of what is typical for a variable: the *mode*, which must be used on nominal data; the *median*, which is appropriate for ordinal data; and the *mean*, which is used extensively on metric data. These three central-tendency measures will be presented in detail in this chapter, along with some other measures that are employed in specific measurement circumstances. The choice of the proper statistic for particular measurement situations will be emphasized, but it should be remembered that it can be useful to employ multiple measures to summarize different aspects of data.

Mode

The simplest summary of a variable is to indicate which category is the most common. The *mode* measures a variable's center by pointing to the most typical category.

The Mode for Nominal Data. If the data are strictly nominal, then the only possible measure of center is assessing which category occurs most often:

Mode = category occurring with greatest frequency.

The mode can also be determined for ordinal and metric data, but it is especially valuable for nominal data. Note that the mode is actually a category, not the frequency of that category.

As an example, say we are dealing with crime statistics during the past year for one city. If there were 10,000 reported cases of homicide, 20,000 rapes, 40,000 robberies, 60,000 assaults, and 70,000 burglaries (see Table 2.1), then burglary would be the mode because more reported crimes were burglaries than any other crime.

The mode is an important statistic for nominal data because it is impossible to take averages to measure the center of a nominal variable. The average crime cannot be determined in Table 2.1, for example, because the categories are not numeric. Even if numbers were assigned to the categories (like 1 for homicide, 2 for rape, 3 for robbery, 4 for assault, and 5 for burglary), finding an average crime of 3.80 would be meaningless because the numbers are arbitrary. Note too that it would not make sense to average the percentages in the categories. Averaging 5%, 10%, 20%, 30%, and 35% to get 20% as the rate of the average crime is not meaningful, because any distribution of cases across five categories would give an average rate of 20% of the cases per crime. Averages only work when the variable has a unit of measurement.

The mode is a measure of central tendency in the sense of showing what the typical category is on a variable. The "average" or the "typical" American is often described as Protestant because more U.S. residents are Protestant than any other single religion. This is a case of using the mode as the measure of center.

Another interpretation of the mode is that it provides the "best guess" as to the category a case has on the variable, *if* the goal is to be accurate as often as possible. That is, no other guess of a category for a random case would be correct as often as the mode is. Using the example in Table 2.1, say a person guessed what the crime was in a particular crime report. Because more burglaries were reported than any other crimes, the "best guess" is that a particular crime would be a burglary. That guess would not always be correct, but it would be correct 35% of the time, a higher success rate than would be achieved from any other guess.

The main advantage of the mode as a statistic is that it is easy to obtain and to interpret. Consequently, the mode is usually simple to communicate and explain to people.

There are four problems involved in dealing with the mode on non-numeric data. First, it may not be very descriptive of the data, because the most common category still may not occur very often. That burglary is the most common crime in a community says little, unless the prevalence of that crime also is indicated. By itself, the mode provides little information.

The second problem with the mode is that it may not be unique. For example, two categories may be equally likely and more common than any other category. A variable with such a distribution is termed *bimodal*. Indeed, several categories may be equally likely and may occur more often than any remaining category, in which case the variable is *multimodal*. In the most extreme case, if each category occurred with the same frequency, there would be no mode for the variable.

A third problem is that the mode can be overly affected by sampling variation. Imagine taking several samples and measuring a variable that has a bimodal distribution with population modes X_1 and X_2. Many samples would have X_1 as their mode, while many other samples would have X_2 as their mode. Thus, the mode would fluctuate considerably from sample to sample.

The fourth problem is that the mode is very sensitive to how categories are combined. The classification scheme should be at the same level of generality for all categories, rather than more general for some categories than others. The mode can, in fact, be manipulated by making the level of generality of different categories unequal. For example, Table 2.1 divides the 70,000 burglary cases into 40,000 cases of minor theft and 30,000 cases of major theft. Should these two categories be used instead of the one, the mode is no longer burglary. It is now assault because there are more assault cases than any other single category of crime. When reading a statistical analysis that reports a mode, always be sure to examine the categories to make sure that the modal category was not manipulated by using categories at different levels of generality.

These problems notwithstanding, the mode is commonly used to measure the center for nominal data because it fits exactly the assumptions appropriate for that level of measurement.

The Mode for Metric Data. Although the mode is particularly important for nominal data, the mode also can be used on other variables, even numeric data. Obtaining the mode for numeric data is just a matter of seeing which value occurs most frequently. If the variable is denoted as X, then

$$X_{mode} = X \text{ value occurring with greatest frequency.}$$

For example, Table 3.1, section a, reports hypothetical data on the number of wars in which seven nations have participated. In this case, the mode is 1 because that value occurs most often.

Occasionally confusion develops as to what the modal value is for metric data. For one thing, the mode is an actual value, not the frequency of occurrence. With the values in Table 3.1, the value of 1 occurs twice, but the mode is 1 rather than 2. Along the same line, the mode is not the largest value (50), it is the value that occurs most frequently: 1.

To shift to a real example, Table 3.2, section a, lists how often each American president from Hoover to Reagan was elected president. Section b displays the same data as a frequency distribution. The first column gives the number of times a president was elected, and the second column shows how many presidents during this time period were elected that number of times. The modal value for such a display is the category with the highest frequency in the frequency column. The most frequently occurring value occurs five times, and that corresponds to electing a president to office once, so the mode is 1.

The Mode for Grouped Metric Data. Grouping is a common strategy for dealing with numeric variables. Rather than listing every possible value for the variable separately, the variable is divided into a set of classes that cover a range of values. The mode then shows which class occurs most often:

$$\text{Mode} = \text{class occurring with greatest frequency.}$$

The example to be used in this section involves daily high temperatures (see Figure 2.2). The exact high temperatures (like 82°) could be recorded, or the data could be grouped by counting how many days had high temperatures in the 70s, in the 80s, and so on.

Some further complications arise when working with grouped metric data. For one thing, the mode is strongly affected by the number

TABLE 3.1
Twentieth-Century Wars (hypothetical data)

Section A. Number of Wars, by Nation		Section B. Frequency Distribution of Wars		
Nation	Number of Wars	Number of Wars	Frequency	Percentage
Algeria	1	1	2	28.6
Australia	2	2	1	14.3
England	3	3	1	14.3
Switzerland	50	4	1	14.3
Tanzania	1	9	1	14.3
Togo	9	50	1	14.3
Turkey	4			
Number of cases	7		7	100.1

Center		Spread	Population	Sample
Mode	1	Mean deviation	11.43	
Median	3	Variance	273.14	318.67
Mean	10	Standard deviation	16.53	17.85
		Coefficient of variation	1.65	1.78
Midextreme	25.5	Gini's mean difference	15.71	
Upper quartile	9 (6.5)*			
Bottom quartile	1 (2.5)	Range	49	
Midhinge	5 (4.5)	Interquartile range	8 (4)	
Trimean	4 (3.75)	Quartile deviation	4 (2)	
Biweight	8.03	Coefficient of quartile variation	.80 (.44)	
		MAD	2	
		AD	8.43	
		Coefficient of dispersion	2.81	
		Leik's D	.63	
		Variation ratio	.71	
		Index of diverstiy	.82	
		Index of qualitative variation	.98	
		Entropy	2.52	
		Standardized entropy	.98	

of class intervals and their sizes. Say we were dealing with high temperatures for a city, each rounded to a whole number (see Table 3.3). Consider, for example, the high temperatures 65°, 65°, 70°, 72°, 73°, 81°, 82°, 86°, and 87°. The mode of those separate temperatures is 65° (section a), but the mode is the 70°-74° range if they are grouped

20

TABLE 3.2
U.S. Presidents, 1928-1984

Section A			Section B		
President	# Times Elected		# Times Elected	Frequency	Percentage
Hoover	1		0	1	10
F. D. Roosevelt	4		1	5	50
Truman	1		2	3	30
Eisenhower	2		3	0	0
Kennedy	1		4	1	10
Johnson	1				
Nixon	2		Total	10	100
Ford	0				
Carter	1				
Reagan	2				
Number of cases:	10				

Center		Spread	Population	Sample
Mode	1	Mean deviation	.80	
Rough median	1	Variance	1.05	1.17
Exact median	1.3	Standard deviation	1.02	1.08
Mean	1.5	Coefficient of variation	.68	.72
		Gini's mean difference	1.13	
Midextreme	2			
Upper quartile	2	Range	4	
Bottom quartile	1	Interquartile range	1	
Midhinge	1.50	Quartile deviation	1	
Trimean	1.25	Coefficient of		
Biweight	1.505	quartile variation	.33	
		MAD	.50	
		AD	.70	
		Coefficient of dispersion	.70	
		Leik's D	.35	
		Variation ratio	.50	
		Index of diverstiy	.64	
		Index of qualitative		
		variation	.85	
		Entropy	1.68	
		Standardized entropy	.84	

into intervals of five degrees (section b), and the 80°-89° range if they are grouped into intervals of 10 degrees (section c). The mode can be very unsteady when data values are grouped together.

TABLE 3.3
Daily High Temperatures

Section A		Section B	
Temperature	Frequency	Temperature	Frequency
65°	2	65°-69°	2
70°	1	70°-74°	3
72°	1	75°-79°	0
73°	1	80°-84°	2
81°	1	85°-89°	2
82°	1		
86°	1	Number of cases	9
87°	1		
		Mode	70°-74°
Number of cases	9	Crude mode	72°
		Refined mode	70.75°
Mode	65°		

Section C	
Temperature	Frequency
65°-69°	2
70°-79°	3
80°-89°	4
Number of cases	9
Mode	80°-89°
Crude mode	84.5°
Refined mode	81.5°

When dealing with grouped numeric data, a distinction is made between the *crude mode* and the *refined mode*. The crude mode is just the midpoint of the interval of the most frequent category. That is,

Crude Mode = midpoint of most frequent interval.

Using the classes of width 10° in Table 3.3, section c, the most frequently occurring category is 80°-89°, so the crude mode would be 84.5°. By contrast, the refined mode adjusts the modal value according to the relative frequencies of the adjacent intervals. It pulls the modal value toward the adjacent interval that has the greater frequency. Let L be the true lower limit of the modal interval, let w be the width of the class interval, let f_{mo} be the frequency of the modal interval, let f_b be the frequency of the interval *below* the modal interval, and let f_a be the frequency of the interval *above* the modal interval. The formula for the refined mode is then

$$\text{Refined Mode} = L + \frac{w\,(f_{mo} - f_b)}{(f_{mo} - f_b) + (f_{mo} - f_a)}$$

In Table 3.3, section c, the width of the class interval is 10°, the modal interval is 80°-89°, the true lower limit of that interval is 79.5°, the frequency of the modal interval is 4, the frequency of the next lower interval (70°-79°) is 3, and the frequency of the next higher interval (90°-99°) is 0. Therefore, the refined mode is

$$79.5° + \frac{10° \times (4 - 3)}{(4 - 3) + (4 - 0)} = 79.5° + \frac{10°}{1 + 4} = 79.5° + \frac{10°}{5}$$

$$= 79.5° + 2° = 81.5°.$$

The refined mode is on the low side of the 80°-89° interval to reflect the fact that more days had temperatures just below that than just above it.

Median

When the categories of a variable are ordered, a measure of center should take that order into account. The *median* does so by finding the value of the variable corresponding to the middle case. It is a positional measure, showing the category for the central observation.

The Median for Ordinal Data. The usual way to summarize the typical value for an ordinal variable is to determine the category in which the "middle" observation falls:

Median = category of the middle case.

The median is a *location* or *positional* or *order* measure, in that it locates the position of the typical value along the variable's ordering. Remember that the median computed on ordinal data is not numeric because ordinal variables are not numeric.

As an example, say that seven people rated a company's service record, three rating its performance as "excellent," and one each rating it "very good," "good," "fair," and "poor." The middle person rated the company's service as "very good," so that is the median on this ordinal scale.

The median is important for ordinal data partly because of the limitations of other measures for such data. The mode can be obtained for ordinal data, but it does not take into account the category order, which is what makes the variable more than just a nominal classification. Furthermore, the mode can be unrepresentative for an ordinal variable. Say that three valedictorians in a graduating class share the top class rank because they all had perfect grade-point averages, and the remaining 97 students each fell in a separate category but with very low grade-point averages. The mode in this example would correspond to the valedictorians, even though they are extremely unrepresentative of the class as a whole.

At the same time, it would not be meaningful to take averages on ordinal data because category numbers are arbitrary. For example, say we asked people to rate the quality of service provided by a company, and used integer scoring to assign numbers to the categories (1 for excellent, 2 for very good, and so on). Finding that the average rating of the service delivery is 2.43 would not be very meaningful, because the units between the five verbal labels are not necessarily equal. Having issued that warning, it is necessary to admit that it is becoming more common to compute averages on ordinal variables. Many researchers are finding that a useful way to summarize their data, even if doing so increases the chances of drawing fallacious conclusions.

There are two main advantages of the median. First, it is relatively easy to obtain. Second, it is based on the whole distribution rather than just a small part of the distribution the way the mode is.

There are two complications to consider in dealing with the median. The first is that a category is middle only with respect to some ordering, so it is essential to think in terms of that ordering when determining the median. Decide what the underlying ordered property is, and then order the cases according to that property before computing the median. The categories *must* be properly ordered before determining the median. For example, say that seven people were asked to rate a company's service record, and the order in which the responses were recorded was "poor," "excellent," "excellent," "fair," "excellent," "very good," and "good." The middle rating is "fair," but that really is not the median category. The ratings should first be put into the proper evaluative order: excellent, excellent, excellent, very good,

good, fair, and poor. The middle rating of the company's service is "very good," so that is the median category.

The second complication involves determining the middle case. *Middle* is well defined when the number of cases is odd, but not when it is even. Imagine a small classroom in which there is a row with only three students in it. The middle student is clearly the second student—and that is the same student whether counting from the left to the right or counting from the right to the left. However, what if there are four students in the row? Who is the middle student? In a sense, the second and third students are together the middle. In another sense, there is no middle. The middle position is between the second and third students. The usual way of thinking about the median for an even number of cases is that it is halfway between the two middle cases.

There is a formula for determining which ordered case is the middle one. If there are N observations, then the middle case is the $(N + 1)/2$th case. That is

$$\text{Median} = \text{category of the } (N + 1)/2\text{th case.}$$

Thus, with three cases, N is 3, and the median is the category of the $(3 + 1)/2 = 4/2 = 2$nd case. With four cases, N is 4, and the median is the category of the $(4 + 1)/2 = 5/2 = 2.5$th case: halfway between the second and third cases.

The Median for Metric Data. Although the median is most important for ordinal data, it is also sometimes used for metric variables. For metric data, the median indicates the value of the variable (which we label X) for the middle case. As with ordinal data, it is essential that the variable be properly ordered before computing the median. If there are N ordered observations, then the middle is the $(N + 1)/2$th observation. So,

X_{median} = value of X for the $(N + 1)/2$th ordered case, for odd N,

and

= average of $N/2$th and $[(N/2) + 1]$th ordered case, for even N.

By the way, $(N + 1)/2$ is *not* the median for odd N; it is the *location* of the median in the ordered set of values.

As an example, we return to the numbers of wars in which different countries participated (Table 3.1, section a). With the countries listed in alphabetical order, the number of wars are 1, 2, 3, 50, 1, 9, and 4. This makes it seem like the middle value is 50, but it is not. The variable is the number of wars in which the country has fought, and the values must be put into the proper order (1, 1, 2, 3, 4, 9, and 50) before obtaining the median. When ordered properly, the median is seen to be 3 wars.

With numeric data for an even number of cases, the median is defined as halfway between the values for the two center cases. For example, say we had data on participation in wars for only four countries, and the number of wars they had been in were 1, 3, 4, and 50, respectively. Would the middle case be the second with 3 wars, or the third with 4 wars, or what? The median is 3.5, halfway between the 3 and the 4, even though no country could be in 3.5 wars.

There are two further advantages of the median for numeric data. First, it is not affected by extreme values on the variable. Some measures of center are considerably deflected by atypical extreme cases (like the 50 value in the above example), but the median is not. It nicely captures where the middle of the distribution is, and that is not affected by unusual "outliers." As a result, the median is considered a *resistant* statistic.

A second special advantage of the median is that it sometimes can be computed even when a distribution is open-ended at the extremes. Consider, for example, the problem of determining the typical age of death of various high school graduating classes. Say that one graduating class had only 5 graduates—one who died young at age 30, a second who lasted until age 67, a third who died at 80, and two more who are still alive and are both 87 years old. The median age of death for this graduating class is clearly 80, and that can be determined without waiting to see how long the two remaining members survive. Neither the mode nor the average can yet be determined in this example, only the median. Note also in this example that the median is not deflected by the outlier, the one person who died unusually young.

Because of these two special advantages, the median is sometimes useful even for metric data. The median should be considered as the measure of center when there are extreme outliers or when the process being observed is open-ended at an extreme.

The median actually has a special optimal property for metric data. Describing this property requires introducing a new concept: the *deviation* of an observation from the measure of center. Some notation is useful here. Label the variable being studied X. Then let X_i be the observation for the ith case. Let X_c be the measure of center. The deviation d_i for the ith case then is $d_i = X_i - X_c$. This deviation shows how much the ith observation's value on the variable differs from the measure of center. Next, define the *absolute deviation* as the unsigned magnitude of that deviation: $|d_i| = |X_i - X_c|$.

The special property of the median is that the sum of these absolute deviations around the median is minimal. In other words, the sum of absolute deviations computed from the median is smaller than the sum of absolute deviations computed from any other possible measure of center. That is, $\Sigma|d_i| = \Sigma|X_i - X_c|$ is minimized when X_c is the median (Blalock, 1972: 60).

As a result of this property, the median is the value that is closest to all the other scores on a variable. (An implication of this property is that the average absolute deviation is minimal when taken from the median, a result that will be used in the next chapter.) This special property gives the median a "best guess interpretation." The median is the best guess of a case's score *if* the goal is to minimize the absolute deviation; if the sign of the error in guessing does not matter but its magnitude does, then the median is the best guess as to a case's score on the variable.

The Median for Grouped Metric Data. A problem occurs with the median for grouped metric data in determining the middle case when there are several cases sharing that value. If the prices of five items at a hardware store were $2, $4, $4, $7, and $30, then is the first 4 or the second 4 the middle value? At first, that might seem like a senseless question, because 4 is 4 (is 4). But say that these prices have been rounded to the nearest dollar. In other words, $4 stands for a cost of $3.50 to $4.49. If the prices are $2, $4, $4, $7, and $30, then there is a real sense in which the middle case is the higher of the two $4 items. We do not know the exact values of the items, but we could assume that any value in that range ($3.50 to $4.49) is equally likely, so the higher item is likely to be closer to $4.49 than to $3.50. Another way of thinking about this is that we are wondering how "deep" into that category (or class) the middle value is. Because there are more cases above $4 than below $4, we have to go well into the $4 category to get to the middle case, so the middle value will be on the high side of $4.

In dealing with the median for such data, a distinction is made between the *rough median* and the *exact median*. The rough median is just the value corresponding to the middle case:

Rough Median = midpoint of class containing middle case.

The formula to obtain the exact median in this situation is

$$\text{Exact Median} = L + \frac{w\,(0.5N - C)}{f_{\text{median}}}$$

where L is the true lower limit of the class containing the 50th percentile, C is the cumulative frequency below the class containing the 50th percentile, f_{median} is the frequency of the class containing the 50th percentile, and w is the width of the interval containing the 50th percentile. This can be thought of as treating the cases in the median class as uniformly distributed through that interval. In the above example, the rough median is \$4, but the exact median is \$4.25. Usually the rough median of a set of numbers is all that is required, but sometimes the exact median is of interest.

Looking back at the earlier example of the numbers of times various presidents were elected to the office, if we looked at the 1928-1984 period (Table 3.2, section a), the values would be 1, 4, 1, 2, 1, 1, 2, 0, 1, and 2. Put in the proper order (section b), these values would read: 0, 1, 1, 1, 1, 1, 2, 2, 2, 4. The rough median would be 1, and the exact median would be 1.3. The exact median is on the high end of the 1 range (0.5 to 1.4999), because we have to go through most of the 1 cases to get up to the middle case.

Mean

Generally the most effective way of summarizing the center of metric data is to average the values on the variable. This statistic is known technically as the *mean*. It is a measure of the central tendency for variables that are fully numeric.

The Mean for Metric Data. The mode and median can be obtained for metric data, but they do not take full advantage of the numeric information inherent in the data. The mean fully considers that metric information.

The most common way to determine the typical value for a numeric variable is to compute the arithmetic average of its values. This is called the *mean* (or *arithmetic mean*) of the variable. To obtain the average, sum all the values and divide by the number of cases.

Although it is easy to calculate the mean from the above description, it is important to become familiar with the notation that will be used for other statistical calculations. The notation for the mean of a variable X is $\overline{X}$, called "X-bar." The formula for the mean is then

$$\overline{X} = \frac{\sum_{i=1}^{N} X_i}{N} = \frac{X_1 + X_2 + \ldots + X_N}{N}.$$

In this formula, the letter N stands for the number of cases. The letter i stands for the case number (the first case, the second case, etc.), and X_i is the ith case's value on the variable X. The Greek letter Σ (capital sigma) stands for "summation." As explained in the appendix to Chapter 2, the notation below and above the sigma is read as "the summation over i, from i equals 1 to N" and is a way of saying that we are summing all values of X_i. After obtaining the sum of the Xs, just divide by N to get the mean, $\overline{X}$.

As an example, Table 3.1, section a, gives hypothetical values for the numbers of wars in which seven nations participated in the 20th century. To obtain the mean of the numbers, first add the values together ($1 + 2 + 3 + 50 + 1 + 9 + 4 = 70$). Then divide by the number of cases (7 nations) to obtain the mean of 10 (= 70/7). Similarly, to obtain the mean number of times the presidents from Hoover to Reagan were elected (Table 3.2, section a), sum the separate numbers (which gives a sum of 15), and divide by the number of presidents (10); the resulting mean is 1.5 (= 15/10).

The mean has several properties that make it unique and useful. In presenting them, it is necessary to use the notation for deviations from the mean. If the mean for variable X is denoted as $\overline{X}$, then the deviation of observation *is* score on X from the mean is denoted as $d_i = X_i - \overline{X}$. This deviation shows how far off each value is from the mean.

The first property of importance for the mean is that *the total sum of deviations around the mean is always zero*. The proof is direct. Recall that $\Sigma X_i / N = \overline{X}$; multiplying both sides by N shows that $\Sigma X_i = N\overline{X}$. Also, adding the mean to itself N times is the same as multiplying it by N, so $\Sigma \overline{X} = N\overline{X}$. Thus

$$\sum (X_i - \overline{X}) = \sum X_i - \sum \overline{X} = N\overline{X} - \sum \overline{X} = N\overline{X} - N\overline{X} = 0.$$

The mean is unique in that sense: the sum total of deviations around any other value would be higher. That the sum of deviations around the mean is zero implies also that the average signed deviation around the mean is zero.

This property leads to an interpretation of the mean as a "best guess" statistic. Say we sought to guess the value of a particular score, such that the sum of the signed errors in guessing (or the average signed error in guessing) is minimized. Because the sum of the signed deviations from the mean is zero, the mean is the best guess of a score on the variable *if* the goal is to minimize the sum (or average) of signed errors.

The second important property of the mean is that *the sum of negative deviations from the mean exactly equals the sum of positive deviations*. This must be the case because the grand total of the deviations is zero, so negative deviations are balanced by positive deviations. This property leads to a special interpretation of the mean as a balance point (or fulcrum) for the distribution of values. It is a balance point in the sense that negative deviations are exactly balanced by positive deviations. To whatever extent some values are below the mean, they are offset by some other values that are equally above that mean.

The third property of the mean involves squared deviations: *The sum of the squared deviations around the mean is smaller than the sum of the squared deviations around any other value*. To prove this, consider the deviation of the observation X_i from an arbitrary value, X_0. The deviation, $X_i - X_0$, is not changed if the same value (say $\overline{X}$), is added to it and subtracted from it:

$$X_i - X_0 = (X_i - \overline{X}) + (\overline{X} - X_0).$$

Squaring both sides of this identity gives

$$(X_i - X_0)^2 = (X_i - \overline{X})^2 + 2(\overline{X} - X_0)(X_i - \overline{X}) + (\overline{X} - X_0)^2.$$

Next, sum both sides over the N observations to get the sum of squared deviations from the arbitrary value X_0, which is to be minimized:

$$\sum (X_i - X_0)^2 = \sum (X_i - \overline{X})^2 + \sum 2(\overline{X} - X_0)(X_i - \overline{X}) + \sum (\overline{X} - X_0)^2.$$

The three terms on the right-hand side of this equation must now each be examined separately. The first term is the sum of squared deviations from the mean. The second term is zero, because $\Sigma 2(\overline{X} - X_0)(X_i - \overline{X}) = 2(\overline{X} - X_0)\Sigma(X_i - \overline{X}) = 2(\overline{X} - X_0) \times 0 = 0$, because the sum of deviations from the mean is zero. The third term is just $N(\overline{X} - X_0)^2$ because $(\overline{X} - X_0)^2$ is a constant that is being added to itself N times. A squared term cannot be negative, so this third term is minimized when $X_0 = \overline{X}$, in which case the term equals zero. As a result, the sum of squared deviations around a fixed arbitrary value X_0 is minimized when that value is the mean, $\overline{X}$. As shall be seen in the next chapter, this *least-squares* property is important in measuring the spread of a metric variable.

In addition to the properties just described, there are two further advantages of the mean as a measure of center. First, it is more stable than other possible measures—over repeated samples, the mean would have less variation than would other measures of center. Second, other important statistics (especially variance and covariance) are based on deviations from the mean. These advantages will become more evident in later chapters.

Three problems with the mean should also be mentioned. First, it can have fractional values, even when the variable itself can sensibly take on only integer values. This problem is evident in Table 3.2, where the mean number of times these presidents were elected to office is 1.5, a value that cannot occur. This actually is a problem for how fractional values of the mean should be interpreted, rather than a limitation of the mean itself.

A second problem with the mean is that it cannot be computed when extreme categories of a variable are open-ended. For example, the mean income would be indeterminate if one category included incomes of $1 million or more.

A final problem with the mean is that it is strongly affected by extreme cases. Recall the earlier example (Table 3.1) involving the number of wars in which seven nations had participated. The mode was 1 and the median 3, but the mean was much larger: 10 wars. The mean here is much larger than the other central-tendency measures because the mean is affected by the 50 case, whereas the mode and median are not sensitive to it. The mode and median tend to be around where the bulk of the values are, but the mean can be drawn away toward the extreme case. Because the mean is affected by atypical outliers, it is considered *nonresistant* in contrast to more resistant measures of center such as the median.

The Mean for Grouped Metric Data. A special version of the mean formula can be used when the data are grouped. When several cases have the same value, the summation in the numerator can be simplified. Instead of summing the separate values, each value is multiplied by its frequency and these products are added together. This sum is then divided by the number of cases as before to get the mean. The grouped mean formula is

$$\overline{X} = \sum (X_i f_i)/N = \sum (X_i f_i)/\sum f_i,$$

where f_i is the frequency of category i.

As an example, consider again the data in Table 3.2 on the numbers of times the ten presidents from Hoover to Reagan were elected to office. We can summarize the data as one president being elected zero times, five being elected once, three being elected twice, and one being elected four times. The original computation of the mean added these values together, but it would be equivalent to multiply 1 times 0 (= 0), multiply 5 times 1 (= 5), multiply 3 times 2 (= 6), and multiply 1 times 4 (= 4), and then sum the products (0 + 5 + 6 + 4 = 15). Dividing by the number of cases, 10, gives the mean of 1.5. Thus the group mean formula gives the same result as the usual formula or the mean; it is just an easier formula when some values occur repeatedly.

When a continuous variable is grouped into classes of interval width greater than one, the mean formula can be used with a minor adjustment—the midpoint of the true class limits defined in Chapter 2 should be used to represent the class. For example, in dealing with daily temperatures, if the true class limits are 79.5° and 89.5°, then 84.5° should be used to represent the class in computing the mean. When possible, it is best to compute the mean and other statistics directly from the raw data rather than use the grouped formulas, though sometimes there is no choice, as when calculating statistics based on published data tables in which variables have already been grouped.

A closely related measure is a *weighted mean.* In most data collection situations, each element is sampled with equal probability. However, sometimes there is intentional oversampling of parts of a population. For example, say the goal of a study is to compare death rates from a particular illness in southern and northern hospitals, and say that 20% of the hospitals in the United States are in the south versus 80% in the north. If resources permitted studying a total of 100 hospitals, equal-probability sampling would lead to selecting about 20 hospitals in the south. That would be too small a sample for reliable inferences about death rates in southern hospitals. In this situation, the researcher might choose to double-sample southern hospitals, so 40 are selected rather than 20. Choosing 40 hospitals in the south and 60 in the north would ensure enough coverage of both areas to permit calculating statistics for each region. Separate means for southern and northern hospitals would be computed using the usual mean formula. However, southern hospitals are being oversampled, so a special "weighted" formula is needed for computing the national mean.

The formula for the weighted mean is

$$\overline{X} = \sum (X_i w_i) / \sum w_i,$$

where w_i represents the weight of the ith observation. The weights compensate for the higher chances for selecting some observations than others. The weight for the ith observation would be

$$w_i = p_i N / f_i,$$

where f_i is the frequency of category i in the sample and p_i is the known population proportion in that category. If a sample includes 40 hospitals in the south, then southern hospitals were double-sampled (40 rather than 20), and so each hospital should be weighted by the factor of .50 (= .20 × 100/40). Northern hospitals were correspondingly undersampled (60 instead of 80), so they should be weighted by a factor of 1.33 (= .80 × 100/60).

Many public opinion surveys purposely oversample particular parts of the population and then use a "weight variable" to compensate. For example, the 1964 American National Election Study double-sampled blacks in order to have more interviews to describe attitudes of African-Americans. The data file for that study includes the weights (the w_i) needed for computing overall means and other statistics.

Another common weighting situation occurs when there are several samples with separate means for each, but a *pooled* mean is of interest. The samples may not be of equal size, so calculating the overall mean requires weighting each separate mean by the number of cases on which it is based. For example, say a variable is measured for each of 3 years, with 1,000 people being in the sample for the first year, 800 for the next year, and 500 for the third year. Because the number of cases for each year is different, it would be inappropriate to add up

TABLE 3.4
Pooled Mean Calculation

Year	Sample Size (N)	Mean ($\overline{X}$)	Sum of $X = N\overline{X}$	Variance
2001	1,000	1.3	1,300.00	.25
2002	800	1.1	880.00	.36
2003	500	0.9	450.00	.16
Total	2,300		2,630	

Mean of means = $(1.3 + 1.1 + 0.9)/3$ = 1.100
Pooled mean = $[(1.3 \times 1,000) + (1.1 \times 800) + (0.9 \times 500)]/2,300 = 2,630/2,300$ = 1.143
Pooled variance = $[(999 \times 0.25) + (799 \times 0.36) + (499 \times 0.16)]/2,297$ = 0.269

the separate yearly means and divide by the number of years. Instead, a combined mean should reflect the unequal numbers of cases underlying each mean, giving greater weight to the years with more people studied. For a pooled mean, use the following formula:

$$\overline{X} = \sum (N_j \overline{X}_j)/\sum N_j,$$

where $\overline{X}_j$ is the mean for sample j, and N_j is the number of cases in sample j. An example of the calculation of a pooled mean is given in Table 3.4.

The Mean for Dichotomous Data. Should dichotomous data be summarized by modes, medians, or means? The answer is that each can be used. The mode shows which of the two categories occurs more often, as does the rough median. The mean has a more special interpretation.

Score the dichotomous variable as 1 for one category (called a *success*) and 0 for the other category. The mean then shows the proportion of cases that fall in the "1" category. If the proportion of cases with the score of 1 is denoted as p, then the mean of the dichotomous variable is

$$\overline{X} = p.$$

To see this, use the mean formula for grouped data. The number of observations with a score of 1 would be pN, and the remaining $N - pN$ observations would have a score of 0. The mean is then

TABLE 3.5
Church Attendance Distribution

Attendance	Code	Frequency	Proportion
Attended	1	30	.15 = p
Did not attend	0	170	.85 = 1 - p
Total		200	1.00
Mean	.15 = [(30 × 1) + (170 × 0)]/200		= p
Variance	.1275 = .15 × .85		= p(1 - p)
Standard deviation	.3571		

$$\bar{X} = \{[1 \times (pN)] + [0 \times (N - pN)]\}/N = [(pN) + 0]/N = pN/N = p.$$

Take, for example, church attendance—whether or not a person went to church during the past week. Say that only 15% of the public went to church (see Table 3.5). The modal category is "not going to church." Likewise, the median person did not go to church. If the variable is scored as 1 for "attended" and 0 for "did not attend," the mean would be .15, showing that 15% of the people attended. The 1/0 scoring of the dichotomous variable (known as creating a *dummy variable*) leads to a mean with an intuitive interpretation—the proportion of cases that fall in the category scored 1.

Discussion

Comparisons of Mean, Median, and Mode. Table 3.6 summarizes several of the properties of the mode, median, and mean that have been discussed in this chapter. The chart also rates these measures according to the various criteria for summary statistics that were presented in Chapter 1. Some of the conclusions in Table 3.6 are debatable, but it still gives a useful beginning point. Further technical properties of these measures will be presented at the end of Chapter 5.

The choice among the three classic measures of center depends mainly on two considerations: the distribution of the values on the variable, and the level of measurement.

First, there are different possible shapes of distributions for metric variables. One of these is the symmetric unimodal distribution as in

TABLE 3.6
Properties of Measures of Center

	Mode	Median	Mean
Level of measurement	nominal or higher	ordinal or higher	metric (usually)
Rigidly defined	yes	yes	yes
Based on all cases	minimally	yes	best
Simple to understand	yes	yes	yes
Easy to calculate	best	yes	yes
Algebraic	no	no	yes
Stable under sampling	no	yes	best
Single valued	not always	yes	best
Resistant to outliers	yes	yes	no
Generalize to two-variable statistics	no	no	yes
Insensitive to combining categories	no	yes	yes
Computed for open-ended variables	indeterminate	yes	indeterminate
Equal to actual data values	yes	for odd N	not always
Interpretation:	most typical value	middle value	average value
Bad guess interpretation:	highest % accuracy	closest to all scores	minimize sum of signed deviations

Figure 3.1, section a. In this instance, the mode, the median, and the mean are all at the center of the distribution. Because the mode, median, and mean are all equal for a symmetric unimodal distribution, the choice among them would not matter.

A contrasting case is a *skewed* distribution, as in section b. Here small values predominate, but there are some atypical large values. This is called *positive skew* because the tail of the distribution goes off to the right. The mode is the value that occurs most frequently. The middle case is higher, so the median is larger. Also, the average is affected by the outliers, so the mean is larger yet. Thus, the mode is smallest, the median second, and the mean largest for positive skewed distributions. By contrast, a distribution with a *negative skew* (section c) has mostly large values, with some atypical small values; the mode is largest, the median second, and the mean smallest. The median is often used to summarize skewed numeric data because the mean can be strongly affected by outliers.[5]

36

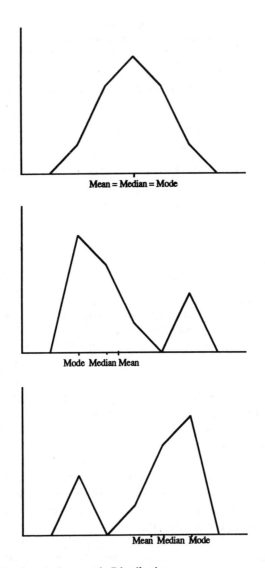

Figure 3.1. Section A. Symmetric Distribution
Section B. Positively Skewed Distribution
Section C. Negatively Skewed Distribution

There was a strong positive skew in our example involving the numbers of wars in which different nations fought (Table 3.1) because of the outlier nation that had been in 50 wars. The values of the measures of center follow the pattern for positively skewed variables: the mode is 1, the median is 3, and the mean is 10. The median value is more typical of the distribution as a whole that the mean is. The median is generally much nearer the mean than to the mode (Yule & Kendall, 1968: 117), although this example shows that that rule does not always hold.

Besides the shape of the distribution of values, the level of measurement must be considered in choosing which of these measures of center to use. The simplest rule is to use the mode for nominal data, the median for ordinal data, and the mean for metric data. Additionally, a lower-level statistic can be safely used for higher-level data, as in using the mode for ordinal data and the median for metric data.

There is actually considerable controversy over using numeric-based statistics, like means, on ordinal data. The strict level of measurement rule is that means should never be computed on ordinal data, but such analysis has become common. Those researchers willing to take the mean of an ordinal variable argue that there are latent continuous variables (albeit with error at the manifest level) underlying ordinal variables (Borgatta & Bohrnstedt, 1980), and that integer scoring of ordinal variables (assigning the score of 1 to the first category, 2 to the second, and so on) usually yields statistical results that would be fairly close to what would be obtained for the true unknown numbered categories (Labovitz, 1970). By contrast, statistical purists argue that there is a chance of making a serious statistical fallacy, because results based on integer scoring could be very different from those based on the true underlying scoring (Grether, 1976). This controversy is unlikely to be resolved anytime soon (Mayer, 1971). In the meantime, it is best to stick close to the level of measurement of the data as a first step and acknowledge directly when violating that level.

In looking at variables, do not feel that it is always necessary to select a single measure of center. The different measures provide different pieces of information, and sometimes it is useful to look at these multiple aspects of the data. Thus, in the war example used throughout this chapter, the median might be the best choice if just one measure were to be reported, but the mode and mean also give relevant information. Multiple measures are shown below the tables in this monograph so readers can compare the results provided by each.

There are some additional measures of center, but they are used less frequently, so some readers might want to skip forward to the next chapter.

Mathematical Properties of Measures of Center. The mean, median, and mode on metric data can be transformed by a linear rule: Adding a constant k to every value on the variable increases the center by that amount k, and multiplying every value by a constant m multiplies the center by m. Mathematically,

$$\text{Center } (k + mX_i) = k + [m \times \text{Center}(X_i)].$$

As an example, if a variable X is measured on a scale of 0 to 100, with 50 as neutral point, and if the researcher wanted to convert the variable to a scale of -100 to $+100$, with 0 as neutral point, the conversion rule would be $2X - 100$, with the mean score being translated as $2\overline{X} - 100$.

Other Order-Based Measures of Center

The interest in exploratory data analysis has led to the development of several new order-based measures of center. In line with the philosophy behind exploratory data analysis, these measures are useful in providing an understanding of the center of the variable. They tend to be particularly resistant to the influence of extreme values. That is, their values are not thrown far off because of outliers.

Some of these measures require prior calculation of the quartile values. Recall that the bottom quartile (Q_1) is where the 25th percentile hits, and the top quartile (Q_3) is where the 75th percentile hits. There are actually two different ways of locating quartiles. One (Tukey, 1977) is that the bottom quartile corresponds to the $(N + 1)/4$th case and the top to the $3(N + 1)/4$th case. These are easy formulas to use, but they often yield quartiles that are between data values. For example, with six cases, the first quartile would be the $1\frac{3}{4}$th case, three quarters of the way up from the bottom case toward the second case. The other way of locating the quartiles (Velleman & Hoaglin, 1981) is to say that they are the medians of the cases up to and including the median. For six cases, the median is between the third and fourth cases, so according to this definition the first quartile is the middle of the first three cases (i.e., case 2) and the third quartile is the middle of the highest three cases (i.e., case 5). The first definitional system is used in the examples in this book.

One set of EDA-based measures involves averages of percentile values. The *midextreme* or *midrange* is the average of the smallest and largest values:

$$\text{Midextreme} = (X_{\text{minimum}} + X_{\text{maximum}})/2.$$

Returning to the war example in Table 3.1, section a, the largest value is 50 and the smallest is 1, so the midextreme is 25.5 wars. The *midhinge* is the average of the bottom and top quartiles:

$$\text{Midhinge} = (Q_1 + Q_3)/2.$$

In this example, the bottom quartile value is 1 and the top quartile value is 9, so the midhinge is their average, 5 wars. More generally, the average of the scores of the bottom *x*th percentile and the top *x*th percentile gives a *midsummary*. The midextreme, midhinge, and other midsummaries can be used as measures of center.

Comparing these different midsummary statistics (Velleman and Hoaglin, 1981) gives an indication of the degree of symmetry of the distribution. In a symmetric distribution, the midextreme, midhinge, median, and all the other midsummaries would be equal. If the variable is skewed with some unusually high cases, the midextreme would be higher than the midhinge, which would be higher than the median (as in the war example). If the variable is skewed with some unusually low cases, this ordering would be reversed.

Another EDA-based measure of center is known as the *trimean* (Tukey, 1977: 46) or *best easy systematic (BES) estimate*. It is a combination of the median and the quartile values, weighting the median more heavily than the quartiles. The formula or the trimean is:

$$\text{Trimean} = [Q_1 + (2X_{\text{median}}) + Q_3]/4.$$

In the war example, the first quartile is 1, the median is 3, and the top quartile is 9, so the trimean equals 4. The trimean is actually the average of the median and the midhinge defined above. An advantage of the trimean as a measure of center is that it combines the median's emphasis on center values with the midhinge's attention to the extremes.

Some computer programs produce one further EDA-based central-tendency statistic, the *biweight* or *bisquare weight*. Its formula (Velleman, 1989: 77) is too complicated to calculate by hand. Mosteller and Tukey (1977: 206-207, 352-356) report the biweight has a low variance from sample to sample, is resistant to the effects of extreme values (as is the median), and is responsive to changes in the middle of its range (as is the mean). It may be useful for exploring data distributions, but it is very nonintuitive.

Other Means

The regular mean discussed above (known technically as the *arithmetic mean*) is the most commonly used average, but there are some other "averages" that are used to avoid the effects of outliers or to handle particular types of ratio-level data.

Trimmed Means. Two ways around the sensitivity of the mean to extreme cases are to *trim* or *winsorize* the outliers from the data before computing the mean. Trimming the data involves removing the most extreme values entirely, as is done in Olympic diving competitions when the top and bottom scores given by the panel of judges to a dive are tossed out before the mean evaluation of the dive is computed. Winsorizing the data instead involves changing the most extreme values to equal the next less extreme values. As examples, the *5% trimmed mean* drops the highest 5% and lowest 5% of the observations before computing the mean, whereas the *5% winsorized mean* with 20 observations changes the highest value (the highest 5%) to the second highest value and changes the lowest value (the lowest 5%) to the second lowest. These are ad hoc solutions, but they are often effective in improving the resistance of the mean.[6] To express these statistics mathematically requires first sorting the variable so that its values are in order from smallest (X_1) to largest (X_N). Then the j/Nth trimmed mean, $T(j)$, is

$$T(j/N) = \frac{1}{N-2j} \sum_{i=j+1}^{N-j} X_i,$$

and the j/Nth winsorized mean, $W(j)$, is

$$W(j/N) = \frac{1}{N} \left(jX_{j+1} + \sum_{i=j+1}^{N-j} X_i + jX_{N-j} \right).$$

One trimmed mean has been proposed as an alternative statistic to the mean. The *midmean* is the average of the central half of the observations. If the observations have been sorted into numerical order, then the formula for the midmean is

$$\text{Midmean} = \frac{2}{N} \sum_{i=N/4}^{3N/4} X_i.$$

This statistic is much more resistant to extreme values than is the mean, though some statisticians would feel that it ignores the extreme cases too much. Rosenberger and Gasko (1983) examined the properties of several trimmed measures, finding the midmean has the most desirable properties.

Geometric Mean. Special means are sometimes used for ratio data. The *geometric mean* is used to summarize a variable when relative change is being measured. Whereas the arithmetic mean adds the different values on the variable before dividing by the number of cases, the geometric mean multiplies together the different values and then takes the root corresponding to the number of cases. The formula for the geometric mean (GM) is

$$\text{GM} = \left(\prod_{i=1}^{N} X_i \right)^{\frac{1}{N}}$$

where the capital pi stands for multiplying the X_i values together. For example, consider the numbers 2 and 8. Their arithmetic average is 5. Their geometric mean is 4, obtained by multiplying the two numbers together (2 times 8 is 16) and then taking the second root of that product (the square root of 16 is 4). If three numbers were being multiplied together, the cube root of their product would be taken, and so on.

The geometric mean is useful when the values of a variable increase exponentially over time. That is often the case for the growth of amounts of money. Say the budget for a public agency doubled one year and increased eightfold the next year (see Table 3.7). Over the two years, its budget would have increased by a factor of 16, as

TABLE 3.7
Means for Growth Rates

Year	Section A. Agency Budget Growth Budget	Growth Rate
2000	$100,000	
2001	$200,000	2
2002	$1,600,000	8
Arithmetic mean		5 = (2 + 8)/2
Geometric mean		4 = sqrt (2 × 8)

Year	Section B. Effects of 5% Annual Growth Rate Budget	Growth Rate
2000	$100,000	
2001	$500,000	5
2002	$2,500,000	5

Year	Section C. Effects of 4% Annual Growth Rate Budget	Growth Rate
2000	$100,000	
2001	$400,000	4
2002	$1,600,000	4

shown in section a. But what is the average annual growth rate for that agency? The arithmetic average would obtain the wrong answer. The arithmetic mean of 2 and 8 is 5, but if the agency's budget had increased by a multiple of 5 two years in a row, its budget would have increased by a factor of 25 (section b), not the observed factor of 16. The geometric mean of 2 and 8 is 4, and indeed the agency experienced the same growth as if its budget had quadrupled both years (section c). The geometric mean properly captures the average growth rate over the two years, whereas the arithmetic mean does not measure any aspect of the budget process.

An alternate way of computing the geometric mean involves using logarithms. Recall that the logarithm of a product is the sum of the logarithms, and that the log of the Nth root of X is $(1/N)\log X$. Therefore, the geometric mean can be obtained by taking the logarithms of all the values, computing the arithmetic average of the logarithms, and then taking the antilogarithm of the result. That is,

$$\log(GM) = \text{Average } [\log(X_i)],$$

so

$$GM = \exp\{\text{Average } [\log(X_i)]\},$$

where "average" is meant as the arithmetic average.

The logarithmic version of the equation implies that the geometric mean weights values extra the closer they are to 1. Values much greater than 1 (and very small fractions) have less effect on the geometric mean than values near 1, which is why the geometric mean of 4 is closer to the value of 2 than to 8 in the example above.[7]

Harmonic Mean. Another average for numeric data is the *harmonic mean*, which is used when averaging rates. Whereas the arithmetic mean takes the average of the values of a variable, the harmonic mean (HM) is based on the reciprocals of the values. It is the reciprocal of the mean of reciprocals:

$$HM = \frac{1}{\frac{1}{N}\sum_{i-1}^{N}\frac{1}{X_i}} = \frac{N}{\sum \frac{1}{X_i}}.$$

The harmonic mean is used mainly to average different rates. Say that in the year 2000 it takes 3 months for Chicago to reach 150 murders, a rate of 50 murders per month. Say that same year it takes Detroit 5 months to reach 150 murders, a rate of 30 murders a month. What is the average murder rate for the two cities combined? It might appear that 40 murders per month is the answer, but that is not the case. All in all, the two cities experienced 300 murders in 8 months, which is an average rate of 37.5 murders per month (see Table 3.8). How can this be the case? Detroit took longer getting to 150 murders at a slower rate, and the longer time at the slower rate pulls down the average rate. To compute this as a harmonic mean, use

$$1/\{[(1/\text{rate}_1) + (1/\text{rate}_2)]/2\} = 1/\{[(1/30) + (1/50)]/2\}$$
$$= 1/\{[(8/150)]/2\} = 1/(4/150) = 150/4 = 37.5.$$

The formula for the harmonic mean also can be represented as taking the reciprocals of each value, computing the arithmetic average of those reciprocals, and then taking the reciprocal of the result. That is,

TABLE 3.8
Murder Rates in Two Cities

City	Murders	Time (# of months)	Rate (per month)
Chicago	150	3	50
Detroit	150	5	30
Total	300	8	
Arithmetic mean		40 = (50 + 30)/2	
Harmonic mean		37.5 = 2/[(1/50) + (1/30)]	

$$\text{reciprocal (HM)} = \text{Average [reciprocal } (X_i)],$$

so

$$\text{HM} = \text{reciprocal \{Average [reciprocal } (X_i)]\}}.$$

The harmonic mean gives greatest weight to smaller values, because the reciprocal of a smaller number is larger than the reciprocal of a larger number. This effect is evident in the above examples, where the harmonic mean is closer to the smaller rates (30) than to the larger rates (50).

A basic result is that the geometric mean is always between the values of the harmonic and arithmetic means: $\text{HM} \le \text{GM} \le \overline{X}$.

Generalized Mean. The alternative formulas given above for the geometric and harmonic mean suggest a more general formulation of a mean. Let T represent a transformation (such as taking a logarithm, or a reciprocal, or a square) and let M denote a *generalized mean.* Then,

$$T(M) = \text{Average } [T(X_i)].$$

Define T^{-1} as the inverse of transformation T—the transformation that undoes the original transformation—so that $T^{-1}[T(X)] = X$. As an example, a square root is the inverse of a square operation. The generalized mean M can then be expressed as

$$M = T^{-1} \{\text{Average } [T(X_i)]\}.$$

The geometric mean is one special case of this formulation, where T is the logarithmic transformation and the inverse T^{-1} of the logarithm is the antilog (also called exponentiation) transformation. The harmonic mean is another special case, where T is the reciprocal and the inverse T^{-1} of the reciprocal is again a reciprocal transformation—because $1/(1/X) = X$. The arithmetic mean also fits this formulation, where T is the identity transformation [$T(X) = X$] and T^{-1} is also the identity transformation.

The generalized mean formulation suggests that the algebraic, geometric, and harmonic means are just three of a larger set of possible means. As a final example of this general formulation, consider the *quadratic mean* (QM), also known as the *root mean square*. Let the transformation T be squaring a value, so the inverse T^{-1} of that transformation is the square-root transformation. Then,

$$\text{square (QM)} = \text{Average [square}(X_i)],$$

so

$$QM = \sqrt{\text{Average [square}(X_i)]} = \sqrt{\text{Average }[(X_i)^2]} .$$

The quadratic mean gives more weight to values with greater magnitudes—large positive and large negative numbers. It will be employed in the discussion of measures of spread for metric variables in Chapter 4.

The geometric mean, harmonic mean, and quadratic mean cannot be transformed by a linear transformation in the way that the mean, median, and mode can. Actually, these three generalized means are transformed appropriately by a multiplier [$\text{Center}(mX_i) = m \times \text{Center}(X_i)$] but not by a constant added to each value [$\text{Center}(k + X_i) \neq k + \text{Center}(X_i)$]. This shows that these means are appropriate only for ratio-level data and not interval data.

Summary. Several different measures of center can be used on numeric data. The most common is the mean, with the median being used when there is an outlier and when the variable is unbounded at an extreme. Special averages are appropriate for dealing with relative growth and with rates. EDA-based measures also are useful for dealing with outliers.

4. MEASURES OF SPREAD

Central tendency is just one property of interest in summarizing the distribution of a variable. Not only do we want to find the typical value for a variable, but we want to know how typical that value is. This concern moves us along to consider the spread of the variable.

The most important measures of spread have been developed for numeric data—the closely related *variance* and *standard deviation* statistics. Other measures have been developed for dealing with dispersion at the lower levels of measurement by adapting the concept of variation.

Measures of spread increase in value with greater variation on the variable. They all equal zero when there is no dispersion. Maximum variation for metric and ordinal variables is defined as occurring when the cases are evenly split between two extreme categories—*polarization*. Maximum dispersion for nominal variables is defined either as when there is an even distribution of cases across the categories regardless of the number of categories (*uniformity*) or when each category occurs just once (*individuality*). Examples of these definitions will be given in this chapter.

Another complexity in dealing with spread measures is their abstract quality. It is not intuitively clear, for example, what meaning to give to a spread of 10. As a result, it is common to norm spread values. One norming procedure is to divide the obtained spread value by the maximum possible spread for the statistic, so a value of 1 represents maximal spread. Another norming procedure, used in the coefficient of variation and other statistics, is to divide the spread by the corresponding central-tendency value; this sometimes is described as yielding an *absolute* measure of dispersion (Yule & Kendall, 1968: 143) because the variable's unit of measurement is removed. Norming procedures will be used several times below.

Standard Deviation
and Other Deviation-Based Measures of Spread

The major measures of spread for metric data are based on deviations from the mean value. Metric data have a unit of measurement, so a deviation shows by how many units the observation differs from the mean:

$$d_i = X_i - \overline{X}.$$

For example, if the mean number of prior convictions of a set of criminal defendants is 4, then the deviation for a defendant with 20 previous convictions is 16 (= 20 - 4), and the deviation for a defendant without any prior convictions is -4 (= 0 - 4). Several spread measures have been devised to summarize the size of these deviations by averaging them—averaging either the raw deviations, absolute deviations, or squared deviations. Each of these possibilities will be described below. The major measures of spread for metric data are the closely related variance and standard deviation statistics,[8] but it is useful to discuss the mean deviation first.

Mean Deviation and Variants. A simple measure of dispersion would seem to be the average deviation from the mean:

$$\sum (X_i - \overline{X})/N = \sum d_i/N.$$

Recall, however, from the discussion of the properties of the mean in Chapter 3 that the sum of the deviations around the mean is always zero. As a result, the average of the deviations from the mean would equal zero for any variable. For example, Table 4.1 shows the numbers of prior convictions of 10 prisoners. If eight defendants had 0 prior convictions and two had 20, the average number of prior convictions is 4. The sum of deviations is $8 \times (-4) + 2 \times (16) = -32 + 32 = 0$, so the average deviation around the mean is zero (see Table 4.1, column 3). Because it is always zero by definition, the average deviation around the mean cannot indicate which distribution of values has greater spread.

Deviations from the mean would yield a more useful measure of dispersion if instead we averaged the absolute values of the deviations from the mean. This is called the *mean deviation* or *average deviation*. The formula is

$$MD = \sum |X_i - \overline{X}|/N = \sum |d_i|/N.$$

The mean deviation has a minimum of R/N and a maximum of $R/2$, where R is the range of the data (the largest value minus the smallest one).

In the criminal example (see Table 4.1), if eight defendants had no previous convictions and the other two had 20 each, the sum of absolute deviations would be 64 (4 for each of eight defendants, plus 16 each for two more defendants), and the mean deviation would then be

TABLE 4.1
Deviation-Based Measures of Spread

Defendant	# of Prior Convictions	Deviation	Absolute Deviation	Squared Deviation	Squared Value
Defendant A	0	−4	4	16	0
Defendant B	0	−4	4	16	0
Defendant C	0	−4	4	16	0
Defendant D	0	−4	4	16	0
Defendant E	0	−4	4	16	0
Defendant F	0	−4	4	16	0
Defendant G	0	−4	4	16	0
Defendant H	0	−4	4	16	0
Defendant I	20	16	16	256	400
Defendant J	20	16	16	256	400
Sum	40	0	64	640	800
Mean	4	0	6.4	64 = variance	
				8 = standard deviation	

Mean = 40/10-4
Variance = $[800-(40^2/10)]/10-[800-160]/10-640/10-64$
Standard deviation = $\sqrt{(64)} = 8$
Coefficient of variation = 8/4 = 2
Gini's mean difference = 320/45 = 7.11

Median = 0
Mean deviation = 64/10 = 6.4
Average absolute deviation from the median = 40/10 = 4
MAD = 0

6.4. That value captures the notion of measuring the typical dispersion well.

The mean deviation is a plausible measure of dispersion. It shows how far off the data values are, on average, from the mean value, when signs of deviations are ignored. However, the mean deviation is not used often. For one thing, dealing with absolute values turns out not to lead to useful generalizations when we move into statistics for more than one variable. For another, the mean deviation around the mean does not have any special statistical uniqueness properties; recall from Chapter 3 that the average absolute deviation is actually minimal when the deviations are taken from the median rather than from the mean. The mean deviation would be an intuitively appealing statistic, but it lacks attractive mathematical properties.

The Variance and Standard Deviation of a Population. A better way of working with deviations from the mean is to square them. Whereas taking absolute values leads to awkward algebraic manipulations when we generalize past one variable, squaring leads to useful statistical properties. As a result, the usual way of measuring spread for metric variables involves squaring the deviations from the mean and averaging these squared deviations. This is termed the *variance* of the variable. (Actually, this definition is for the variance parameter for the full population; estimating the variance statistic on the basis of a smaller sample from that population requires slight modification of this formulation as will be shown in the next section.)

The population variance is the average squared deviation from the mean:

$$\sigma^2 = \sum (X_i - \mu)^2/N = \sum d_i^2/N,$$

where the Greek letter σ^2 (sigma squared) is used to represent the population variance and the Greek letter μ (mu) is used to represent the population mean.

The variance statistic is unusual in an important sense—the squaring operation means that the variance is not in the original units of measurement. For example, if we were measuring the gross domestic products of countries in dollars, the variance would be in squared dollars. We can return to the original unit of measurement by taking the square root of the variance. The resulting statistic, termed the *standard deviation*, is a very common measure of spread. The formula for the population standard deviation is

$$\sigma = \sqrt{\sum (X_i - \mu)^2/N} = \sqrt{\sum d_i^2/N}\ .$$

As an example, consider again the previous convictions of criminal defendants as shown in Table 4.1. The mean number of convictions is 4. The first eight defendants had 4 convictions less than the mean, leading to squared deviations of 16. The last two defendants had 16 convictions more than the mean, leading to squared deviations of 256. The squared deviations sum to $(8 \times 16) + (2 \times 256) = 128 + 512 = 640$. The average squared deviation is then $640/10 = 64$, which is the variance (see Table 4.1). Because that variance is in the unusual unit of "squared convictions," we would take its square root to obtain a standard deviation of 8 convictions.

Although the above formulas for variance and standard deviation in terms of deviations from the mean are easy to follow conceptually, they are difficult to employ when doing hand calculations. For example, it would be painful to calculate squared deviations from a mean of 2.634. Fortunately, there are computational formulas for the variance and standard deviation that are easier to employ. Three equivalent computational formulas for the population variance are

$$\sigma^2 = [\sum (X_i^2) - (1/N) (\sum X)^2]/N$$

$$= [\sum (X_i^2) - N(\overline{X})^2]/N$$

$$= \sum (X_i^2)/N - \overline{X}^2,$$

and the computational formulas for the standard deviation are the square roots of those formulas.

The computational formulas involve summing squared data values, which is not the same as squaring the sum of the data values. For example, say the data values are 1 and 2; their sum is 3, so the squared sum of the data values is 9. However, the squares of the data values are 1 and 4, which adds to 5, and that is the sum of squared data values used before the minus sign in the computational formulas. Scientific calculators can compute sums of X and X^2 with fewer operations than required if deviations from the mean were used.

The computational version can easily be shown to be equivalent to the definitional formula. First, expand the squared deviation:

$$(X_i - \overline{X})^2 = X_i^2 - 2\overline{X}X_i + \overline{X}^2.$$

The variance then can be represented as

$$\sigma^2 = \sum (X_i - \overline{X})^2/N = \sum (X_i^2 - 2\overline{X}X_i + \overline{X}^2)/N$$

$$= \sum X_i^2/N - 2\sum \overline{X}X_i/N + \sum \overline{X}^2/N.$$

Since $\overline{X}$ is a constant, it can be moved before the summation sign, so

$$\sigma^2 = \sum X_i^2/N - 2\overline{X} \sum X_i/N + N\overline{X}^2/N.$$

Notice that the formula for the mean appears in the middle term, permitting simplification of that term; also the last term can be simplified. This gives

TABLE 4.2
Housing Price Data for Three Cities (in dollars)

	City A	City B	City C
	96,000	45,000	45,000
	101,000	83,000	47,000
	105,000	100,000	43,000
	99,000	117,000	155,000
	101,000	150,000	154,000
	98,000	105,000	156,000
Mean	100,000	100,000	100,000
Variance	8,000,000	1,021,333,333	3,026,666,667
Standard deviation	2,828.43	31,958.31	55,015.15
Coefficient of variation	.03	.32	.55

$$\sigma^2 = \sum X_i^2/N - 2\overline{X}^2 + \overline{X}^2 = \sum X_i^2/N - \overline{X}^2.$$

Returning to the criminal defendants example with eight defendants having no convictions and two having 20 convictions, the variance calculation would entail summing the square of 0 eight times (which leads to a partial sum of 0) and summing the square of 20 twice (2 × 400 = 800) to get a sum of squares of 800. Next, sum the actual values (40), square that sum (40^2 = 1,600), and divide that by the number of cases (10) to get 160. To calculate the variance, subtract the latter (160) from the sum of squares (800) to obtain 640, and divide by the number of cases (10) to get 64. The standard deviation is, of course, still the square root of the variance, or 8 convictions.

The standard deviation is increased by outliers. Thus, in the above example, the standard deviation of 8 is larger than the mean deviation of 6.4, because squaring deviations increases the impact of the large deviations caused by outliers. This lack of resistance to outliers could be seen as a problem with the standard-deviation measure, but the advantage of working with squares rather than absolute values more than compensates, so the standard deviation is the usual measure of spread.

As another example, Table 4.2 shows hypothetical prices for houses sold in three cities during the past week, along with the means and variances for each city. These cities have the same mean housing price, but the variances differ. The house prices in city A show very little dispersion; there is greater dispersion in city B; city C seems sharply split between expensive housing and inexpensive housing. This example also shows why it is useful to summarize a distribution in terms of its spread as well as its center: These three cities have identical centers, but their different spreads call attention to differences in the distributions of prices in these cities.

Several further interpretations can be given to the variance and standard deviation. First, the standard deviation is often interpreted as a *root mean square deviation*. Recall the discussion of the quadratic mean in the previous chapter—it is the square root of the average squared values. The standard deviation is similar, except that it squares the deviations from the mean rather than raw data values. The standard deviation is the square root of the average squared deviations, so it is a quadratic mean of the deviations, also known as the root mean square deviation.

A second interpretation of the variance and standard deviation is based on what is termed a *least-squares* logic (Blalock, 1972: 59). One property of the mean mentioned in Chapter 3 was that the sum of squared deviations around it is minimal. We can restate that as a property of the variance: *The variance calculated around the mean is smaller than the average squared deviation around any other value.* This minimization is a special property of the variance. Recall that the average deviation around the mean is not minimal; the only dispersion statistics calculated off the mean that are minimal are the variance and standard deviation.

A third interpretation of the variance and standard deviation involves another possible measure of spread—the average squared difference between all pairs of observations:

$$\sum (X_i - X_j)^2 \Big/ \binom{N}{2}$$

where the binomial coefficient in the denominator reduces to $N(N - 1)/2$. It can be shown (Hays, 1963: 180) that this average squared difference equals $2\sigma^2 N/(N - 1)$; therefore, *the variance is proportional to the average squared difference between all pairs of observations.* The more that pairs of cases are unequal in their scores, the higher the variance and standard deviation of the set of scores. Indeed, if we took the average squared difference between all pairs of observations, including the observation with itself (Yule & Kendall, 1968: 147), we would have $\Sigma(X_i - X_j)^2/N^2 = 2\sigma^2$. Thus the standard deviation is proportional to the root mean square of all the possible pairs of differences:

$$\sigma = (1/\sqrt{2N}) \times \sqrt{\sum (X_i - X_j)^2/N} \ .$$

That leads to the question of when the variance and standard deviation are maximal. According to the result just obtained, they are maximal when the average squared difference between all pairs of observations is maximal. That turns out to be when the data are polarized, with half the observations at the maximum and the other half at the minimum, because the squared deviations from the mean are then maximal. Say there are an even number (N) of observations, exactly $N/2$ of these observations equal X_{max} and the other $N/2$ observations equal X_{min}. The deviations $(X_{max} - \overline{X}) = d = (\overline{X} - X_{min})$, so the sum of squared deviations from the mean is Nd^2. The population variance is d^2 and the standard deviation would be d. For example, a variable that could range from 0 to 100 would have its maximum variance if its mean were 50, half the cases were 0, and the other half 100. Its variance would be 2,500 and its standard deviation would be 50. More generally, if we let R represent the range of the variable ($R = X_{max} - X_{min}$), then the maximum variance is $(R/2)^2$ and the maximum standard deviation is $R/2$.

A further property of the variance should be mentioned here: Variances are additive under one special circumstance. *If two variables are strictly independent of one another, then the variance of their sum equals the sum of their variances.* If, for example, one variance is labeled A and the other is labeled B, then the variance of their sum is

$$\sigma^2_{A+B} = \sigma^2_A + \sigma^2_B$$

if A and B are independent of one another. This rule is important because it sometimes permits the decomposition of the variance of a variable X into separate parts that are due to independent elements, as will be discussed below. Note, incidentally, that this rule for variances does not apply for standard deviations:

$$\sigma_{A+B} = \sqrt{\sigma^2_A + \sigma^2_B} \neq \sigma_A + \sigma_B \ .$$

The standard deviation satisfies most of Yule and Kendall's rules for good statistics listed in Chapter 1—it is rigidly defined, based on all the observations, algebraic, and minimally affected by sampling fluctuation. However, it is awkward to compute, not resistant to extreme values, and, more important, it is not readily comprehended. The mean deviation is fairly simple to understand, but the standard deviation is so abstract that its values are more difficult to interpret. Yet the standard deviation is the most important measure of spread for metric variables. The usefulness of the standard deviation will become more clear shortly.

The Variance and Standard Deviation of a Sample. Technically, the variance and standard deviation have been defined so far for full populations, rather than for samples of cases. However, the variance and standard deviation thus defined lack some optimal properties when dealing with samples. This problem will be discussed in Chapter 5 more directly, but here it suffices to say that a simple modification of the definitional formula is required for samples. Instead of dividing the sum of squared deviations by the number of cases, the sum of squared deviations should be divided by the number of cases less 1. The formulas for the sample versions of the variance (denoted as s^2) and standard deviation (denoted as s) are

$$s^2 = \sum (X_i - \overline{X})^2/(N-1) = \sum d_i^2/(N-1),$$

and

$$s = \sqrt{\sum (X_i - \overline{X})^2/(N-1)} = \sqrt{\sum d_i^2/(N-1)}.$$

Note that this slight modification will have negligible impact when the number of cases is large. After all, a quotient is about the same whether a numerator is divided by a large number or by that large number less 1. The modification can have a more substantial impact when the number of cases is small, say less than 100 and particularly if less than 60.

Computational formulas for a sample variance are

$$s^2 = [\sum (X_i^2) - (1/N)(\sum X)^2]/(N-1) = [\sum (X_i^2) - N(\overline{X})^2]/(N-1).$$

The computational formulas for the standard deviation are just the square roots of those formulas. Once again, the sum of squared values in the formula is not the same as squaring the sum of the values.

A further complication occurs when sampling from a finite population. The formulas given so far assume sampling from an infinite population. However, the population size must be taken into account when sampling from a finite population without replacement (Hays, 1963: 210). If the sample size is denoted as N and the population size as T, then the variance is

$$s^2 = [(\sum d_i^2/(N-1)] \times [(T-1)/T] = [\sum d_i^2/(N-1)] \times [1 - (1/T)].$$

The correction factor $1 - (1/T)$ is near 1 except for small populations, so this adjustment has little effect unless the population size is under 100.

The Variance and Standard Deviation for Grouped Metric Data. Other versions of the variance and standard deviation formulas can be used when the data are grouped. When working from a frequency distribution in which each value of the variable X is listed along with its corresponding frequency f, the population variance can be calculated as

$$\sigma^2 = \sum f_i(X_i - \mu)^2/N = \sum f_i d_i^2/N,$$

or the computational formulas

$$\sigma^2 = [\sum f_i(X_i^2) - (1/N)(\sum f_i X_i)^2]/N = [\sum (f_i X_i^2) - N(\overline{X})^2]/N$$

$$= \sum (f_i X_i^2)/N - \overline{X}^2.$$

The appropriate sample variance formulas are

$$s^2 = \sum f_i(X_i - \overline{X})^2/(N-1) = \sum f_i d_i^2/(N-1),$$

or the computational formulas

$$s^2 = [\sum f_i(X_i^2) - (1/N)(\sum f_i X_i)^2]/(N-1) = [\sum (f_i X_i^2) - N(\overline{X})^2]/(N-1).$$

The standard deviation is the square root of these variance formulas.

When dealing with a continuous variable that has been grouped into classes, the above formulas can be employed with the midpoint of the interval used to represent the interval. Thus, if the true limits of the interval are from 2 to 3, the value 2.5 should be used to represent the interval.

Sometimes it is also necessary to pool variances obtained from different samples. For example, consider combining the variances from separate samples for three different years (say with different numbers of cases for each sample) into an overall variance. If there are J samples and we represent the variance for sample j by s_j^2 and the corresponding number of cases as N_j, then the *pooled variance* formula is

$$s^2 = \sum [(N_j - 1) s_j^2]/(\sum N_j - J).$$

This calculation is illustrated in Table 3.4. If the sample sizes happen to be equal, say N, the formula reduces to the average sample variance:

$$s^2 = (N - 1) (\sum s_j^2)/(NJ - J) = \sum s_j^2/J.$$

The Variance and Standard Deviation for Dichotomous Data. The variance and standard deviations formulas can be further simplified for dichotomous data. The variance of a dichotomous variable (Blalock, 1972: 195) is

$$\sigma^2 = p(1 - p),$$

where p is the proportion of successes. To see this, say that a binary variable is scored 1/0 with p being the proportion of the cases scored 1, so $1 - p$ is the proportion scored 0. According to the computational version of the variance formula, the variance would be

$$\sigma^2 = \sum (X_i^2)/N - (\mu)^2 = \{(N \times p \times 1^2) + [N \times (1 - p) \times 0^2]\}/N - p^2$$

$$= [(Np) + 0]/N - p^2 = p - p^2 = p(1 - p).$$

The standard deviation, of course, is the square root of the variance:[9]

$$\sigma = \sqrt{p(1 - p)}.$$

Note that the variance is maximal when the proportion p is near one half. Thus, the maximum variance is .25 when $p = .5$, and it diminishes to .16 when $p = .2$ or .8 and to .09 when $p = .1$ or .9.

Gender is a typical example of a dichotomous variable, as it takes on only two possible values: male or female. Say it is scored 0/1, with men coded zero and women coded one. If 53% of the population were women, then the variance for gender would be .53 × .47 = .249.

Coefficient of Variation. It is difficult to interpret standard deviation values directly, as what is large depends on the unit in which the variable was measured. For example, is a standard deviation of 100 large or small? It would be large if we were analyzing the weight of people, but it would be small if we were analyzing yearly income values.

The *coefficient of variation* or *coefficient of relative variation* is a statistic that is used to give a better sense of how large a standard deviation is. It divides the standard deviation by the mean of the variable, as shown in the following formula:

$$CV = \sigma/\overline{X}.$$

For example, if a group of people have an average weight of 150 pounds with a standard deviation of 100, the coefficient of variation of weight would be .667. If the average yearly income were $20,000 and the standard deviation were 100, the coefficient of variation of income would be .005. These coefficients of variation can legitimately be compared to find that the weights are more variable than the incomes.

An alternative interpretation of the coefficient of variation is in terms of relative variation. Define the *relative deviation* for observation i as $(X_i - \overline{X})/\overline{X}$. Next, square the coefficient of variation $(\sigma/\overline{X})$. Squaring the standard deviation of a variable divided by its mean gives the variance divided by the mean squared. This can be simplified: $[\Sigma(X_i - \overline{X})^2/N]/\overline{X}^2 = \Sigma[(X_i - \overline{X})/\overline{X}]^2/N$. The latter is just the average of the squared relative deviations $[(X_i - \overline{X})/\overline{X}]^2$. Thus, the squared coefficient of variation equals the average of the squared relative deviations. This is why the coefficient of variation is sometimes called the *coefficient of relative variation*.

Gini's Mean Difference. A final measure of spread for metric variables is based on differences rather than deviations. *Gini's mean difference* (Yule & Kendall, 1968: 146-147) is the mean of the absolute value of the differences between all pairs of values:

$$g = \sum |X_i - X_j| / \binom{N}{2} \qquad \text{summing over } i \leq j$$

$$= \sum |X_i - X_j| / [n(n - 1)] \qquad \text{summing over all pairs } i \neq j.$$

Gini's mean difference has intuitive appeal, as it shows the typical difference between a pair of values. For example, in Table 4.1, the mean difference is 7.11, showing that the typical difference in prior convictions between a pair of defendants was 7.11, a value that is close to the standard deviation of 8 but is more readily interpretable. However, it does not generalize beyond the single-variable case in useful ways, so the mean difference is not used often in statistical analysis.

Summary. The variance and standard deviation are the most important measures of spread for metric variables. The mean deviation and Gini's mean difference are conceptually simpler, but the variance and standard deviation are the statistics that generalize beyond the single-variable case and that have important mathematical properties.

Uses of Variance

So far, it has been claimed that the standard deviation and variance are important statistics without showing why. Some of their uses will be described in this section; others will be explained in the next chapter. This discussion is brief and introductory, and is designed mainly to emphasize the widespread use of the variance concept in data analysis and research design.

Assessing Unusual Values. One use of the variation on a variable is to assess how unusual any particular value on the variable is. The measure employed for this is called a *standard score* or *Z-score*. If the variable is labelled X, the ith observation on X is labeled X_i, the mean on X is labeled μ, and the standard deviation of X is labeled σ, then the Z-score corresponding to the ith observation is

$$Z_i = (X_i - \mu)/\sigma.$$

As an illustration, the standard score for people with 20 previous convictions in the criminal example above is 2.0 if the mean is 4 and the standard deviation is 8. They score 2 standard deviation units above the mean.

The Z-scores on a variable are termed *standardized* because they always have a mean of 0 and a variance of 1. First, consider their mean:

$$\bar{Z} = \sum (Z_i)/N = \sum (X_i - \mu)/(\sigma N) = [1/(\sigma N)]\sum (X_i - \mu) = 0,$$

because the sum of the deviations around the X mean is always 0. Next, consider their variance:

$$s_Z^2 = \sum \{[(X_i - \mu)/\sigma]^2 - 0\}/N = (1/\sigma^2)\sum (X_i - \mu)^2/N = (1/\sigma^2)\sigma^2 = 1.$$

Because standardized variables have a variance of 1, they also have a standard deviation of 1.

Variables are often standardized in statistical analysis to remove some sources of differences between the variables. A typical example would involve constructing an additive index from separate variables. Usually, additive indices are created by just adding up the raw scores on the variables. However, that would be inappropriate if the variables have very different magnitudes or variances (as when constructing a measure of people's status on the basis of the values of their houses and their barbecues) and particularly if they are measured in different units (as when constructing a measure of status based on income in dollars and education in years). In such cases, the variables should be standardized first, and then an index can be created by summing the standardized scores.

What makes standard scores particularly useful is that the laws of statistics and probability provide information on what is an unusual standard score. Z-scores near zero are more likely than values far from zero. According to Chebychev's inequality, regardless of the shape of the distribution of X, no more than $(1/k)^2$ proportion of the cases will have standard scores more extreme than k. That is,

$$\text{Prob}(|X_i - \bar{X}|/\sigma \geq k) \leq (1/k)^2.$$

For example, the probability that a Z-score's absolute value is greater than or equal to 2 is no more than $1/4$.

If the variable has a symmetric distribution, then the probability of a Z-score whose absolute value is greater than or equal to k is no more than $(4/9)(1/k^2)$. That is,

$$\text{Prob}(|X_i - \bar{X}|/\sigma \geq k) \leq (4/9)(1/k)^2.$$

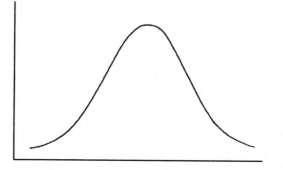

Figure 4.1. Normal Distribution

So, if the variable has a symmetric distribution, the probability of the magnitude of a Z-score being greater than 2 is at most 1/9.

If the variable has the bell-shaped distribution that is called a normal curve (Figure 4.1), then the distribution follows tabulated results. For example, the probability of a Z-score greater than or equal to 1.96 (or less than or equal to −1.96) is .05, versus the 1/4 for values beyond 2 for the more general Chebychev inequality or the 1/9 for a general symmetric distribution. The table showing the likelihood of particular values under a normal curve is included in most statistics texts.

Assessing the Covariation Between Variables. Another statistical use of variance involves comparing the variance on two variables to see the extent to which they *covary*. This is usually measured by a *correlation coefficient.* The correlation coefficient used for metric variables is called *Pearson's r*, and it is the average of the products of the standardized values on variables X and Y:

$$r = \frac{1}{N} \sum_{i=1}^{N} Z_{X_i} Z_{Y_i}.$$

The values of this statistic range from 0 when there is no covariance between the variables to 1 (or −1) when there is maximal covariance.

Correlations are often examined when assessing causation. Correlation does not in itself prove that one variable "causes" the other. However, finding no correlation between two variables certainly suggests the lack of a causal connection between them. In studying causation, a distinction is made between the *dependent variable,* which is the one being caused, and the *independent variable,* which may be producing the observed differences on the dependent variable. The square of Pearson's r (r^2) shows the proportion of the variance of the dependent variable Y that can be accounted for by a linear prediction rule based on the independent variable X. For example, a correlation above .7 shows that more than half of the variance in the dependent variable can be accounted for by the independent variable. Thus, correlations are interpreted in terms of variances.

The variance statistic is especially important in analysis of multiple variables, because the variance of the dependent variable can often be decomposed in useful ways. Recall the rule in the previous section that variances (but not standard deviations) are additive when independent results are being summed. This rule is often employed in multivariate analysis, when particular effects can be proven to be independent of one another. The interpretation of Pearson's r^2 in the last paragraph was based on this idea, decomposing the variance of the dependent variable into *explained variance* due to a linear relationship with the predictor variable and the remaining *error variance* that cannot be accounted for by linear prediction.

The Choice of Variables. Variation is also important to consider at the research-design stage. The simplest lesson is that variation is required in a variable if that variable is to be useful. Say that the determinants of criminal behavior were being studied. A researcher could record the ages of prisoners and use the results to summarize the typical age of criminals. However, without similar data for noncriminals, the study could not be used to check whether criminals are older or younger than the rest of the population. By studying only prisoners, there is no variance on the dependent variable. Variables that lack variation are rarely useful to examine.

Similarly, there must be variation on independent variables. To examine the effects of gender on income, for example, studying only women would not suffice. The interesting part is how men and women differ, because that would allow an examination of the causes of variation between genders. Creating a research design without variance on one of the variables destroys the ability to draw conclusions from the study.

Sources of Variability. Why are there differences in scores on a variable? A classification of sources of variability in measurement focuses on the distinction between *true values* and *observed values*. According to this classification, the observed value of a variable is composed of its true value plus an *error* term. That error term can in turn be decomposed into two terms: a *systematic-bias* term and a *random-error* term. Assume that the true values, the systematic bias, and random error are uncorrelated, meaning that the only kind of systematic bias would be a constant added to the true score. The observed variance of a variable then can be decomposed into its true variance and its error variance (because a constant-bias term would lack variance). The random-error term is sometimes further divided into its various sources, such as measurement error, coder error, and sampling error, and each of these errors can have a variance associated with it. Measurement is thus a matter of minimizing particular sources of error variance.

In experimental research, the part of the variance associated with the manipulated variables is considered *systematic variance,* which is to be maximized. The part of the variance associated with other factors is considered *extraneous variance,* which is to be controlled as by random assignment of subjects to different experimental groups. The remaining variance due to random fluctuations is considered *error variance,* which is to be minimized by controlling experimental conditions or by increasing the reliability of the measures. This classification leads to the suggestion by Kerlinger (1973) in his research-design textbook that the researcher should "maximize systematic variance, control extraneous variance, and minimize error variance." Thus, research design itself can be considered an exercise in variance control. All in all, the variance concept is of critical importance in research design as well as in data analysis.

Order-Based Measures of Spread

The concept of spread is also applicable to ordinal data, though spread is rarely measured at a purely ordinal level. Measures of spread for ordinal data will be described in this section, along with measures that are based on the order of numeric values. The major measures of spread discussed in this section are the range and, especially, the interquartile range (IQR).

Range. The simplest order-based measure of spread is the range of values: the difference between the largest and smallest data values.

Let X_{max} represent the largest data value and X_{min} denote the smallest data value, so

$$\text{Range} = X_{max} - X_{min}.$$

The range indicates how much the variable varies in practice. Its minimum value is zero when there is no spread on the variable.

As an example, say that we counted the number of prior convictions of 10 criminal defendants. If each defendant had exactly 4 prior convictions, the range would be 0. The range would be 20 if the numbers of prior convictions went from a maximum of 20 down to a minimum of 0.

The main advantage of the range as a measure of spread is its ease of calculation. However, it is very much affected by extreme values, even if they are not atypical. For example, if nine defendants had no prior convictions and the remaining defendant had 20, the range would be 20 because of the single outlier. As a result, the range is considered to be a nonresistant measure of spread. More resistant measures are generally preferred.

Interquartile Range and Variants. This sensitivity of the range to extreme cases is sometimes remedied by switching to such variants as the *interquartile range* (also known in the EDA literature as the *midspread, H-spread,* or *F-spread*). For this measure, determine what data value corresponds to the 75th percentile of cases (Q_3: the upper quartile) and what data value corresponds to the 25th percentile (Q_1: the lower quartile). The IQR is the difference between those values:

$$\text{IQR} = Q_3 - Q_1.$$

By lopping off the extreme cases, the IQR is less sensitive to outliers than is the full range, so it is a more resistant measure of spread.

As described in Chapter 1, exploratory data analysis emphasizes becoming familiar with the data at an intuitive level. Also, EDA emphasizes the use of resistant statistics. The IQR is a statistic favored in EDA, because it is intuitive, resistant, and has desirable properties over a variety of different distributions for the variable (Iglewicz, 1983).

The limitation of the IQR is that there is an ad hoc quality to its calculation, because there is nothing magical about the 75th and 25th percentiles. Indeed, some EDA advocates would suggest computing a variety of IQR-like statistics, such as the difference between the top and bottom eighths of the distribution, and so on. This multiplicity of possible ranges serves as a reminder that EDA-based statistics are intended for exploration of a set of data more than as final summary statistics.

Several variants of the IQR also have been proposed as measures of spread. The *quartile deviation* (QD); (also *semi-interquartile range* or *quartile range*) is the interquartile range divided by 2:

$$QD = (Q_3 - Q_1)/2.$$

The division by 2 is intended to give the statistic the feel of a typical deviation from the center, here how much the quartiles typically deviate from the median. The QD also can be thought of as the average of the range from the 25th percentile to the 50th percentile and the range from the 50th percentile to the 75th percentile.

The interquartile range and related ranges have a zero value when there is no spread on the variable. Their values are unlimited as the spread on the variable increases. The IQR is fairly easy to compute, but it does not lead to useful generalizations beyond the single-variable case.

The interpretation of the size of range-based spread coefficients depends on the units in which the variables are measured. Following the coefficient of variation logic, a normed version can be obtained by dividing the spread statistic by a measure of center. The *coefficient of quartile variation* (CQV) is the interquartile difference divided by the sum of the first and third quartiles (Leabo, 1972: 110):

$$CQV = (Q_3 - Q_1)/(Q_3 + Q_1).$$

This statistic equals the quartile deviation divided by the midhinge (defined in Chapter 3), which emphasizes its use of coefficient of variation logic.

Box Plots. One of the most inventive developments in statistics in recent years has been the creation of new graphic procedures for data exploration. In particular, *box plots* (also known as *box-and-whisker diagrams*) have been devised for displaying the ordinal distribution of variables. The box plot simultaneously shows the median of a variable, its range, and its interquartile range, and emphasizes which observations are outliers. Thus, box plots give a quick view of both center and spread.

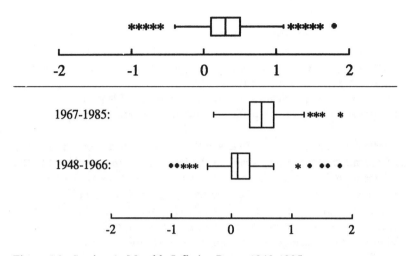

Figure 4.2. Section A. Monthly Inflation Rates, 1948-1985
Section B. Monthly Inflation Rates, by Years

Figure 4.2, section a, shows the box plot corresponding to the monthly inflation rates for the U.S. economy from 1948 through 1985. The horizontal axis shows the values of the variable, from −2 through +2. Note the three vertical lines in the plot. The middle one represents the median, showing that the median for these data is roughly 0.3. The other two vertical bars show the first quartile (about .1) and third quartile (about .5). There is a box around these three vertical lines; the horizontal width of this box represents the interquartile range. Beyond the interquartile range, values within 1.5 times the midspread (interquartile range) of the first or third quartiles are shown and are connected to the main box with lines, colorfully termed *whiskers*. Outliers between 1.5 and 3 times the interquartile range from the first or third quartiles (said to be outside the *inner fences*) are plotted with stars. Extreme outliers more than 3 times the interquartile range from the first or third quartiles (said to be outside the *outer fences*) are plotted as filled circles.

Box plots are particularly useful when comparing the distribution of the same variable for different subgroups of observations. Figure 4.2, section b, shows box plots for inflation for 1948-1966 and 1967-1985 separately. The median inflation rate is seen to be higher in the later period. Also, the interquartile range was larger in the later period, though the earlier period experienced more atypical monthly values. The subgroup differences are apparent from a glance at these plots. Comparing different box plots can highlight differences in medians, quartiles, spreads, and/or outliers.

The remaining measures in this chapter are used less often, so some readers might want to skip ahead to the next chapter at this point.

Median Absolute Deviation. Another possible order-based measure of spread is the average absolute deviation from the median. Let the deviation d_i be defined as the arithmetic difference between the value for an observation X_i and the median, $d_i = X_i - X_{median}$, and let the absolute deviation $|d_i|$ be $|X_i - X_{median}|$. The *median absolute deviation* (MAD; sometimes also called the *mean deviation* and the *average deviation*) is the average of these absolute deviations:

$$\text{MAD} = \underset{i}{\text{median}} |X_i - X_{median}|.$$

As an example, the median for Table 4.1 is 0, the absolute deviations from that median sum to 40, and the number of cases is 10, so the average deviation from the median is 4.

This mean deviation from the median is minimal compared to the mean deviation from any other possible measure of center (Yule & Kendall, 1968: 138). EDA work suggests that the MAD has desirable properties over a variety of distributions for the variable (Iglewicz, 1983).

Just as the coefficient of variation is the standard deviation normed by dividing through by the mean, the *coefficient of dispersion* (CD) is the median absolute deviation normed by dividing through by the median:

$$\text{CD} = \sum |X_i - X_{median}|/(NX_{median}).$$

This is a spread measure that corrects for the magnitude of the variable.

Although the MAD has some useful interpretations, absolute values are awkward to manipulate algebraically. Because of this, the MAD does not lead to useful generalizations when we move into statistics for more than one variable. As a result, this measure of spread is rarely used.

Leik's D. The purest ordinal measure of spread was developed by Leik (1966) in his study of consensus (Rae & Taylor, 1970: 125-127). First, assume that the variable has been placed in its proper order. Denote the proportions of the observations in each of the K different categories as $p_1, p_2, \ldots, p_K$. Define the cumulative proportion for category k as $c_k = \Sigma p_j$ for $j \leq k$. Then let the difference $d_k = c_k$ if $c_k \leq 0.5$ and $1 - c_k$ otherwise. Leik proposes as a measure of dispersion:

$$D = 2\sum d_k/(K - 1).$$

As an example, say that there are four individuals and three categories, with one person in the first category, two in the middle category, and one in the last category (see Table 4.3, section a). The cumulative proportions for the three categories are $c_1 = 0.25$, $c_2 = 0.75$, and $c_3 = 1.00$. The corresponding differences are $d_1 = 0.25$, $d_2 = 0.25$, and $d_3 = 0$. Leik's $D = 2(0.25 + 0.25 + 0.00)/(3 - 1) = 2 \times 0.50/2 = 0.50$. This statistic is zero if there is no dispersion: if all people fall in the same category (section b). Maximum dispersion occurs when the cases are polarized, with half at each extreme, in which case D takes on a maximal value of 1 (section c).

Leik's D logic is fully appropriate for ordinal data, without requiring a conversion to numeric scores, but it is used infrequently.

Summary. There are several order-based measures of spread. The range is too nonresistant to be useful. The interquartile range and median average deviation have some useful properties, but they do not generalize to more than one variable. Leik's D is very purely ordinal, but it is rarely used. Putting these considerations together, order-based measures of spread are limited in their value. As a result, the variance and standard deviation are frequently employed even on ordinal data.

Frequency-Based Measures of Spread

Spread can be measured for nominal variables in terms of the degree of heterogeneity on the variable. Zero spread denotes complete homogeneity (all cases falling in the same category), whereas higher values indicate greater heterogeneity. Spread measures for nominal variables are based on the frequencies of the categories. In reading this section, it should be kept in mind that there is no single agreed-upon measure of spread for nominal data.

TABLE 4.3
Examples for Illustrating Leik's D

Section A. Calculation of Leik's D			
	Category 1	*Category 2*	*Category 3*	*Sum*
Frequency	1	2	1	4
Proportion	.25	.50	.25	1.00
Cumulative proportion	.25	.75	1.00	
Difference	.25	.25	.00	.50
$D = 2 \times 0.5/(3 - 1) = 2 \times 0.5/2 = 0.5$				

Section B. No Dispersion			
	Category 1	*Category 2*	*Category 3*	*Sum*
Frequency	0	4	0	4
Proportion	.00	1.00	.00	1.00
Cumulative proportion	.00	1.00	1.00	
Difference	.00	.00	.00	.00
$D = 2 \times 0/(3 - 1) = 0$				

Section C. Maximal Dispersion			
	Category 1	*Category 2*	*Category 3*	*Sum*
Frequency	2	0	2	4
Proportion	.50	.00	.50	1.00
Cumulative proportion	.50	.50	1.00	
Difference	.50	.50	.00	1.00
$D = 2 \times 1/(3 - 1) = 2 \times 1/2 = 2/2 = 1.00$				

Variation Ratio. The simplest measure of spread for nominal data is called the *variation ratio*. It is just the proportion of cases that do not fall into the modal category

$$\text{Variation Ratio} = 1 - (f_{\text{mode}}/N),$$

where f stands for frequency, f_{mode} is the frequency of the modal category, and N is the total number of cases. This is a useful measure of spread because it shows how descriptive the mode is of the data.

For an example of the variation ratio, look at data on religious affiliations in Table 4.4. The modal religion for column 2 is Protestant, with 40% of the sample being Protestant; the variation ratio is .60.

TABLE 4.4
Distributions of Religions

Religion	Actual	Unanimity	Polarized	Individuality	Uniform
Protestant	80	6	3	1	2
Catholic	60	0	3	1	2
Jewish	10	0	0	1	2
Muslim	—	0	0	1	0
Other	20	0	0	1	0
None	30	0	0	1	0
Total	200	6	6	6	6
Mode	Protestant	Protestant	not unique	not unique	not unique
Variation ratio	.600	.00	.50	.83	.67
Index of diversity	.715	.00	.50	.83	.67
IQV	.894	.00	1.00	1.00	1.00
Entropy	2.009	.00	1.00	2.58	1.58
Standardized entropy	.865	.00	1.00	1.00	1.00

The variation ratio would be zero if all cases fell into the same category. Its maximal value depends on the number of categories of the variable. If there are K categories and each occurs equally with frequency N/K (a uniform distribution), then the variation ratio is $1 - (1/K)$, which approaches 1 as the number of categories K becomes infinitely large. Thus, it is maximal under individuality—when each case is in a separate category.

The variation ratio is simple to compute, but it has the disadvantage of being based only on the proportion of cases in the modal category. Other measures of nominal spread take the full distribution of cases into account.

Index of Diversity. A second measure of spread for nominal variables is the *index of diversity*, D. This is a dispersion measure based on the proportion of cases in each category. It squares each of those proportions, sums the squares, and subtracts the sum of squares from 1:

$$D = 1 - p_1^2 - p_2^2 - \ldots - p_K^2 = 1 - \sum_k p_k^2,$$

where p_k is the proportion of cases in category k, K is the number of categories, and Σ stands for summation—the summation of the p_k^2

terms for each category. This index shows the degree of *concentration* of the cases in a few large categories, because squaring proportions emphasizes the large proportions much more than small ones (Coulter, 1984).

In the religions example (Table 4.4), with 40% Protestant, 30% Catholic, 5% Jewish, 10% other, and 15% none, the sum of squared proportions is .16 + .09 + .0025 + .01 + .0225 = .285, so D is 1 − .285 = .715.

The index of diversity has been developed independently in many fields as a measure of heterogeneity. For example, it is the same as the fractionalization measure developed by Taylor and Hudson (1972: 216; also Waldman, 1976) to summarize the spread between the numbers of votes received by political parties in multiparty elections.

The index of diversity approaches zero if nearly all cases fall into the same category. It is maximal under individuality—when each case is in a separate category. However, its maximum value depends on the number of categories, so D values cannot be compared across distributions with differing numbers of categories. If there were K categories, with an equal proportion of cases in each category, D would have the maximum value of $(K - 1)/K$. Thus in the religions example, the maximum diversity is .80 (= 4/5), because there are five religious groups. What makes this unusual is that the maximum would increase if there were more categories. For example, if we subdivided the Protestant category into Baptist, Presbyterian, Methodist, Lutheran, and other Protestants, we would have 10 categories, with a maximum diversity of .90 (= 9/10). For many purposes, it would be more useful were the diversity index normed to go from 0 to 1 regardless of the number of categories.

Index of Qualitative Variation. A third measure of spread for nominal variables, the *index of qualitative variation* (IQV), norms the diversity index so that the value of 1 always represents maximum spread. To do this, it simply divides the index of diversity by its maximum for the actual number of categories: $(K - 1)/K$. The formula is

$$\text{IQV} = (1 - p_1^2 - p_2^2 - \ldots - p_K^2)/[(K - 1)/K].$$

In the religions example of Table 4.4, with five religious categories the index of qualitative variation is .715/.80 = .894. This high IQV indicates that there is considerable dispersion across religions in this sample. It is 0 when all cases fall into a single category, and 1 under uniformity, when the cases are evenly spread across the K categories.

Which nominal measure of spread is more useful depends partly on how we define nominal spread. Say we were comparing party competition in two nations: a two-party system in which each party won 50% of the vote and a multiparty system in which each of 10 parties obtained an equal 10% share of the vote. The IQV value would be 1.00 in each case, because the diversity is maximal given the number of categories. Yet there is a real sense in which there is more dispersion in the 10-party case than in the two-party system. If we felt this dispersion was important to capture, we would have to return to the index of diversity, where we would find a value of .90 for the 10-party nation versus a value of .50 for the two-party system. Thus, correction for the number of categories would be inappropriate when the existence of more categories in itself signifies greater diversity.

Entropy. A fourth measure of spread for nominal variables is based on information theory (Krippendorff, 1986). Information-theory-based statistics gauge how much information is conveyed by a distribution. There is no uncertainty when all cases fall in the same category. The greater the spread of cases across categories, the more uncertainty.

Independent bits of information are counted. By definition, there is exactly one bit of uncertainty in a choice between two equal alternatives. Less uncertainty would exist if one alternative were more popular than the other. An even choice among two alternatives provides one bit of uncertainty, an even choice among four alternatives (two-squared) provides two bits of uncertainty, an even choice among eight alternatives (two-cubed) provides three bits, and so on. Thus, the number of independent bits of information can be calculated by taking the logarithm to the base 2 of the number of alternatives, adjusted for their differential popularities.

Entropy (or *uncertainty*) is measured by looking at the proportion of cases in each category k. This proportion is multiplied by the negative[10] of its logarithm (usually to the base 2), which gives $-p_k \log_2(p_k)$. The uncertainty of a distribution is defined as the sum of this value over all categories:

$$H'(X) = -\sum_k p_k \log_2(p_k) = -3.3219 \sum_k p_k \log_{10}(p_k).$$

The second version of the formula states entropy in terms of common logs to the base 10.

In the religions example of Table 4.4, the entropy is 2.009. This can be interpreted as saying that the spread among the religious categories is approximately that of choosing between four equally prevalent religions.

There is no uncertainty when all observations are in the same category. In that case, $p_1 = 1$. By definition, the logarithm of 1 is 0, so the entropy value for this situation is zero. By contrast, if there is a uniform distribution across K categories, then entropy equals $-\Sigma(1/K)\log_2(1/K) = -K(1/K)[\log_2(1) - \log_2(K)] = -[0 - \log_2(K)] = \log_2(K)$. In other words, the more categories, the greater the uncertainty. Its maximum value thus depends on the number of categories, with the greatest value under individuality.

The entropy statistic can be normed so its maximum is 1 regardless of the number of categories of the variable. The entropy formula can be modified to have this characteristic by dividing through by its maximum value to obtain what is termed *standardized entropy*:[11]

$$J' = - \sum_k p_k \log(p_k) / \log(K) .$$

In the religions example, the standardized entropy is .865.

Entropy statistics are little used because logs to the base 2 are awkward to compute and because most researchers are uncomfortable with logarithms. However, the theoretical basis of these statistics is very strong. Other nominal measures of spread have an ad hoc basis to them, whereas entropy statistics are elegantly based on information theory. A further advantage is that entropy statistics generalize readily to multiple variables, so uncertainty-based measures of association between two variables can be used to determine how much an explanatory variable helps reduce the uncertainty as to the dependent-variable category in which a case belongs.

Other Measures. Several other measures of spread for nominal variables have been devised, usually by researchers solving their own substantive problems. Thus, political scientists developed several measures of the dispersion of the seat totals won by different parties in multiparty legislatures (Waldman, 1976). A typical example is Rae and Taylor's (1970) *fragmentation* statistic, which is the proportion of pairs of cases that are not in the same category; it approximately equals the index of diversity for large numbers of cases. Similarly, biologists constructed several *indices of ecological diversity* (Kotz, Johnson, & Read, 1983, vol. 2: 409), where the existence of a large number of species nearly equal in size is considered high diversity. Also, several disciplines developed measures of *equality* (Coulter, 1984) or integration, such as $1 - \Sigma|p_k - (1/K)|$, which is based on the difference between proportional shares and the average proportional share.

Summary. There is no common agreement as to which frequency-based measure of spread is best. Indeed, computer programs rarely provide *any* of them. Each has a value of zero when all cases are in the same category. The greater the heterogeneity of the observations, the higher the value for these statistics. As shown in the last four columns of Table 4.4, they differ in their maximal values. The index of qualitative variation and standardized entropy have maximum values of 1 when the distribution is uniform; the others are maximal when each case is in a separate category, with their maximum value depending on the number of categories.

Discussion

Comparisons of Measures of Spread. Spread measures all accept the same definition of zero variation, but they use different interpretations of maximum spread (see Table 4.5). The metric and order-based measures are maximal when the variable is polarized, with half of the cases at the maximum value and the other half at the minimum. The frequency-based measures instead are maximal when there is a uniform distribution of cases across the categories, or when there are as many categories as observations. Also, some spread measures are normed, either to have a maximum value of 1 or by dividing through by a central-tendency value to control for the unit in which the variable is measured. Normed values are generally more interpretable, although raw values may be purer measures of spread.

Table 4.6 compares the major measures of spread described in this chapter along the desirable criteria for descriptive statistics listed in Chapter 1. Some of the evaluations in the table are debatable, but they give a useful beginning point for considering the statistics. The advantages of the standard deviation (and variance) are that they are

TABLE 4.5
Maximum Value Conditions for Measures of Spread

Measure	Maximum Value	Maximum Condition for Fixed # of Cases	Maximum Dependent on # Categories	Normed
Mean deviation	unlimited	polarized	no	no
Variance	unlimited	polarized	no	no
Standard deviation	unlimited	polarized	no	no
Coefficient of variation	unlimited		no	yes
Gini's mean difference	unlimited	polarized	no	no
Range	unlimited		no	no
Interquartile range	unlimited	polarized	no	no
Quartile deviation	unlimited	polarized	no	no
Coefficient of quartile variation	unlimited		no	yes
Median absolute deviation	unlimited	polarized	no	no
Coefficient of dispersion	unlimited		no	yes
Leik's D	1	polarized	yes	no
Variation ratio	→1	individuality	yes	no
Index of diversity	→1	individuality	yes	no
Index of qualitative variation	1	uniformity	no	0-1
Entropy	unlimited	individuality	yes	no
Standardized entropy	1	uniformity	no	0-1

algebraic, stable under sampling, and generalizable to two or more variables. The interquartile range is easier to understand and to calculate, more resistant to outliers, and can often be computed for open-ended variables. The frequency-based measures generally do not excel on the criteria, but they are appropriate for nominal data. Rather than choose a single measure of spread, often it is more appropriate to use several of these measures together to highlight different aspects of the dispersion.

The values of these measures of spread can be compared for some known distributions. In particular, say that the variable has a normal distribution, the bell-shaped distribution shown in Figure 4.1. This distribution has well-known mathematical properties that have been extensively studied over the years. For such a distribution, the interquartile range is 1.349 times the standard deviation (Velleman & Hoaglin, 1981: 54), and the mean deviation is .7979 times the standard deviation (Leabo, 1972: 114). This suggests that the standard devia-

TABLE 4.6
Properties of Measures of Spread

Property	Index of Diversity	Interquartile Range	Standard Deviation
Level of measurement	nominal or higher	ordinal or higher	metric (usually)
Rigidly defined	yes	yes	yes
Based on all cases	yes	yes	yes
Simple to understand	medium	yes	no
Easy to calculate	yes	yes	medium
Algebraic	yes	no	yes
Stable under sampling	unknown	unknown	yes
Single valued	yes	yes	yes
Resistant to outliers	yes	yes	no
Generalize to two-variable statistics	no	no	yes
Insensitive to combining categories	no	yes	yes
Computed for open-ended variables	no	yes	no
In same units as data values	no	yes	yes

tion will generally be larger than the average unsigned deviation from the mean (as measured by the mean deviation) and smaller than the interquartile range. These values could differ considerably for other distributions, although the 1.349 value for the interquartile range should not be terribly sensitive to the exact distribution because the measure is based on quartiles.

Mathematical Properties of Measures of Spread. A measure of spread should have two mathematical properties when applied to metric data. First, if a constant k is added to every value on the variable, the spread statistic should remain unchanged. Adding the constant changes the location of the values, but not the spread between them. Second, if a multiplier m is multiplied by every value of the variable, the spread then should be multiplied by the absolute value of m. Putting these two points together, the measure of spread on a variable transformed in a linear fashion should be

$$\text{Spread } (k + mX_i) = |m| \times \text{Spread}(X_i).$$

The range, interquartile range, mean deviation, and standard deviation all satisfy these conditions. Linear transformations of the data values increase these measures of spread in a multiplicative fashion. Consider, for example, a variable measured on a scale of 0 to 100, with 50 as neutral point. If a researcher wanted to convert this variable to a −100 to 100 scale, with 0 as neutral point, the conversion rule would be $2X - 100$, so the spread would double. Notice that the variance does not satisfy these conditions; its value would be multiplied by m^2, the square of the multiplier.

Summary. The most common measures of dispersion for metric data are the variance and its unsquared cousin, the standard deviation. These two measures must be understood well if the statistics of relationships between two or more variables are to be comprehended. Dispersion measures exist for other types of data, some (particularly the interquartile range) based on order-properties of the data and others based on the frequencies of the categories. Most of these measures do not generalize well beyond one variable, but they are effective in gauging the amount of dispersion when the variable is nonmetric.

5. CENTER AND SPREAD IN SAMPLES

Measures of center and spread have been presented in Chapters 3 and 4 from the *descriptive* point of view, showing how to summarize the results for the observed cases. An alternative *inferential* perspective is to use the *sample* of cases to describe a larger *population* of interest.

Often the researcher is interested in determining the value of a population *parameter*, such as a mean for the population. By convention, population parameters are denoted by Greek letters, such as mu (μ) for the population mean and sigma (σ) for the standard deviation. A sample does not permit the researcher to view the value of the population parameter directly. Instead, it permits the researcher to compute a sample *statistic*, such as the mean for the sample. These sample statistics are denoted by italic (Latin) letters, such as $\overline{X}$ for the sample mean and s for the standard deviation. Even when computing sample statistics, researchers generally are more interested in estimating the population parameters.

This chapter will introduce the estimation of center and spread for samples. In doing so, the importance of the variance statistic in classic statistics will be emphasized further.

Sampling Distributions

In addition to the distribution of the variable for the sample and the distribution of the variable for the population, a third distribution is of interest. It is called a *sampling distribution*. Imagine taking an infinite series of random samples of a given size and computing the variable's mean for each sample. The distribution of those sample means is known as the *sampling distribution of means*. Of course only one sample is taken in research applications, but this hypothetical distribution of sample means is important in statistical theory. Statistical inference is based on this sampling distribution; its variation and shape must be determined before statistical inference can be explained.

Standard Error of the Mean. The computational formula for the variance presented in Chapter 4 can be applied to obtain the variance of this sampling distribution of means:

$$\sigma_{\overline{X}}^2 = \sigma^2/N.$$

This formula can be derived by applying the formula for the variance of a weighted sum of independent results: $\text{Var}(cA + dB) = c^2\text{var}(A) + d^2\text{var}(B)$, where c and d are constants and A and B are independent results. When a sample of N independent observations is taken, the mean $\overline{X}$ can be expressed as $(1/N)X_1 + (1/N)X_2 + \ldots + (1/N)X_N$. Applying the weighted rule above, the variance of sample means must then be $(1/N^2)\text{Var}(X) + (1/N^2)\text{Var}(X) + \ldots + (1/N^2)\text{Var}(X) = N[(1/N^2)\text{Var}(X)] = \text{Var}(X)/N = \sigma^2/N$.

The *standard error of the mean* is defined to be the standard deviation of the sampling distribution of means—the standard deviation of the means of the several samples. It is the square root of the variance of the mean just defined. This standard error equals the population standard deviation divided by the square root of the number of cases:

$$s_\text{m} = \sigma/\sqrt{N}.$$

When using an estimated sample standard deviation, the estimated standard error for the mean is

$$\text{est } s_{\text{m}} = s/\sqrt{N} = \sqrt{\sum (X_i - \bar{X})^2/N(N-1)} \ .$$

The standard error is an important measure when using sample data to make inferences about populations, as will be shown shortly.

A correction factor is necessary when sampling from a finite population without replacement. If the sample size is N and the population size is T, then the estimated standard error of the mean is

$$\text{est } s_{\text{m}} = s/\sqrt{N} \times \sqrt{1 - (N/T)} \ .$$

When the sampling fraction N/T is small, as in most samples where less than 1% of the total population is being sampled, the multiplier $\sqrt{1 - (N/T)}$ is near 1 and does not have much effect on the standard error. This correction becomes more important when a large fraction of the population is sampled. For example, if half of the population is sampled, then the multiplier is about .7, so the standard error is 30% lower than it would otherwise be for a sample of that size.

Similarly, the standard error of a proportion is its standard deviation divided by the square root of the number of cases:

$$s_p = \sqrt{p(1-p)/N} \ ,$$

or, when sampling without replacement from a finite population of size T,

$$s_p = \sqrt{p(1-p)/(N-1)} \times \sqrt{1 - (N/T)} \ .$$

Again, that last term is a correction factor that has little effect unless a large fraction of the total population is being sampled. The use of this standard error for a proportion in polling is described below.

Central-Limit Theorem. Most variables do not have the normal distribution that was shown in Figure 4.1. However, that distribution is vital in statistics because of an important theorem. The theorem involves the sampling distribution of the mean—the distribution of means that would be obtained if a large number of samples were taken and the mean was computed for each of these samples. According to the *central-limit theorem*, for large sample sizes the sampling distribution of the mean $\overline{X}$ is approximately normal, with mean equal to the population mean μ and standard deviation equal to the standard error just defined.

The central-limit theorem holds regardless of the shape of the variable's distribution (so long as it has a finite standard deviation), so that the mean of a variable can be considered to have a normal distribution even if the variable itself does not. As a result, the normal distribution can be used to assess the statistical significance of sample means.

Statistical Inference

Statistical tests about the mean can be conducted by putting together the various results already obtained.

Recall from the discussion of standard scores in Chapter 4 that when a variable has a normal distribution, the probability of a Z-score greater than or equal to 1.96 (or less than or equal to −1.96) is .05. We have just seen that the sample mean $\overline{X}$ has a normal distribution with mean μ and standard deviation s_m. Define the *test statistic* as the Z-score for $\overline{X}$: $|\overline{X} - \mu|/s_m$. The probability of a test statistic greater than or equal to 1.96 by chance alone is .05. That is,

$$\text{Prob}(|\overline{X} - \mu|/s_m \geq 1.96) \leq .05.$$

Therefore, there is only a .05 chance of a sample mean being more than 1.96 standard errors from the population mean.

To see how significance testing works, say that we want to test whether the population mean on a variable equals some value, such as 100. Say also that a particular sample of 64 cases gives a mean of 125 with a standard deviation of 120, which translates to an estimated standard error of $120/\sqrt{64} = 120/8 = 15$. The statistical question then is whether it is likely that we would have a sample 25 points away from the hypothesized population mean of 100 with a standard error this size.

The test is conducted by computing the test statistic $|\overline{X} - \mu|/s_m$. If the test statistic is at least 1.96, then we can conclude with considerable confidence that the population mean does not equal the hypothesized value of 100; if the test statistic is less than 1.96, then we cannot reject the hypothesis that the true mean equals 100. The test statistic $|\bar{X} - \mu|/s_m = |125 - 100|/15 = 25/15 = 1.667$, which is less than 1.96. As a result, the sample mean 125 would not be considered statistically different from the hypothesized population mean of 100 at the .05 level of significance. With a sample of only 64 cases, we could have a sample mean of 125 even if the population mean were 100. On the other hand, were our sample mean 145, we would reject the hypothesis that the true mean is 100.

Significance tests for proportions are similar. As indicated above, the standard error of a proportion is $\sqrt{p(1-p)/N}$. So to test whether a sample proportion p significantly differs from .50, for example, the test statistic would be $|p - .50|/\sqrt{p(1-p)/N}$. The possibility that the true population proportion is .50 could be rejected at the .05 level of significance if this test statistic is greater than 2 (or, more precisely, 1.96).

In public-opinion polling, it is more common to use sample surveys to try to estimate population proportions. Say that a *simple random sample* is taken, each element having the same chance of being included in the sample. In that case, the *sampling error* usually is defined as

$$se = 1.96\sqrt{p(1-p)/(N-1)} \, ,$$

which is maximal when $p = .50$. This simplifies to a maximum sampling error of *roughly* $1/\sqrt{N}$. Thus, 95% of proportions estimated from simple random samples of size 900 should be within 3.33% (= $1/\sqrt{900}$) of the true population proportion. If a sample survey of 900 people finds that 60% favor a particular policy, it really is showing that $60\% \pm 3.33\% = 56.67\% - 63.33\%$ of the larger population probably favor that policy.

Other significance tests are used for testing whether there is a significant difference between two means, for the size of a variance (a *chi-square* test), and for whether one variable has a greater variance than another (an F test). These tests are beyond the scope of this book.

Summary. When dealing with metric variables, it is possible to make statistical inferences about the center and spread for the population of interest based on sample statistics. For example, the sampling distribution of the mean has a normal distribution, centered around the true population mean and with a standard deviation corresponding to the estimated standard deviation of the variable divided by the square root of the number of cases. As a result, 95% of the sample means will be within approximately two standard-error units of the true population mean. This permits testing of statistical hypotheses regarding whether a sample mean is compatible with a hypothesized value of the population mean. Significance tests have been developed for some ordinal and nominal measures of center and spread, but they are too specialized to present here.

Appendix: Technical Properties of Estimators

Statisticians have defined several technical properties of estimators by which to evaluate how well sample statistics, such as $\overline{X}$, estimate population parameters, such as μ. These properties were not mentioned in Chapters 3 and 4 because of their complexity, though the basic points are easy to follow.

The first technical property is called *consistency*. According to this criterion, as the sample size N becomes larger, the sample statistic should approximate the population parameter more closely. This criterion is stated in terms of the difference between those two values:

$$\text{Prob}(|\text{sample statistic} - \text{population parameter}| < \delta) \to 1 \text{ as } N \to \infty,$$

regardless of the value of δ (delta). The arrows in this equation are read as "approaches," so the condition is that the probability that the difference between the sample statistic and population parameter becomes arbitrarily small approaches certainty as the number of cases approaches infinity.

Consistency also can be stated in terms of the expected value of the square of the difference between the sample statistic and the population parameter: This expected value should approach zero as the number of cases approaches infinity. An *expected value* is similar to a mean—if the statistical operation were performed several times and then the average of the results were taken, that is the expected value. More technically, an expected value is a weighted mean, where each value is weighted by its probability:

$$E(X) = \sum x p_x, \quad \text{summed over all possible values of } X.$$

Consistency implies that

$$E(\text{sample statistic} - \text{population parameter})^2 \to 0 \text{ as } N \to \infty.$$

Some texts use that as the definition of consistency. Whether an estimator is consistent can be determined only by a mathematical proof.

The sample mean is a consistent estimator of the population mean:

$$\text{Prob}(|\overline{X} - \mu| < \delta) \to 1 \text{ as } N \to \infty.$$

Although that may not be surprising, for a symmetric population distribution the sample median is also a consistent estimator of the population mean:

$$\text{Prob}(|X_{\text{median}} - \mu| < \delta) \to 1 \text{ as } N \to \infty.$$

If many large samples were taken, the average difference between the sample median and the population mean would approach 0. Incidentally, the sample variance is a consistent estimator of the population variance:

$$\text{Prob}(|s^2 - \sigma^2| < \delta) \to 1 \text{ as } N \to \infty.$$

Consistency is a large-sample property—it describes the behavior of the sample statistic as the sample size is made very large. An inconsistent statistic is a poor choice, even for large samples. However, consistency does not guarantee that a statistic is useful for small samples. The remaining properties to be discussed involve properties of estimators for small samples.

An estimator should also be *unbiased*. An unbiased sample statistic has as its expected value the population parameter being estimated:

$$E(\text{sample statistic}) = \text{population parameter}.$$

An expected value is an average, so this says that if several samples are taken, the sample statistic is calculated on each, and these several sample statistics are averaged, then that average should equal the population parameter. Bias can be determined only by mathematical proof.

The sample mean is an unbiased estimator of the population mean: $E(\overline{X}) = \mu$. To see this, substitute on the left-hand side the formula for the mean:

$$E\left(\sum X_i/N\right) = E\left(\sum X_i\right)/N = \sum E(X_i)/N = (N\mu)/N = \mu.$$

Although the sample median is a consistent estimator of the population mean for symmetric distributions, that estimate is biased: $E(X_{\text{median}}) \neq \mu$. The sample mean is the preferred estimator of the mean because it is not biased.

A more surprising result is that applying the formula for the population variance to sample data leads to biased estimation. Let σ^2 represent the true population variance, and define $s_X^2 = \Sigma(X_i - \overline{X})^2/N$, or the computational equivalent: $(\Sigma X_i^2)/N - \overline{X}^2$. When the s_X^2 formula is applied to a sample, the resulting estimate is biased: $E(s_X^2) \neq \sigma^2$. The expected value of s_X^2 is

$$E(s_X^2) = [(N - 1)/N]\,\sigma^2.$$

To see this, use the computational formula $s_X^2 = (\Sigma X_i^2)/N - \overline{X}^2$. The expectation of this is $E(s_X^2) = E[(\Sigma X_i^2)/N - \overline{X}^2] = E[(\Sigma X_i^2)/N] - E(\overline{X}^2) = \Sigma E(X_i^2)/N - E(\overline{X}^2)$. To simplify the first term, recall the definition of a population variance, $\sigma^2 = E(X_i^2) - \mu^2$, so $E(X_i^2) = \sigma^2 + \mu^2$, and $\Sigma E(X_i^2)/N = \Sigma(\sigma^2 + \mu^2)/N = \sigma^2 + \mu^2$. To simplify the second term, recall that the sampling distribution of means has variance $\sigma_{\overline{X}}^2 = E(\overline{X}^2) - \mu^2$, so $E(\overline{X}^2) = \sigma_{\overline{X}}^2 + \mu^2$. Substituting these back, $E(s_X^2) = \Sigma E(X_i^2)/N - E(\overline{X}^2) = (\sigma^2 + \mu^2) - (\sigma_{\overline{X}}^2 + \mu^2) = \sigma^2 - \sigma_{\overline{X}}^2$. Thus, the sample variance is, on average, smaller than the true population variance, σ^2. Earlier in this chapter it was shown that $\sigma_{\overline{X}}^2 = \sigma^2/N$, so $E(s_X^2) = \sigma^2 - \sigma^2/N = \sigma^2[(N - 1)/N]$.

The sample variance must be adjusted to remove this bias. Multiplying the sample variance by the fraction $N/(N - 1)$ yields an unbiased estimate: $E\{[N/(N - 1)]s_X^2\} = \sigma^2$. Thus, an unbiased estimate of the population variance can be obtained by using the following formula:

$$s^2 = [N/(N - 1)] \sum (X_i - \overline{X})^2/N = \sum (X_i - \overline{X})^2/(N - 1).$$

That is why the sample variance formula in Chapter 4 divides the sum of squared deviations by the number of cases minus one.

Although s^2 is an unbiased estimator of σ^2, its square root is a biased estimator of the population standard deviation. For example, if the population distribution is normal, then an unbiased estimator of the population standard deviation σ is $[(4N - 3)/(4N - 4)]s$. This tends to have minimal effect for large N, so such a correction is rarely made.

Unbiasedness is a small-sample property. The bias renders the statistic inaccurate when the sample size is small. The correction for bias in the variance is important to use for small samples (i.e., less than 60).

A third desirable property of an estimator is that it be *efficient*. This property involves the relative stability of the estimator over repeated samples. The most efficient unbiased sample statistic (termed the *best unbiased estimator*) would be the one with minimum variance across different samples. Stated in terms of expectations, efficiency requires that E(sample statistic – population parameter)^2 be minimized.

Consider first the sample mean as an estimator of the population mean. Say that a large number of samples were taken of size N, and the mean was computed for each of those samples to generate a sampling distribution of sample means. We have labeled the variance of this sampling distribution as $\sigma_{\bar{X}}^2$. The sample mean is an efficient estimator of the population mean, because this variance is smaller than that of any other possible estimator of the population mean. For example, the sample median may be a consistent estimator of the population mean, but when the variable has a normal distribution, the sampling distribution of medians has a variance of $(\pi/2)\sigma_{\bar{X}}^2 = 1.5708$ $\sigma_{\bar{X}}^2 > \sigma_{\bar{X}}^2$. Thus, the sample median is a less efficient estimator of the population mean than is the sample mean. The adjusted sample variance is an efficient estimator of the population variance.

The best estimators are consistent, unbiased, and efficient. Some estimators are consistent, but lack the other properties, as is the case in using the sample median to estimate the population mean or in using the unadjusted sample variance to estimate the population variance. Such statistics are fine for very large sample situations but not for small ones. Some estimators are both consistent and unbiased, but are still not the most efficient estimators. The best unbiased estimators are those that are the most efficient, such as the sample mean and the adjusted sample variance.

APPENDIX A: COMPUTER APPLICATIONS

Single-variable graphs can be obtained from many computer statistics programs, including microcomputer statistics and spreadsheet programs. Bar charts, histograms, and frequency polygons are the most readily available, but modern programs also give pie charts, stem-and-leaf plots, and box plots.

Computer statistics programs invariably provide the common measures of center and spread for metric variables: the mean, variance, and standard deviation. Some also calculate the median, range, and interquartile range.

One problem is that these statistics are usually calculated regardless of the measurement level of the data. The fact that the computer prints them out does not show that they are appropriate; instead the researcher must decide if these statistics are appropriate for the data. In doing so, be sure to graph the variable and examine the shape of the distribution, rather than relying on summary measures.

Typically computer programs and statistical calculators report the sample variance and standard deviation, rather than the population values. Unfortunately, the results are usually not labeled as sample values, leading to occasional confusion in interpreting the computer output.

Most computer programs do not include the EDA-based measures, though some modern microcomputer-based statistics programs do calculate them. The nominal measures of spread reviewed in this book are rarely calculated by computer programs, making them difficult to obtain.

The statistics shown at the bottom of the tables in this monograph were calculated using a program written by the author.

APPENDIX B: LIST OF MEASURES

Measures are listed in the order they are presented; alternative names for the same measure are listed in parentheses.

Measures of Center

Mode: mode, crude mode, and refined mode.

Median: median, rough median, and exact median.

Mean: mean, grouped mean, weighted mean, pooled mean, and mean of dichotomous variable.

Other order measures: midextreme (midrange), midhinge, trimean, and biweight.

Other means: trimmed mean, winsorized mean, and midmean; geometric mean, harmonic mean, generalized mean, and quadratic mean.

Measures of Spread

Numeric: mean deviation (average deviation), population variance, population standard deviation, sample variance, sample standard deviation, pooled variance, variance of dichotomous variable, coefficient of variation (coefficient of relative variation), and Gini's mean difference.

Ordinal: range, interquartile range (midspread), quartile deviation (semi-interquartile range, quartile range), coefficient of quartile variation, median absolute deviation, coefficient of dispersion, and Leik's D.

Nominal: variation ratio, index of diversity, index of qualitative variation, entropy, and standardized entropy.

Sampling distributions: variance of sampling distribution of means, standard error of the mean (standard deviation of sampling distribution of means), standard error of a proportion, and sampling error.

NOTES

1. Note that technically the issue is whether the property underlying the measurements (e.g., heat) has a unit of measurement, so that attitudes are not metric variables because they lack such a unit of measurement.

2. Sometimes numbers are assigned to objects that are fundamentally nonorderable, such as the numbers put on the backs of baseball shirts so that players can be kept track of numerically instead of just by name. However, baseball jersey numbers are not metric, because they are not based on any scale. If the numbers do not correspond to an ordered trait of the objects (and the numbers of baseball players are assigned fairly arbitrarily rather than according to a single ordered property), then the variable is nominal and should not be treated as metric.

3. Some metric scales are neither ratio nor interval. The most common example is the Richter scale that is used to measure the severity of earthquakes. It is a logarithmic scale, set up so that an quake of 7.0 is 10 times as severe as a quake of 6.0, which is 10 times as bad as a quake of 5.0, and so on. Such scales cannot be multiplied by a constant nor have a constant added to them without destroying their properties.

4. When there are large amounts of missing data, it is worth thinking about why the data are missing. In some situations, missing data are meaningful substantively, as when "don't know" is really an intermediate neutral category. In other situations, a systematic process may have produced the missing data. Instead of omitting the missing data, sometimes it may be better to code them at the average of the variable.

5. In addition to measuring the center and spread of a variable, there are statistics to measure the skewness and even the peakedness of a variable's distribution. The sign of the skewness statistic shows whether there is positive or negative skewness. The kurtosis statistic measures how flat or peaked the distribution is.

6. Incidentally, the median itself can be considered an extremely trimmed mean, trimming all but the very central observations. A *broadened median* is a more general form of the median, averaging a few of the central observations (such as the middle three or four or five observations) instead of just using the exact central observation; it also can be thought of as a trimmed mean.

7. The geometric mean cannot be computed if an odd number of the values are negative. That is not a problem in dealing with growth rates, which are always positive—greater than one for positive growth and less than one if deceleration is occurring.

8. The range and interquartile range also can be used on metric data. The median absolute deviation also can be used on metric data, but spread measures based on the median are rarely used with metric data.

9. Many texts report the standard error of the proportion, $\sqrt{p(1-p)/N}$, as its standard deviation. The standard error is discussed in Chapter 5.

10. The negative is used because of a property of logarithms of proportions. Numbers larger than one have positive logarithms and the logarithm of one is zero. Numbers between zero and one, such as proportions, have negative logarithms. Taking the negative of the logarithm thus makes entropy values positive because the negative of a negative number is positive.

11. The base for the logarithms is not critical in this formula—the same numerical result would be obtained regardless of whether the logs are taken to the base 2, the base 10, or the base e. Changing from one base to another is a multiplicative relationship, and multiplying the numerator and denominator of the standardized entropy formula by the same multiplicative constant would cancel out.

REFERENCES

BLALOCK, H. M., Jr. (1972) Social Statistics (2nd ed.). New York: McGraw-Hill.

BORGATTA, E. F., and BOHRNSTEDT, G. W. (1980) "Level of measurement: Once over again." Sociological Methods and Research 9: 147-160.

COULTER, P. B. (1984) "Distinguishing inequality and concentration." Political Methodology 10: 323-335.

GRETHER, D. M. (1976) "On the use of ordinal data in correlation analysis." American Sociological Review 41: 908-912.

HARTWIG, F., and DEARING, B. E. (1979) Exploratory Data Analysis. Beverly Hills, CA: Sage.

HAYS, W. L. (1963) Statistics for Psychologists. New York: Holt, Rinehart and Winston.

IGLEWICZ, B. (1983) "Robust scale estimators and confidence intervals for location," in D. Hoaglin, F. Mosteller, and J. W. Tukey (eds.) Understanding Robust and Exploratory Data Analysis. New York: John Wiley.

JACOBY, W. (1991) Data Theory and Dimensional Analysis. Newbury Park, CA: Sage.

KERLINGER, F. (1973) Foundations of Behavioral Research. New York: Holt, Rinehart and Winston.

KOTZ, S., JOHNSON, N. L., and READ, C. B. (1983) Encyclopedia of Statistical Sciences. New York: John Wiley.

KRIPPENDORFF, K. (1986) Information Theory. Newbury Park, CA: Sage.

LABOVITZ, S. (1970) "The assignment of numbers to rank order categories." American Sociological Review 35: 515-524.

LEABO, D. A. (1972) Basic Statistics. Homewood, IL: Irwin.

88

LEIK, R. (1966) "A measure of ordinal consensus." Pacific Sociological Review 9: 85-90.

MAYER, L. S. (1971) "A note on treating ordinal data as interval data." American Sociological Review 36: 519-520.

MOSTELLER, F., and TUKEY, J. W. (1977) Data Analysis and Regression. Reading, MA: Addison-Wesley.

RAE, D. W., and TAYLOR, M. (1970) Analysis of Political Cleavages. New Haven, CT: Yale University Press.

ROSENBERGER, J., and GASKO, M. (1983) "Comparing location estimators: Trimmed means, medians, and trimean," in D. Hoaglin, F. Mosteller, and J. W. Tukey (eds.) Understanding Robust and Exploratory Data Analysis. New York: John Wiley.

TAYLOR, C., and HUDSON, M. (1972) World Handbook of Political and Social Indicators (2nd ed.). New Haven, CT: Yale University Press.

TUKEY, J. W. (1977) Exploratory Data Analysis. Reading, MA: Addison-Wesley.

VELLEMAN, P. F. (1989) Learning Data Analysis with DATA DESK. San Francisco: Freeman.

VELLEMAN, P. F., and HOAGLIN, D. C. (1981) Applications, Basics, and Computing of Exploratory Data Analysis. Boston: Duxbury.

WALDMAN, L. K. (1976) "Measures of party systems' properties: The number and sizes of parties." Political Methodology 3: 199-214.

WEISBERG, H. F., KROSNICK, J. A., and BOWEN, B. D. (1989) An Introduction to Survey Research and Data Analysis (2nd ed.). Glenview, IL: Scott, Foresman.

YULE, G. U., and KENDALL, M. G. (1968) An Introduction to the Theory of Statistics (14th ed.). New York: Hafner.

PART II

UNDERSTANDING SIGNIFICANCE TESTING

LAWRENCE B. MOHR

1. INTRODUCTION

Significance tests are extremely common in social science research. Many people would say that they are entirely too common, and there are two basic reasons for that claim. The first is that the tests do not provide enough information, and the second is that the situations in which they are truly and legitimately applicable are less frequently encountered in social science than one might think. There is some truth in both of these bases for the claim, but not enough, I think, to make us abandon significance testing or put less effort into teaching and learning about it than we do. I will postpone treating the second of the two reasons until the very end. The first — that the tests do not provide enough information — will pop up in several places, and I think that a few words about it are in order right at the beginning.

A significance test is a test of a hypothesis; for example, the hypothesis that a certain population correlation is zero or that a certain population mean is 37.5. There is an alternative to testing such hypotheses, based on the same statistical reasoning, that in many cases would give more valuable information. Instead of testing such a specific, exact hypothesis, one can fashion an estimate of what the value in question really is. One can find, for example, that the magnitude of the focal relationship in a population is probably 0.6 ± 0.3 ("0.6 plus or minus 0.3," that is, a magnitude between 0.3 and 0.9), or perhaps 0.3 ± 0.6. In so doing, one may also be taken as testing an exact hypothesis, but by an indirect route; the first of the two interval estimates just mentioned, for example, would lead you to reject the hypothesis that the relationship is exactly zero, whereas the second one would not. But you obviously know more than just enough for a simple decision about rejecting a hypothesis when you also have the probable range in which the relationship actually does lie. For that reason, many would advocate interval estimation of this sort (commonly called "confidence intervals") in place of significance testing. However, significance testing is far more common. Why?

There are probably many reasons, but the main one, I think, is that significance tests really do satisfy the goals of social scientists more frequently than do interval estimates. We are in most cases not far enough along theoretically to be concerned with the range in which an estimated value probably lies; we just want to know whether or not a certain relationship or other quantity is worth further thought — whether it might repay additional research effort. If the relationship, insofar as we have been able to observe or estimate, is zero or close to it, then it may not merit further exploration, especially in competition with other ideas. If we are looking at only one such relationship, then perhaps we would get the most for our time and trouble out of an interval estimate, but we may and often do consider hundreds of them. Instead of examining a welter of interval estimates, involving many more numbers in most cases than we have any desire to think about, we simply look at a list of essentially qualitative results — "significant" or "nonsignificant," that is, "perhaps worth more thought" or "probably not." (This rule would rarely be followed slavishly; there are always cases in which one would distribute further effort on the basis of other considerations, as well.)

Clearly, though, the interval estimate provides so much information that it also has a great deal to recommend it. Both procedures are important, and both should be learned. Since they are based on what is at bottom the same statistical reasoning, although this is not always apparent to the newcomer, it can also be quite efficient to learn both. Then the question becomes: Which should be learned first? My experience suggests that the logic of interval estimation is less tortuous and more appealing. Furthermore, interval estimation may be seen to encompass significance testing, but the reverse is not true. The statistical reasoning behind both is generally referred to as "classical statistical inference." In this monograph, we will approach classical inference mainly by the path of interval estimation, adding direct significance testing as a special twist. But I will also, at the end, cover the uses and misuses of significance testing in itself because it is both so common and so controversial a procedure.

Before continuing, it is also important to say a word about the function of classical inference. When we speak of classical inference, just what is it that we are inferring? Basically, it is one of two things. The first, as the above examples suggest, is that we infer something about the characteristics of an unobserved population on the basis of the characteristics of an observed sample from that population. For example, if a sample relation measures 0.6, we might infer that the population relation is, with high probability, 0.6 ± 0.3 (confidence interval), or at least that the population relation is probably not zero (significance test). The second kind of inference, which comes into play primarily when an experimenter has implemented a randomized, controlled experiment, is to infer that a relation is probably *causal*, or that an instance of causation has probably taken place. Most of the rest of this monograph will deal with the first sort of inference; in the concluding section, in the context of the uses of significance testing, I will add the reasoning necessary to understand the second, or causal, sort of inference.

2. SOME DEFINITIONS

I assume that the reader is familiar with such basic quantitative terms as percentage and proportion. A large number of additional concepts will be introduced and defined as we go along. In fact, understanding significance testing may largely be seen as coming to understand the meanings of a few dozen special terms.

At the outset, it is necessary to cover a number of basic concepts. The first is a *variable*. *A variable is a property of individuals that may take on two or more "values," or scores, but not at the same time for the same individual.* For example, "Sex" is a property of individuals that may take either the value "male" or the value "female." "Ease of understanding" is a property of individuals that, in a study of innovations (so that each "individual" is one innovation), might be able to take the values "easy," "moderately difficult," or "difficult." "Expenditures" is a property of individuals that, in a study of cities (so that each individual is one city), might take on such values as $1.3 million, $2.1 million, and so on. Note that "individuals" in this context may be people and they may be inanimate objects or other entities, such as innovations. Also, they may be single ideas, objects, or organisms, such as individual people or individual innovations, but they may also be collectivities, such as cities. In the latter sort of case, the collectivities are thought of as individuals because many of them are being considered in a single study and each one is taken as a whole, or as a unit. Examples of such collectivities are classes in a school, forests in the western United States, and countries in the United Nations.

The reader has probably studied beginning statistics, but the concepts of mean, variance, and standard deviation are so important for understanding classical inference that a very brief review of them will be prudent. These three concepts become relevant as summarizers of scores on a variable when those scores are quantitative, that is, when we deal with variables like expenditures rather than gender (I skip lightly here over what can be a highly technical subject; the reader is referred to the chapters on scales of measurement in most beginning statistics books for a basic treatment and references).

A *mean*, or an arithmetic mean, is of course a synonym for an average, as commonly understood. To arrive at it, one simply adds up all the scores and divides by N, the number of such scores.

Variances and *standard deviations* are a bit more complicated. Instead of giving information about the midpoint of a set of scores, they convey information about the spread of those scores *around* their mean. These summarizers help us to make quick distinctions between some sets of scores that are closely clumped together and others that are spread out quite widely. The best measure for accomplishing this in an intuitively clear fashion is neither the standard deviation nor the variance, but the "average absolute deviation": (1) Subtract the mean from each score in order to get the distance of that score from the mean, (2) consider all of these distances or deviations from the mean as positive (otherwise, if you added them up you would always get zero), and (3) take the average of these positive or "absolute" deviations. For example, if we had the scores 4, 5, and 6 inches, the mean would be 5 inches. The deviations would be −1 inch, 0, and 1 inch, respectively. Changing these to absolute values gives 1, 0, and 1. The mean of these three numbers is 0.667 inches. To say that the average absolute deviation here is 0.667 is to say that each of the three scores is an average of 0.667 inches away from the original mean of 5 inches. This tells us something. For example, if the three scores were 1, 5, and 9 inches, the average absolute deviation would be 2.667 inches. The second set of scores is clearly more spread out around its mean than the first one. In fact, if we want to know dispersion, or "spread-outness," it is hard to think of a clearer way to think about the concept than in terms of the average distance of the various scores from their mean, recognizing that some are generally nearby and some farther away.

As it happens, however, clarity and simplicity are not the only concerns in developing such summary measures. Another kind of consideration is mathematical utility and connectedness. The variance and standard deviation are also measures of dispersion, and they score extremely well on this other, more mathematical dimension. At the same time, the average absolute deviation is quite pathetic in this perspective; it connects mathematically with practically nothing. Which should be used? If the contest were only between the average absolute deviation and the variance, the race might be close, because the variance provides very little information intuitively about dispersion. Instead of being an average *absolute* deviation, *the variance is the average squared deviation from the mean.* For the numbers 1, 5, and 9, the variance is $[(-4)^2 + (0)^2 + (4)^2]/3 = 32/3 = 10.667$ inches. What possible information can this quantity convey about the numbers 1, 5, and 9? None at all! Thus, although the variance clearly dominates the average absolute deviation in mathematical utility, just the reverse is true with respect to intuitive meaningfulness.

But let us move on to the *standard deviation.* This measure is simply the square root of the variance. It cannot be arrived at in any other way and has no *intrinsic* meaning other than as the square root of the variance. It is not, for example, the average of anything. For almost all sets of scores that we deal with, however, the standard deviation turns out to be reasonably close in magnitude to the average absolute deviation! In fact, it will generally be a little larger, the average absolute deviation being about four-fifths as great as the standard deviation (the standard deviation of the scores 1, 5, and 9 inches is 3.27 inches, as compared to the average absolute deviation of 2.667). Thus, the standard deviation has the great advantage of mathematical connectedness and, by being a rough guide to the average distance of a number of scores from their mean, it also tells us almost exactly what we want to know intuitively about dispersion. The standard deviation, then, is the summary measure of choice for this purpose (there are others, but none so commonly used.) The variance is used frequently as well, but more because of its mathematical convenience and relation to the standard deviation than for any intrinsic communicative value.

The remaining concepts that we need at the beginning make a pair: *statistic* and *parameter. A statistic is a summarizing property of a collectivity when that collectivity is considered to be a sample.* The term has other uses and meanings, many of which will also arise in this monograph, but this is a particular, technical meaning that will be of great importance. I will try to be sure that it is always clear when "statistic" is being used in this technical sense. The word to note most carefully in the above definition is "sample." It is highly restrictive, since it turns out that in a great deal of quantitative work we either do not deal with samples at all or do not consider them in their true statistical role of representatives of a larger population. Statisticians rarely break the rule of using "statistics" to refer only to samples, but practicing scientists frequently do, to the great disadvantage of those who need to understand just what is being accomplished in research. The "collectivity" referred to in the definition is, of course, composed of individuals of some sort, and those individuals have scores on one or more variables. For example, the collectivity might be a sample of children from a school, and each child might have been given a score on the variable, "father's income." An example of a statistic, then, would be the average father's income of the children in the sample, or the median father's income, or the maximum father's income, the variance in father's income, and so forth. A statistic may also summarize the relations among several variables, still all in one quantity: for example, the multiple correlation coefficient denoting the accuracy with which (1) the school performance of children in the sample may be predicted from (2) father's income and (3) birth order (only child, first child, second child, etc.). In this monograph, by the way, the term "sample" will refer to a random sample. It is not that nonrandom samples are "bad," but simply that classical inference is in principle irrelevant to sampling that is not rooted somehow in a random procedure.

A parameter is a summarizing property of a collectivity when that collectivity is not considered to be a sample. The collectivity might be a population from which a sample is drawn; or it might just be a group (large or small) that is considered, at least at the moment, for its own sake; or it might be a hypothetical population, such as the infinite population to which a true, universal causal law applies.

The distinction between a statistic and a parameter is important for classical inference because what is generally involved there is an inference about a population parameter on the basis of a sample statistic. For that reason, we need to have and do have notation that serves to keep the two distinct, so that we may always know what sort of thing we are talking about. In most cases, a parameter is symbolized by a Greek letter, and the corresponding statistic is symbolized by the corresponding Roman letter usually italicized. For example, a standard deviation in parameter notation is written as "σ," whereas in statistic notation it is written as "*s*." Similarly, the regression slope coefficient is written as β for parameter, and "*b*" for the corresponding statistic. The convention does not always hold, however. In particular, the population mean of X or Y is symbolized as μ_X or μ_Y whereas the sample mean is given by $\overline{X}$ or $\overline{Y}$, pronounced "X-bar," "Y-bar."

So much for introductory comments and definitions. We turn now to the all-important notion of a sampling distribution.

3. THE SAMPLING DISTRIBUTION

The idea of the sampling distribution is fundamental to an understanding of classical inference. It is the keystone of the entire process; without clarity in regard to the sampling distribution, only a muddy and confused notion of significance testing and confidence intervals is possible. Furthermore, it is a difficult idea to grasp. The student should not suppose that he or she is expected to assimilate the material on this topic in one quick reading. On the contrary, it seems for most people to take careful and repeated study, probably because the concept is a strange one from the standpoint of ordinary experience.

Roughly speaking, the sampling distribution functions in the following way: The basic task in classical inference, as noted above, is to learn something about an unobserved population on the basis of an observed sample. More specifically, it is to learn something about a population parameter on the basis of a sample statistic. Not much of this task can be accomplished directly. Let us say that the sample yields a correlation of 0.43. All we can say directly from there about the population from which the sample was drawn is "My best guess is that the corresponding correlation in the population is also 0.43." That is fine as far as it goes, but it generally does not go far enough. One would often have quite an insecure feeling about a guess of that nature because one would not know how much confidence to put in it or how accurate it is likely to be. To add these sorts of dimensions to our statements about the unobserved population, the sample itself is not enough. We will see that the sampling distribution is the extra tool that is necessary. It forms a kind of bridge between the sample and the population. In the sampling distribution, certain bits of information about the sample and the population come together in such a way that one can make the desired statements about population parameters with varying degrees of confidence and with varying degrees of accuracy. As the reader might guess, great accuracy and great confidence do not go together; one must be traded off for the other, and all of that is accomplished within the mediating or bridging context of the sampling distribution.

Frequency Distributions

A sampling distribution is a type of frequency distribution, and so it is first necessary to understand the latter term. *A frequency distribution is a depiction of the number of times each value of a variable occurs in a sample or population.* Very often, a frequency distribution is referred to simply as a "distribution"; the two terms are essentially synonomous. The depiction mentioned in the definition might be just a series of numbers, as in Male: 42; Female: 39, meaning that there were 42 males and 39 females in the collectivity. Sometimes the frequencies are depicted by means of a bar graph or a pie chart. Often, the frequency distribution is given by a curve rising above a horizontal axis, such that the height of the curve above a point on the axis depicts the number of times the score represented by that point occurs in the collectivity. In an ordinary bell-shaped curve, for example, the scores in the middle of the axis occur most frequently, while those toward the ends occur least frequently, as one can quickly tell by the shape of the curve. It is possible also, and we will take advantage of this variant, to let the height of the curve represent *relative* frequency instead of simple frequency. The relative frequency is the *proportion* of times a value occurs, rather than the number. For example, for the distribution of the variable "sex" in the illustration just offered, the relative frequencies of Male and Female are 52% and 48%, respectively. Thus, the sum of all the relative frequencies in a single distribution is always equal to 1.0, or 100% of the cases.

If the divisions or points along the horizontal axis are infinitely small because any decimal is possible, a score cannot accurately be represented by a true, physical point. In that instance, a better way to think of the whole is as 100% of the area under the curve, rather than 100% of the cases. Moreover, a score must then technically be considered as a small interval, or neighborhood of scores, along the line, and its relative frequency as the proportion of the area occupied by the bar rising above that interval, rather than the infinitely thin bar rising above a point (see figure 3.1).

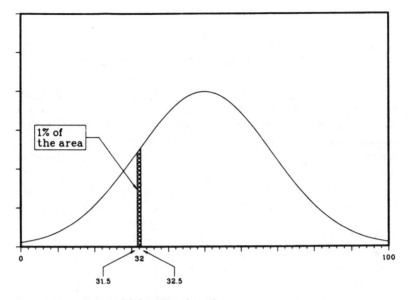

1% of
the area

0   32   100

31.5   32.5

Figure 3.1. Infinitely Divided Number Line

It is important to keep in mind that a frequency distribution always has two components. One component is the scores on the variable concerned, such as Male-Female, High-Medium-Low, or all of the possible numbers and fractions between, say, 0 and 20. When the distribution is given as a curve over an axis, these scores are ranged along the axis. The other component is the frequency (or relative frequency) of each score, given by the height of the curve above each relevant point. Sometimes, people make the mistake of thinking of a distribution as those scores on a variable that happen to occur in a particular sample or population, forgetting about the other component that gives the number or proportion of times each such score occurs, that is, the number or proportion of cases represented by each score. If we say without further clarification that a distribution is "infinite," the statement is ambiguous with respect to component; it could mean that the axis stretches out to plus or minus infinity along the number line, and it could also mean that there is an infinite number of cases or individuals in the collectivity (even if the range of scores is finite). Or, it could mean both of these things.

The Unit of Analysis

There is one more concept to introduce before we can come to grips with the sampling distribution. *The unit of analysis is the kind of individual described by a variable or set of variables.* It is unfortunately not always clear what the unit of analysis is, and unless the investigator gives us this information directly, we must do the best we can to glean it by thinking about the variables employed and the sorts of entities they describe. The unit of analysis may be people, and it very often is in social research. It may also be unmarried women, or U.S. voters, or innovations, or forests, trees, or cities. If the variable is height, with such scores as 50 feet, 125 feet, and so forth, the unit of analysis may be trees, but if the variable is *average* height (of trees), the unit of analysis is clearly a *group* of trees, something like a forest, or a grove, which means that many such groups are apparently under consideration in one study (or else the *average* of something would not be a *variable*).

If we are talking about a relationship, in which one or more variables are being considered as determinants of another one, all of the variables must be descriptors of the same unit of analysis. It is sometimes difficult to be certain of one's *own* unit of analysis when thinking about a relation or set of relations in a potential study. Confusion can reign when all variables being considered do not apply to the same unit of analysis and the investigator fails to recognize this. One might reasonably think, for example, that interest groups are influential in determining the adoption of policies to the extent that they have access to relevant governmental officials, and that the success of proposed policies in gaining adoption reflects the influence of rich and powerful interest groups more than any other groups in society. Here we have what might seem to be one integrated theory, but two analyses, or two different studies, or at least a study in two analytic stages. In the first, the unit of analysis is the interest group, and the two variables involved are the extent of access of each group and its (average) degree of influence over policy adoption. In the second, the unit of analysis is the policy proposal, and the variables are the degree of success of each and the (average) degree of wealth/power of its supporting groups. Because the two units of analysis are different, the first and last studies cannot be *statistically* combined. Similarly, one might think that organizations with more technical expertise than others adopt innovations faster, and that the kinds of innovations that take the most time to diffuse through a population of organizations are those that demand the most technical expertise. Again, there would seem to be one general subject being discussed here, but what is in reality reflected is two studies. The first is a study of organizations: the greater their technical expertise, the earlier they adopt. The second is a study of innovations: the more technical expertise they demand, the slower they diffuse. I cannot provide a set of rules for determining what the unit of analysis is or should be; I can only urge that the reader think about this issue in all cases and make a point of puzzling out what the various variables describe. Technical expertise and earliness of adoption describe organizations; technical expertise required and diffusion time, however, describe innovations. A good approach to almost any but the simplest study is "First, just what is the unit of analysis here?"

For our purposes, the unit of analysis is critical because the sampling distribution is a special kind of frequency distribution, special in that it has a unique unit of analysis. The unit of analysis is not the person, or the innovation, or the tree. It is a collectivity. But it is not an ordinary collectivity, either; it does not come in bunches such that a large number of the collectivities is observed in a given study, such as classes in school, or forests, or Congressional delegations. It is a special collectivity: the sample. But in most studies, only one sample is observed; how can the sample be an "individual," that is, one of many such individuals represented in a distribution? We will see that in a moment. First recognize, however, that the variables that describe this unit of analysis must also be special. Since a variable is a description of an individual, what is that description when the individual is a sample? The answer is "a statistic." Thus, "The mean diffusion time in this sample of innovations I have selected is eight months," or "The mean family income for the census tract in this sample of census tracts is $20,000," or "The correlation (a statistic) between need for achievement and grade-point average in this sample of sophomores is 0.55." Clearly, if there were a lot of *samples* of innovations, or of census tracts, or of sophomores, in a study (which there almost never are), each of the samples could be characterized by a different score for mean diffusion time, or mean tract income, or correlation between need for achievement and grade-point average. Thus, in this very special and apparently nonreal sense, a statistic can be a variable, and can have a distribution.

The Distribution of a Statistic

What can possibly be meant, then, by this idea of a sampling distribution, or the distribution of a statistic? It is this. Think of a situation in which you are about to draw a sample from a population. You have numbered each individual in the population (that is, each person, voter, tree, forest, etc.), and you are about to draw some numbers from an urn, or read random numbers from a table, in order to take a random sample of a certain size from your population. At that moment, it is possible for you to have in mind a statistic that you will calculate once you have drawn the sample and made your measurements. For example, you may have in mind that you will measure intelligence by means of an IQ test and then calculate the mean intelligence (your statistic) of the individuals in the sample. Of course, the mean that you will find depends on the individuals who happen to fall into your sample. One sample would yield one mean intelligence, another might yield a different mean, and a third might yield the same as the first would have yielded even though it involved a different set of individuals.

At that moment, then, before you sample, there is a host of possibilities for the outcome of the statistic. *It is these possibilities for the resulting calculated statistic that are ranged along the horizontal axis of a sampling distribution.* That is why the statistic (e.g., the mean) can be a variable and the unit of analysis can be a sample even though there is only one sample in the study; it is because at the time when you establish the sampling distribution there is actually no sample at all, and the distribution is merely hypothetical — a distribution of possibilities. Note that the numbers ranged along the horizontal axis in your sampling situation would be different if you were going to calculate a different statistic — the median intelligence, for example, or the variance of the individual intelligence scores in the sample, or the correlation between intelligence and parents' income — and they would also be different if the population were a different group. Thus, a sampling distribution is not just one entity, but there may be any number of them, even in just the matter of the numbers ranged along the horizontal axis, depending on such things as the statistic and population we are talking about.

Furthermore, that is only one component. In addition to the numbers along the axis, there is also the matter of the number of times each such value occurs. In the case of the sampling distribution, of course, these calculated values do not in principle occur at all; they are merely possibilities. But what is meant here by "all the possibilities" is to think of continuing to draw samples of that same size forever and writing down the mean (or other statistic) that is calculated each time. In that case, the same sample might be drawn over and over again; furthermore, the same number might come up repeatedly, even if the same exact sample is not imagined as being repeated, simply because two or more different samples can have the same mean. Thus, the sampling distribution is infinite in its second component (whatever it may be in its first component); there is no end to the number of samples it includes. Clearly, though, some numbers are more probable than others; that is, in the sort of hypothetical situation we are visualizing, some numbers would come up more often than others. Still, since the number of individual samples in the sampling distribution is infinite, there is no sense in trying to have the second component be frequency itself. Even though some means occur more frequently than others, no mean occurs an exact number of times in an infinite collection of means. We can, however, think in terms of relative frequency or probability, and that is exactly what we do. In the long-run situation, some numbers result two or three times or one and a half times as often as others, or (to be more faithful to this hypothetical situation in which no numbers have resulted at all) some outcomes are more *probable* than others. Which are the most and least probable depends on such things as the nature of the population and the size of the hypothetical sample.

A sampling distribution is therefore a compendium of the probabilities of calculated outcomes when one is about to draw a sample of size n from a certain population and calculate a certain statistic. Examples of sampling distributions will be shown many times in the pages that follow, but there is no point in providing a picture now; we need to base it on more specific information. Still, given that this concept is probably the most important one in the monograph and that it is generally found to be a difficult one to master — even if it seems easy at first glance — the reader is advised to go over the above section more than once, if necessary, to achieve clarity on the meaning of a sampling distribution in the abstract.

Mathematical Sampling Distributions

It would not be surprising if a certain question were now puzzling the reader a great deal. "How is it possible that a hypothetical distribution like the sampling distribution can be so important and useful? If it is only a distribution of possibilities, it is not likely to be very concrete;

we may not even know what the various outcomes are and what may be their respective probabilities." But of course we can know, in the same sense that we can know what the possible outcomes are when we roll two dice, and how probable each of the various outcomes actually is. If we know a lot of relevant facts about the population from which a sample is to be drawn at random, then we may deduce quite a bit about the outcomes of the sampling process. For example, if we know how many people in the population have each IQ score, then we automatically know which scores are more and which are less probable when selecting strictly at random (just as we know that the numbers on a die are *equally* probable because in that case there is exactly one of each), and therefore which *mean* IQ scores are more and less likely to result. In fact, there is not even a need to have such exact and detailed information about the population. Such is the science of mathematics in regard to probability that we can actually know quite a bit about certain sampling distributions on the basis of only some rough, summary information about the population from which a sample is about to be drawn (and a good thing, too, because if we already had detailed information about the population there would obviously be no need to take a sample).

Before continuing, let us pause to appreciate how important the random sampling procedure is to classical inference. The sampling distribution is the foundation of all, but if we did not use some sort of random sampling procedure, then the specifics of the sampling distribution would be anybody's guess. What if I were to sample using the technique: "Pick any individual to start, look that selection over, then pick others in the population by looking them over, too, and trying your best to balance things out"? Or perhaps I might use another technique: "Given that the individuals in this population are widely scattered and that the sample has to be observed and measured, pick a sample in such a way that travel,time to make those observations will be reasonably small." These are not necessarily "bad" sampling procedures; it is just that the rules of probability do not apply to them so as to yield a predetermined sampling distribution. Who can tell ahead of time what the results of such sampling procedures will be? The predetermined sampling distribution is simply irrelevant to such procedures, and so, therefore, is the entire edifice of classical inference. Thus, everything we say from now on assumes a random sampling procedure, or something close enough to it that an investigator and his or her audience are willing to consider it as amounting to the same thing.

The Normal Curve

Predetermined sampling distributions, which we will refer to simply as "sampling distributions" from now on, are given by mathematical formulas. The normal distribution is a curve defined by a certain formula and many statistics are found to have a sampling distribution that is normal. (I have now begun to write conversationally about the sampling distributions of different statistics, as though the idea were second nature. If it is not, then it would be best for the reader to stop and back up a bit.) The t distribution is another curve, defined by a different formula, and many statistics are found to have a sampling distribution that is the t distribution. Many people believe that the normal curve means simply a bell-shaped curve. That is incorrect. The t distribution is also a bell-shaped curve, looking so much like a normal curve that the two are essentially indistinguishable to the eye, yet it has a totally different formula. The formula I am speaking of in each case is the formula that, given a certain score on the horizontal axis, yields the height of the curve above that point. For both the normal distribution and the t distribution, the formula yields a curve that is bell-shaped, symmetrical around its mean, tapering into its tails, and asymptotic to the horizontal axis, that is, coming closer and closer but never actually touching the axis — never dropping to zero probability.

The normal curve was not simply discovered; it was approached by mathematicians gradually over a period of a great many years, largely in conjunction with trying to figure out the sampling distribution of the mean. You could not arrive at this result empirically (that is, by taking millions of samples and plotting their means) because the second component of a sampling distribution is infinite. Since it never ends, it never settles down in such a way that you can reach a conclusion about the exact shape that is taken by the lineup of probabilities. If you flip a fair coin a billion times, it doesn't necessarily come out half a billion heads, and, even if it did, ten more flips might spoil the 50-50 split. Although empirically the distribution definitely seems to tend towards half and half, the truth is that it comes out however it comes out. We simply have to make our definitions and formulas such that a fair coin is one that comes out half and half "in the long run." It is the same with the sampling distribution of the mean and the normal curve. The relation between the two is largely a matter of great mathematical convenience coupled with great empirical plausibility. From the normal curve as a beginning point, however, all of the other major curves used in classical statistical inference follow mathematically; the t distribution, the chi-square distribution, and the F distribution are all curves that specify the sampling distributions of a number of different statistics, and all are based on the normal distribution. The whole makes a remarkable, close-knit family that is wonderful in mathematical elegance and momentous in practical utility.

The Sampling Distribution of the Mean

Consider a large population of individuals about whom little is known in detail. We would like to learn as much as we can about what some of those details are, but we cannot undergo the expense of doing so by direct observation. Consider, for example, that this is the population of individual, noninstitutionalized Americans over 18 and that we wish to know their mean tolerance of the views of others. We have an instrument to measure tolerance on a scale of 0 to 100. We call this tolerance variable X. The population mean tolerance (a parameter) that is at present unknown we will symbolize by the notation μ_X, and the population standard deviation, another unknown parameter, we will symbolize by σ_X.

We might draw a random sample of size 500 from this population. In fact, there are organizations such as the Survey Research Center at the University of Michigan, the National Opinion Research Center at the University of Chicago, and others that have the capability of drawing such national samples and regularly do so. The samples are not strictly random samples, but they have a vital core of random selection that makes the notion of a sampling distribution relevant to them. Let us therefore continue to think of our samples as random.

As the sample is about to be drawn, and given that we are interested in calculating the sample mean tolerance, $\overline{X}$, there exists conceptually a sampling distribution of $\overline{X}$. That is, there are specific values that the sample mean tolerance $\overline{X}$ can take, and each such value has a probability, some greater, some less. It has been shown mathematically, summarized in a device called the Central Limit Theorem, that this distribution is approximately normal. Furthermore, the mean of the sampling distribution of $\overline{X}$, which would be symbolized as $\mu_{\overline{X}}$, is μ_X, in our case, the unknown mean tolerance in the population. This is a wonderfully convenient result. It means that, *on the average*, a sample mean tolerance is the same as the population mean tolerance. Note that the term "on the average" in the last sentence is a reference to this hypothetical distribution, this distribution of possibilities, that we call the sampling distribution of the mean; μ_X is the average of the infinite iterations of the possibilities for $\overline{X}$.

The Central Limit Theorem also tells us that the standard deviation of the sampling distribution of $\overline{X}$, which would be symbolized as $\sigma_{\overline{X}}$, is $\sigma_X/\sqrt{n}$, that is, the population standard deviation divided by the square root of the sample size. The standard deviation of the sampling distribution of any statistic has a special name that has become conventional. It is called the "standard error" of the statistic. Thus, we are now talking about the standard error of the mean. Whenever the term "standard error" is used instead of "standard deviation," the distribution referred to is a sampling distribution.

In sum, the Central Limit Theorem tells us (1) that the sampling distribution of $\overline{X}$ is normal, (2) that it has a certain mean, and (3) that it has a certain standard deviation. Why do we care about this information? It is intuitively plausible that we would feel we want to know $\overline{X}$ itself because it is so reasonable to use it to get an idea of the unknown population mean. The fact that the *average* $\overline{X}$ (the mean of the sampling distribution) is that very population mean is then a welcome and pleasing characteristic of the sampling distribution. For this piece of information, we are grateful to the Central Limit Theorem. It is not so intuitively clear why it would be important for us to know the other two pieces: that the sampling distribution is normal and that it has a standard deviation of a certain size. These latter two facts are not used directly to get an idea of the population mean, it is true; however, they will be a great help because they will enable us to figure out approximately how far off from the population mean (the target) our actual sample mean, when we draw it, is likely to be. Let us consider these two bits of information further.

To say that the sampling distribution of $\overline{X}$ is *normal* around the mean μ_X is rather a remarkable revelation. We did not stipulate that the population tolerance scores themselves must have a normal distribution. That distribution could in fact be lopsided in any fashion. Yet the sampling distribution is approximately normal about μ_X even so, as long as the sample size is large. Why is that so? It is because, whenever you draw a large sample, say 100 or more, from a population, that sample will tend to mirror the population itself. That is what random selection is all about. The sample will not always reflect the population exactly, of course, and sometimes it may look quite different. But large random samples generally are pretty representative. That implies that of all the possibilities for $\overline{X}$, those that are most probable are the ones that are close to μ_X. Furthermore, there is no more reason for them to be off on the high side than the low side, no matter what sort of lopsidedness the population shows. The reason is this: A mean is the center of gravity of a population of scores, meaning that there is just as much weight on either side of it. Therefore, if there are more actual people on one side of the population mean, say the low side, then balance must be achieved by the high scores being on average more extreme, or further away from the middle — what you might quite precisely call the teeter-totter principle. Any large random sample from such a population will tend to have a similar balance — more individuals with low scores, but high scorers that are more extreme — and there is no reason for one of these factors to influence the outcome more than the other. Thus, an auspicious sampling situation, which is what a large sample gives us, results in a sampling distribution that represents both ways of being wrong (low side or high side) about equally often, that is, it is symmetric around μ_X.

In this consideration of normality, it is also clear, and for the same sort of reason, that the sampling distribution will have a tall middle and low tails. If the contemplated sampling is "with replacement," that is, putting each selection back into the pot so that it has a chance of being drawn again, it is possible to draw the same individual 500 times. In our case, that means that the sample mean could be as low as the lowest score on tolerance in the population, or as high as the highest. What, however, is the probability of drawing the same individual 500 times in a row? Obviously, it is very low. If sampling is "without replacement," the sample mean could be as low as the average of the 500 lowest scorers. But in an auspicious sampling situation, such sample values will also be rare. They are possibilities and must therefore be considered as having *some* probability, but their probabilities are very low compared to the probabilities of values that are close to the population mean. All of this is quite simply and directly reflected by the tapering curve of the sampling distribution, which shows the differing probabilities for sample means that are close to and far from the population mean.

The same sort of reasoning applied once more indicates why the sampling distribution has the sort of *dispersion* that it does. Let us say that, by some standard, we considered the distribution of tolerance scores in the population to be wide. Another way of saying the same thing is that we are considering the population standard deviation, σ_X, to be large. Then it follows that, by the same standard, we must consider the *sampling* distribution to be extremely thin by comparison, because it has a standard deviation that is $1/\sqrt{n}$ times the population standard deviation. In our case, the square root of 500 being around 22, the standard deviation of the sampling distribution (not the *sample*, whose standard deviation should be quite similar to that of the population) is only about 1/22 times as large as the standard deviation of the population (see Figures 3.2 and 3.3). That is a huge difference! Why is it so? It is because in an auspicious sampling situation, although extreme values are possible, most of the infinitely many hypothetical sample means will hit pretty close to the population mean; they will deviate only a small amount on either side. That is, the central values are far more probable than the extreme values, so that the average distance off center is very small. We will see that this is a result of great power; it means that, once the real sample is actually drawn and its mean is calculated numerically, if it is off target at all, it is not likely to be off by very much. The probability of being off by a lot is quite low.

The Task

Having established what a sampling distribution is, it remains to detail how it is used in classical inference. Recall that the point of such inference is to learn something about a parameter that we cannot observe, such as a particular population mean, from bits of observed data on a single sample. Learning "something" about the parameter boils down to accomplishing one or both of two tasks.

One task that can be performed relative to the unobserved parameter is to *estimate its magnitude*. It was noted above that a direct estimate based on the sample value would often not be considered good enough. This sort of estimate is called a "point estimate." If our sample mean tolerance is 27.5, for example, then our best point estimate of the unobserved mean tolerance in the population would naturally be 27.5. Another possibility, however, and the one supported by classical inference, is an interval estimate. Here, we would make some estimate on the order of "27.5 ± 3," rather than just 27.5 all by itself. This may seem a peculiar thing to do. Can we really be better off by judging that the mean tolerance score in the population is probably between 24.5 and 30.5, let us say, than by judging that it is probably 27.5? Actually, the answer is yes, we can, in the sense that we have a better chance of being right with the interval estimate because we have allowed ourselves more latitude. But how much better? Perhaps if we knew that, we would have a basis for choosing which estimate to make. Classical inference sup-

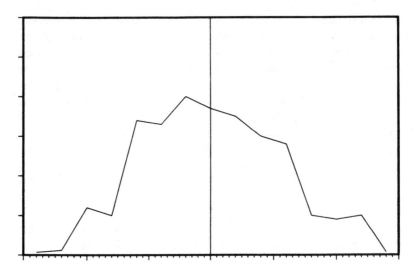

Figure 3.2. Population Distribution

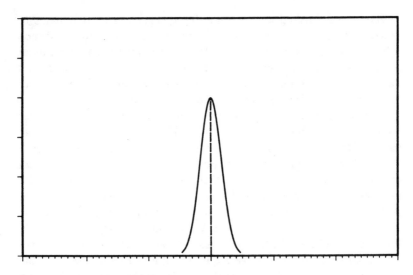

Figure 3.3. Sampling Distribution

plies the answer to that question. It will be the main business of the next section, and in a sense the main business of this monograph, to show just how such a feat is accomplished (as you might guess, the sampling distribution is at the heart of the method). Let it be said here, though, that whereas one may be able to have only very little confidence in the correctness of an estimate such as 27.5 ± .01, it is not at all unusual to be able to reach a conclusion such as 27.5 ± 2, or ± 3, with 95% confidence in the correctness of the estimate, or even more. That classical inference is often able to supply what are still fairly narrow interval estimates with a bare minimum of uncertainty makes it one of the more powerful applied mathematical tools available.

The other sort of task that is often performed relative to the unobserved parameter is to *test specific claims about its magnitude.* Such tests are called tests of significance. The claims might be serious claims advanced by oneself or others, such as a claim that the difference in pay for men and women in comparable jobs is some very large amount, or perhaps some very small one. On the other hand, they might be claims advanced only as straw men, with the hope and expectation of shooting them down. The primary sort of claim in the latter category is a claim that the relationship between two variables is zero. Most tests of significance are of that nature, and the following is the reason why: In social science, researchers are in general engaged in a search for the sorts of factors that make a difference in people's lives, with different aspects of life being salient for different disciplines. To say which factors make a difference is often to say that there is a relationship between such factors and the behaviors or events of concern in the discipline — for example, the factors that make people turn out to vote, or that make them tolerant, or innovative, or apt to be leaders. Thus, if the investigator is able to *reject* the straw-man claim that such a relationship is zero, so that it must be accepted to exist in *some* degree (at least in the group studied), then one has potentially identified such a factor. It is not that simple, of course. For one thing, to have found a relationship is not necessarily to have found a causal relationship. And for another, factors that seem to be important in one population or at one time have an annoying way of appearing to be inconsequential later on. But the identification of such factors at work in at least one setting is a strong beginning for much of the thought and research that must then go on at a deeper level.

Thus, we have indicated two tasks for classical inference in connection with population parameters: interval estimation and significance testing. As noted earlier, we will consider interval estimation first, and then add the twist that is necessary to extend the basic reasoning to significance testing.

4. INTERVAL ESTIMATION

The task, then, is to provide an interval estimate of a population parameter and to know how much confidence to have in its accuracy; our approach to the task will feature the use of a sample statistic together with our knowledge of the relevant sampling distribution. We might as well take a simple statistic for our first illustration: Let us begin by thinking about an interval estimate of a population mean, say the mean tolerance score.

The conceptual procedure for accomplishing the task is best seen as a series of seven steps, some of them a bit tricky. These steps apply, with minor changes, to the case of any parameter and its corresponding statistic, as long as the form of the sampling distribution of the particular statistic is known (a few of the statistics in common use in social science do not have known sampling distributions — the form has not, or at least not yet, been figured out by statisticians). In what follows, you must consider that we know which parameter we want to estimate (e.g., the mean tolerance in a particular population) and we know also that we are going to estimate it by taking a sample of a certain size from the relevant population and calculating the corresponding statistic (the sample mean tolerance). We have not yet, however, drawn the sample. The thinking represented by the seven steps is thinking that we are able to do before the sample is actually observed.

Seven Steps to Interval Estimation for the Population Mean

I will present the seven steps all together first, so that their flow may be comprehended, and then I will elaborate on each. The initial, brief listing will no doubt appear cryptic to the reader, but once the meaning of the steps is fleshed out, so that they communicate adequately even though they are brief, the terseness of this form becomes convenient.

$\bar{X}$1. The $\bar{X}$ I will calculate once I draw my sample is an element located *somewhere* in *some* sampling distribution.

$\bar{X}$2. That sampling distribution of $\bar{X}$ happens to be normal, with mean $\mu_{\bar{X}}$ and standard deviation $\sigma_{\bar{X}}/\sqrt{n}$.

$\bar{X}$3. Select a "worst case" level in percentiles, for example, 5%. In other words, we are working with a confidence level of 95%.

$\overline{X}$4. Working with that level, I recognize the following: The probability is .95 that the single $\overline{X}$ I will calculate will be within *some* certain distance of $\mu_{\overline{x}}$. Call that distance the *critical distance.*

$\overline{X}$5. Express the critical distance in terms of number of standard deviations from the mean, as follows: The probability is .95 that the single $\overline{X}$ I will calculate will be within $1.96\sigma_{\overline{x}}$ of $\mu_{\overline{x}}$.

$\overline{X}$6. Express the critical distance in terms of the values of the statistic on the horizontal axis: The probability is .95 that the single $\overline{X}$ I will calculate will be within $1.96(\sigma_X/\sqrt{n})$ of $\mu_{\overline{x}}$.

$\overline{X}$7. Since the probability is .95 that $\overline{X}$ will be within the established critical distance of μ_X, then the probability is .95 that μ_X will be within the established critical distance of $\overline{X}$. This last statement is equivalent to a 95% interval estimate, as follows: With 95% confidence, the interval $\overline{X}\pm 1.96(\sigma_X/\sqrt{n})$ includes μ_X.

Let us expand on the meaning of these seven steps.

$\overline{X}$1. "The $\overline{X}$ I will calculate once I draw my sample is an element located *somewhere* in *some* sampling distribution." Of course this is always true, even if we happen to know nothing about the form and parameters of the particular sampling distribution needed. Note that it makes sense to talk about a sampling distribution even though no sample has yet been drawn; it is the distribution of possibilities.

$\overline{X}$2. "That sampling distribution of $\overline{X}$ happens to be normal, with mean μ_X and standard deviation $\sigma_X/\sqrt{n}$." For the statistic $\overline{X}$, these facts are known on the basis of the Central Limit Theorem. The distribution is depicted in Figure 4.1, which the reader is urged to consult throughout the discussion of these seven steps.

$\overline{X}$3. "Select a 'worst case' level in percentiles, for example, 5%. In other words, we are working with a confidence level of 95%." If the "worst case" selected is 1%, the confidence level is 99%, and so forth. By the term "worst case," I mean the following: Knowing that the $\overline{X}$ I will calculate is located somewhere in some sampling distribution, and that I will use it as a tool for estimating the mean of that sampling distribution, the question of how far away from the mean it is becomes extremely important. We do not know the answer to this, of course, and never will. We can, however, take a worst case, hoping that even that is not so bad. That is, it may be that the sampling distribution is so thin (see Figure 3.3) that even if $\overline{X}$ were about as far away from $\mu_{\overline{x}}$ as it could get, it would still be close enough to be a reasonable estimator. In fact, that is very often the case.

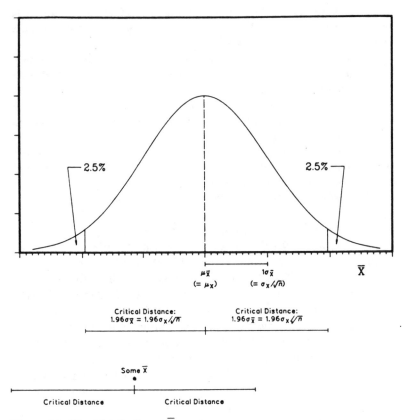

Figure 4.1. The Distribution of $\overline{X}$

Here, then, is the focal point of the method. We are able to do wonderful things with inferential statistics because sampling distributions are often extremely thin distributions. This in turn, remember, results from the fact that, in auspicious sampling, every statistic *tends to be* very representative, that is, very close in magnitude to the corresponding population parameter. We will see that sometimes it does not work out as well as we would like; the sampling distribution for a particular case may be thin, but not really thin enough. When that happens, it is simply too bad. We will have done the best we can, but the best is sometimes not good enough.

Of course (returning to the situation in general, good or bad), we cannot actually afford to take a "worst" case because we must conceive of the sampling distribution as having infinite tails; that is a feature of the mathematical formula that defines a normal distribution. Thus, "worst" will have to mean some location far out in a tail, but not so penalizing as to be infinitely far. We locate the worst-case point in terms of percentiles — always. Considering all of the infinite samples that result from the idea of sampling over and over again forever as being 100% of the cases, we define "worst case" as a location so far out in one of the tails that only, say, $2\frac{1}{2}\%$ of the cases are beyond it (see Figure 4.1). That location would be either the 2.5th percentile (left-hand or negative tail) or the 97.5th percentile (right-hand or positive tail). In either case, 5% of the cases are farther away from the mean, since a case can be farther away in absolute distance by being in either of the two tails. To assume the worst as 5%, therefore, is to assume that the $\overline{X}$ I will calculate is so far out that only 5% of the cases are farther away from the mean. (Remember that 5% of the cases does not mean 5% of the values along the horizontal axis — the first component; it means 5% of all the sample means that would be calculated when sampling forever, some of them coming over and over again — the second component.)

The reader might well ask, "What level or percentile shall I choose as the 'worst'?" The textbook answer is that it depends on how much error you are willing to risk. That is, if you estimate "with 95% confidence," then your procedure, if always followed, would lead you into error 5% of the time. In point of fact, however, social scientists generally do not know how much error they are willing to risk. That is not a very meaningful or relevant concept for us. It is hard to say that there are risks involved as there are, for example, in statistical quality control in industry. If we are truly interested in an interval estimate at all, we are usually trying to get just a rough idea of the magnitude of a parameter, so that if the sampling distribution is thin enough to yield any reasonably narrow interval estimate, that is good enough. Thus, we tend simply to follow convention, and 95% confidence intervals have become conventional. If a 95% interval is too wide to be useful, try 90%. If that still seems too wide, well perhaps this is a case when our best is not quite good enough. We will return below to the factors that make for wider and narrower confidence intervals.

$\overline{X}$4. "Working with that level, I recognize the following: The probability is .95 that the single $\overline{X}$ I will calculate will be within *some* certain distance of $\mu_{\overline{X}}$. Call that distance the *critical distance*." Steps $\overline{X}$4 to $\overline{X}$6 concentrate on measuring the critical distance, that is, the distance between the worst-case point, which is out in a tail, and the mean of the sampling distribution. Step $\bar{X}4$ simply recognizes the existence of such a distance and gives it a name.

$\bar{X}5$. "Express the critical distance in terms of number of standard deviations from the mean, as follows: The probability is .95 that the single $\bar{X}$ I will calculate will be within $1.96\sigma_{\bar{X}}$ of $\mu_{\bar{X}}$." This must seem like a bizarre distraction. Knowing from Step $\bar{X}4$ that the $\bar{X}$ I will calculate is probably not more than a certain distance from $\mu_{\bar{X}}$, I need now to express that distance in terms of points on the tolerance scale. The job of estimating μ_X would be essentially finished now if I could just say that, with .95 probability, the $\bar{X}$ I will calculate will be within three tolerance points of $\mu_{\bar{X}}$, or 2.15 points, or whatever. Why do I not do that? Why begin speaking of standard deviations? The answer is that I do not know (yet) how to associate numbers of points on the tolerance scale with percentiles of the sampling distribution of $\bar{X}$. By simple arithmetic, I can say with .95 probability that $\bar{X}$ will be between the 2.5th and the 97.5th percentile, but how many tolerance points does that represent? How densely are sample mean tolerance scores ranged along the axis of the sampling distribution? Is the distance between the mean of the distribution and the 97.5th percentile a great many tolerance points or just a few? This question, as it happens, is answerable, but not directly; the present step must come between Steps $\bar{X}4$ and $\bar{X}6$.

Two facts make the bridge between Steps $\bar{X}4$ and $\bar{X}6$ possible. One is that in all normal distributions, there is a known and invariable relation between percentiles of the distribution and its standard deviation. The other is that there is a connection between the standard deviation of the sampling distribution of $\bar{X}$ and the standard deviation of the population of scores, such as tolerance scores, on which the sampling distribution is based. We leave the second, which is quite simple, for Step $\bar{X}6$.

It is a property of the normal distribution that a certain distance from the center in terms of standard deviations always represents coverage of the same proportion of the area under the curve, or coverage of the same amount of territory in terms of percentiles. For example, to proceed one standard deviation to the right, starting from the midpoint, is to cover 34.1% of the area under the curve (see Figure 4.2). Since the midpoint is at the 50th percentile, this would place one at the 84.1st percentile. Similarly, proceeding 2.33 standard deviations from the mean covers 49% of the area, bringing one to the 1st or 99th percentile, depending on the direction of travel. Given this property, it is a simple

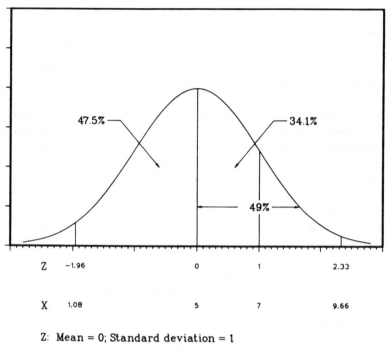

Z: Mean = 0; Standard deviation = 1

X: Mean = 5; Standard deviation = 2

Figure 4.2. Normal and Standard Normal Distributions

matter to express any "worst-case" point in terms of standard deviation units. All one needs is a table giving these invariant relations. *The Z distribution makes such a table convenient,* as we will see in a moment.

What would this table look like? It need not give standard deviation units both above and below the mean because the normal distribution is symmetrical; giving just one-half is adequate. For the half shown, it would merely present standard deviation units, proceeding perhaps by tenths or by hundreths, and associate a percentile or proportion of the area under the curve with each such increment. We would have the number 1 associated with the number 34.1, 2.33 associated with 49, and so on.

Since "1" and "2.33" stand for "1 standard deviation from the mean" and "2.33 standard deviations from the mean," and so forth, it turns out that such a table essentially invents a normal distribution in which the mean is 0 and the standard deviation is equal to 1.0. The reason is the following: For such a distribution, the scores along the axis that are 1 standard deviation above the mean, or 2.33 standard deviations above the mean, would simply be the scores 1 (because in the invented distribution, 1 standard deviation of 1.0 above a mean of 0 would yield a score of 1) or 2.33 (because 2.33 standard deviations of 1.0 above a mean of 0 would equal a score of 2.33), respectively. These are precisely the numbers that would appear in the table we have been discussing. Thus, these numbers do double duty as meaning (1) scores on a normally distributed variable with mean 0 and standard deviation 1.0, and (2) number of standard deviations (of any size) from the mean (no matter what it is) in any normal distribution.

Thus, the table that is generally presented to supply the proportions of area under the curve and number of standard deviations from the mean associated with one another is considered to be a tabular presentation of the normal distribution whose mean is 0 and whose standard deviation is 1.0. That distribution is conventionally called the distribution of the variable, "Z." Since Z is also a surrogate for "number of standard deviations from the mean in a normal distribution," the scores in any normal distribution can be converted to Z scores by expressing them as number of standard deviations from their mean, as follows:

$$Z = \frac{X - \mu_X}{\sigma_X}$$

The numerator of the Z score (or "standard score," as it is often called) gives the distance of a score from the mean of the collectivity, and the denominator serves to express this distance in standard deviation units. For example, if $\mu_X = 5$ and $\sigma_X = 2$, then the Z score corresponding to 7 is 1, and the Z scores corresponding to 9.66 and 1.08 are 2.33 and -1.96, respectively (see Figure 4.2).

Table 4.1 is a table of the Z distribution. It presents exactly the association between proportion of the area under the curve and number of standard deviations from the mean that we have just discussed. $Z = 2.33$ (meaning 2.33 standard deviations above the mean in any normal distribution and, in particular, 2.33 standard deviations of 1.0 above the mean of 0 in *this* distribution) is found by locating the row headed 2.3 and the column headed .03. At the intersection of this row and column is the cell with the entry, 4901, meaning 0.4901 or 49.01% of the area under the curve. $Z = 1.00$ is found by locating the row headed 1.0 and the column headed .00. The cell entry at the intersection is 3413.

TABLE 4.1

Areas under the Normal Curve

Fractional parts of the total area (10,000) under the normal curve, corresponding to distances between the mean and ordinates, which are Z standard-deviation units from the mean.

Z	.00	.01	.02	.03	.04	.05	.06	.07	.08	.09
0.0	0000	0040	0080	0120	0159	0199	0239	0279	0319	0359
0.1	0398	0438	0478	0517	0557	0596	0636	0675	0714	0753
0.2	0793	0832	0871	0910	0948	0987	1026	1064	1103	1141
0.3	1179	1217	1255	1293	1331	1368	1406	1443	1480	1517
0.4	1554	1591	1628	1664	1700	1736	1772	1808	1844	1879
0.5	1915	1950	1985	2019	2054	2088	2123	2157	2190	2224
0.6	2257	2291	2324	2357	2389	2422	2454	2486	2518	2549
0.7	2580	2612	2642	2673	2704	2734	2764	2794	2823	2852
0.8	2881	2910	2939	2967	2995	3023	3051	3078	3106	3133
0.9	3159	3186	3212	3238	3264	3289	3315	3340	3365	3389
1.0	3413	3438	3461	3485	3508	3531	3554	3577	3599	3621
1.1	3643	3665	3686	3718	3729	3749	3770	3790	3810	3830
1.2	3849	3869	3888	3907	3925	3944	3962	3980	3997	4015
1.3	4032	4049	4066	4083	4099	4115	4131	4147	4162	4177
1.4	4192	4207	4222	4236	4251	4265	4279	4292	4306	4319
1.5	4332	4345	4357	4370	4382	4394	4406	4418	4430	4441
1.6	4452	4463	4474	4485	4495	4505	4515	4525	4535	4545
1.7	4554	4564	4573	4582	4591	4599	4608	4616	4625	4633
1.8	4641	4649	4656	4664	4671	4678	4686	4693	4699	4706
1.9	4713	4719	4726	4732	4738	4744	4750	4758	4762	4767
2.0	4773	4778	4783	4788	4793	4798	4803	4808	4812	4817
2.1	4821	4826	4830	4834	4838	4842	4846	4850	4854	4857
2.2	4861	4865	4868	4871	4875	4878	4881	4884	4887	4890
2.3	4893	4896	4898	4901	4904	4906	4909	4911	4913	4916
2.4	4918	4920	4922	4925	4927	4929	4931	4932	4934	4936
2.5	4938	4940	4941	4943	4945	4946	4948	4949	4951	4952
2.6	4953	4955	4956	4957	4959	4960	4961	4962	4963	4964
2.7	4965	4966	4967	4968	4969	4970	4971	4972	4973	4974
2.8	4974	4975	4976	4977	4977	4978	4979	4980	4980	4981
2.9	4981	4982	4983	4984	4984	4984	4985	4985	4986	4986
3.0	4986.5	4987	4987	4988	4988	4988	4989	4989	4989	4990
3.1	4990.0	4991	4991	4991	4992	4992	4992	4992	4993	4993
3.2	4993.129									
3.3	4995.166									
3.4	4996.631									
3.5	4997.674									
3.6	4998.409									
3.7	4998.922									
3.8	4999.277									
3.9	4999.519									
4.0	4999.683									
4.5	4999.966									
5.0	4999.997133									

SOURCE: Rugg (1917:389-390)

What number is associated with a worst-case point of 97.5%? Translating from percentiles to proportion of the area under the curve, we recognize that the 97.5th percentile is at the point such that 47.5% of the area under the curve lies between it and the mean. We work backwards now, from cell entry to column and row headings. Looking for the cell entry closest to 4750, we find that exact number at the intersection of the row headed 1.9 and the column headed .06. Thus, a score at the 97.5th percentile is 1.96 standard deviations of 1.0 above the mean of 0 in the Z distribution, and, in fact, 1.96 standard deviations above the mean in *any* normal distribution. Symmetrically, a score at the 2.5th percentile is 1.96 standard deviations below the mean. Between these two points we have 47.5% plus 47.5%, or 95% of the area (see Figure 4.2).

We see here, then, the origin of our statement in Step $\bar{X}5$: "The probability is .95 that the single $\bar{X}$ I will calculate will be within $1.96\sigma_{\bar{X}}$ of $\mu_{\bar{X}}$." Note that it is not necessary to know what the magnitudes of $\sigma_{\bar{X}}$ and $\mu_{\bar{X}}$ truly are. These symbols merely designate the standard deviation and the mean of the sampling distribution of $\bar{X}$; given that the distribution is normal, the statement is true no matter what these magnitudes may be.

$\bar{X}6$. "Express the critical distance in terms of the values of the statistic on the horizontal axis: The probability is .95 that the single $\bar{X}$ I will calculate will be within $1.96(\sigma_X/\sqrt{n})$ of $\mu_{\bar{X}}$." The statistic on the horizontal axis in our original case is $\bar{X}$, and each point on the axis represents a mean tolerance score for a sample. Having expressed the critical distance in terms of numbers of standard deviations (of the sampling distribution) from the mean in Step $\bar{X}5$, the task is now to convert that metric into the original metric of tolerance scores or, in other research projects, into dollars, voter turnout, points on other attitude scales, and similar, presumably meaningful, measures. This is quite readily and simply accomplished by the knowledge, based on the Central Limit Theorem, that $\sigma_{\bar{X}}$ is equal to $\sigma_X/\sqrt{n}$. (Of course, in real research situations one would essentially never know the magnitude of σ_X, and this is a major problem to be dealt with in the next two sections; for now, let us act as though the quantity were known.) The end result is now in tolerance scores because, it will be remembered, σ_X, or the standard deviation of the tolerance scores in the population, is the "standard" (roughly the average) number of *tolerance points* that each score is away from the mean; it is a statistic expressed in the metric of the original distribution. If n = 500, for example, and if σ_X were, let us say for illustration, 14 points, then $1.96(\sigma_X/\sqrt{n})$ would equal 1.23 points on the tolerance scale. We would know that, with .95 probability, the sample mean we will calculate when we draw the sample of 500 individuals will be within 1.23 points of the population mean tolerance, the value to be estimated.

One is reluctant to be overly dramatic, but it might with some justification be said that we have arrived here at the climax of the tale. We have seen how one sample value plus knowledge of the theoretical sampling distribution enables us to say, at a certain selected level of confidence based on probabilities, that the sample value is within a certain meaningful, interpretable distance of the desired population parameter. We have thus put the unknown parameter squarely and practically within our sights. There is much more to be established, but in a sense it is all elaboration of this basic idea, plus the filling in of some details.

One important caveat is no doubt understood, but should be noted explicitly at this point. To say with 95% confidence that the sample value is within a certain number of tolerance points from the population parameter is also to say that 5% of the time *it will not be within that distance.* Here is the 5% error that results from having to stop somewhere in the infinite tails and say, "this is the worst," when it is truly not; we could possibly draw a sample that is, unknown to us, farther out. Using this exact procedure regularly, we would obtain an interval estimate that did *not* contain the parameter 5% of the time.

$\bar{X}$7. "Since the probability is .95 that $\bar{X}$ will be within the established critical distance of μ_X, then the probability is .95 that μ_X will be within the established critical distance of $\bar{X}$. This last statement is equivalent to a 95% interval estimate, as follows: with 95% confidence, the interval $\bar{X} \pm 1.96(\sigma_X/\sqrt{n})$ includes μ_X." This step may seem obvious, and we have strongly suggested its content in the previous few paragraphs, but it is an important one to specify anyway, for later purposes. It details how the exact statement of the interval estimate is derived by converting a statement about the distance from sample value to population value into an equivalent statement about the reverse, that is, the distance from population value to sample value. Knowing (with 95% confidence) that the parameter to be estimated is within a certain distance of the sample mean, we merely place that critical distance on either side of the sample mean and infer probabilistically that the parameter is contained in the resulting interval.

Seven Steps, Using the Z Distribution

In this section and the next, we must deal with the problem previously postponed, the problem that we are expressing the critical distance in terms of an unknown quantity — the standard deviation of tolerance scores in the population. It is necessary to sneak up on the solution to this problem, and we do so by beginning with consideration of interval estimation for μ_X in terms of Z, rather than directly in terms of $\overline{X}$. The procedure will be to show, by exploiting the Z distribution, that the central task of interval estimation for μ_X can be accomplished by means of the sampling distribution of a statistic that is not $\overline{X}$ itself, but is related to $\overline{X}$ in important ways. That done, we will turn to the t distribution, which connects both with general interval estimation and with $\overline{X}$ in the same ways as the Z distribution does, and which also avoids the need to know the magnitude of σ_X.

The seven steps presented above do not pertain only to the estimation of μ_X by means of $\overline{X}$. With minor changes, they present a basic pattern of interval estimation useful in connection with all parameters. In particular, one might consider estimating the mean of a population of Z scores. We do not do this because it is a meaningful real-world task — we already know just by definition that the mean of a population of Z scores is 0. We do it, rather, because it shows a valuable, indirect method of estimating μ_X by means of $\overline{X}$. Admittedly, we have already developed a method — a direct method — just above, but while pedagogically indispensable, that method is ultimately inadequate; it depends on the knowledge of an unknown parameter.

Here are the same seven steps as they would pertain to Z. The reader is reminded that Z is any normal variable with mean 0 and standard deviation 1.0; such a variable might be composed and calculated as a sample statistic in any number of ways, one of which would be

$$Z = \frac{\overline{X} - \mu_{\overline{X}}}{\sigma_{\overline{X}}}$$

$Z1$. The Z I will calculate once I draw my sample is an element located *somewhere* in *some* sampling distribution.

$Z2$. That sampling distribution of Z happens to be normal, with mean 0 and standard deviation 1.0 (see Figure 4.3).

$Z3$. Select a "worst case" level in percentiles, for example, 5%. In other words, we are working with a confidence level of 95%.

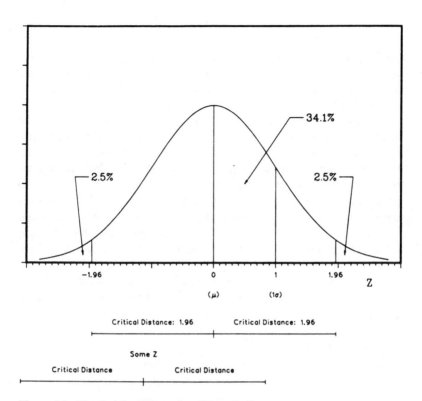

Figure 4.3. The Standard Normal or Z Distribution

Z4. Working with that level, I recognize the following: The probability is .95 that the single Z I will calculate will be within *some* certain distance of 0. Call the distance the *critical distance*.

Z5. (Not necessary, since the standard deviation in this case is simply 1.0.)

Z6. Express the critical distance in terms of the values of the statistic on the horizontal axis: The probability is .95 that the single Z I will calculate will be within 1.96 points of 0.

Z7. Since the probability is .95 that Z will be within the established critical distance of 0, then the probability is .95 that 0 will be within the established critical distance of Z. This last statement is equivalent to a 95% interval estimate, as follows: With 95% confidence, the interval Z ± 1.96 includes 0.

Thus, we have asserted that if we sample and calculate the statistic Z, assuming that our Z is based on a variable that has a normal distribution (such as $\overline{X}$ in the formula above), the probability is .95 that we will obtain some value between -1.96 and $+1.96$. We might not; in fact, we would expect to get a value outside these limits 5% of the time if we constantly used this procedure.

This procedure would seem to be useless, however, because in order to calculate Z in our case, as the above formula clearly shows, one would need not only to know $\sigma_{\overline{X}}$, but $\mu_{\overline{X}}$ as well, and we know neither. We will continue to defer attention to σ_X until later, but $\mu_{\overline{X}}$ may be considered here. It is true that this value is unknown and, in fact, is equal to the mystery parameter that started this whole search. We must therefore give up on the calculation of Z. We may use the seven steps in Z, however, to accomplish exactly what was accomplished in the last section through the first series of seven steps, but in another way. That is, we may use this approach to make the same interval estimate of μ_X on the basis of a sample $\overline{X}$ as before. We begin at step 6 in Z and proceed simply to convert it into step 6 in $\overline{X}$ by means of very simple algebra (to be explained momentarily) as follows:

Z6. $\Pr\{-1.96 < Z < 1.96\} = .95$
Z6A. $\Pr\{-1.96 < [(\overline{X} - \mu_X)/(\sigma_X/\sqrt{n})] < 1.96\} = .95$
Z6B. $\Pr\{-1.96(\sigma_X/\sqrt{n}) < (\overline{X} - \mu_X) < 1.96(\sigma_X/\sqrt{n})] = .95$
$\overline{X}6.$ $\Pr\{\mu_X - 1.96(\sigma_X/\sqrt{n}) < \overline{X} < \mu_X + 1.96(\sigma_X/\sqrt{n})\} = .95$

Thus, we end with the precise statement made in step $\overline{X}6$ in the previous section. The algebra is explained as follows: We begin in $Z6$ with a restatement of step $Z6$ just above, but in algebraic rather than narrative language. It says simply that, with probability .95, the Z to be calculated from our yet-to-be-drawn sample will be greater than -1.96 and smaller than $+1.96$.

To move to $Z6A$, simply substitute one way of saying Z for another, as given in the formula for Z above, but with μ_X and $\sigma_X/\sqrt{n}$ replacing their respective equivalents, $\mu_{\overline{X}}$ and $\sigma_{\overline{X}}$.

To move to $Z6B$, multiply all three sides of the inequality by $\sigma_X/\sqrt{n}$. This is done in order to move toward the isolation of $\overline{X}$, about which we wish to make a statement.

This process is completed in the final step by adding μ_X to all three sides. The resulting statement is an algebraic version of what is stated narratively in Step $\overline{X}6$ of the previous section, namely, that $\overline{X}$ is within the critical distance of μ_X. We are not quite finished, however, because the true aim is to make a statement isolating μ_X, the parameter to be estimated. This is done by starting back at step $Z6B$ and taking the path that isolates μ_X rather than $\overline{X}$:

$Z6B.$ $\Pr\{ -1.96(\sigma_X/\sqrt{n}) < (\overline{X} - \mu_X) < 1.96(\sigma_X/\sqrt{n})\} = .95$

$Z6C.$ $\Pr\{ -\overline{X} - 1.96(\sigma_X/\sqrt{n}) < -\mu_X < -\overline{X} + 1.96(\sigma_X/\sqrt{n})\} = .95$

$\overline{X}7.$ $\Pr\{\overline{X} + 1.96(\sigma_X/\sqrt{n}) > \mu_X > \overline{X} - 1.96(\sigma_X/\sqrt{n})\} = .95$

$\overline{X}7A.$ $\Pr\{\overline{X} - 1.96(\sigma_X/\sqrt{n}) < \mu_X < \overline{X} + 1.96(\sigma_X/\sqrt{n})\} = .95$

To isolate μ_X in $Z6C$ we have subtracted $\overline{X}$ from all three sides. This does not succeed completely, however, because it leaves us with $-\mu_X$ instead of the positive value. The next step, then, labeled $\overline{X}7$, is to multiply $Z6C$ by -1. That is simple enough, except that when inequalities are concerned rather than ordinary equations (the term "inequalities" refers to statements like equations that use $<$ or $>$ rather than $=$), the direction of the inequality signs must be reversed when multiplying by a negative number. (The reader can check this quickly by taking an inequality such as $2 < 4 < 6$. To make the resulting statement true when multiplying by -1, we must reverse the directions to yield $-2 > -4 > -6$.) $\overline{X}7A$ is an exact restatement of $\overline{X}7$, but reordering the sides from right to left instead of from left to right. Whereas the previous conclusion, statement $\overline{X}6$, said that $\overline{X}$ is within the selected critical distance of μ_X, the final statement now says that μ_X is within the selected critical distance of $\overline{X}$.

Thus, we have used the estimation logic in conjunction with the sampling distribution of Z to accomplish exactly what was accomplished more directly using $\overline{X}$. This substitution achieves no progress in results toward the goal of estimating μ_X, but it does yield a crucial insight: It is possible to arrive at the estimate using the sampling distribution of a *function* of $\overline{X}$ (namely Z) rather than the sampling distribution of $\overline{X}$ itself. Very simple algebraic manipulations allow us to move from one to the other. This principle does not pertain to $\overline{X}$ and μ_X alone; it is used as well in connection with a large number of totally different parameters.

Seven Steps, Using the *t* Distribution

With the realization that the sampling distribution of a function of $\overline{X}$ may be utilized rather than $\overline{X}$ itself, the thought must naturally occur that other such functions would do just as well as Z, if only their sampling distributions were known. For example, if "G" were some statistic that, unlike $\sigma_X/\sqrt{n}$, could be calculated from the sample to be drawn, and if the sampling distribution of $(\overline{X} - \mu_X)/G$ happened to be known, then we could go through exactly the same algebraic steps as above and obtain the desired interval estimate without confronting the nuisance of the unknown σ_X. What sort of denominator should be used? The most likely thing to try is an estimate of σ_X rather than σ_X itself. Might we simply use the standard deviation of the tolerance scores in the sample to be drawn, s_X, in the denominator in place of σ_X? After all, if the sample is large, then s_X should be quite close in magnitude to σ_X.

In fact, it can be shown that the very best estimator of $\sigma_X/\sqrt{n}$ that we can obtain from a sample is not $s_X/\sqrt{n}$, but $s_X/\sqrt{n-1}$. (The derivation of this fact need not concern us here, but the interested reader might consult Hays, 1981:187-189.) There is a problem, however, in using this statistic in the denominator in place of $\sigma_X/\sqrt{n}$: Technically speaking, the result no longer has the Z distribution. That means that the Z table is no longer any good to us for associating the value we would calculate, $s_X/\sqrt{n-1}$, with proportions of area under the curve in a sampling distribution. Whereas before we had a known sampling distribution but were unable to calculate the relevant statistic, we now have a statistic we can calculate completely but have lost our connection with the known sampling distribution. The solution to the problem is to recognize that $(\overline{X} - \mu_X)/(s_X/\sqrt{n-1})$ also has a sampling distribution of some sort and, if possible, to figure out what it is; if not, we must try for another denominator, or perhaps another function of $\overline{X}$ and μ_X altogether.

The task of figuring out the sampling distribution of $(\overline{X} - \mu_X)/(s_X/\sqrt{n-1})$ was accomplished by W. S. Gosset in 1908. Since Gosset wrote under the pen name "Student" and called his distribution the t distribution, it is often known as Student's t distribution. It is not only $(\overline{X} - \mu_X)/(s_X/\sqrt{n-1})$ that has this particular sampling distribution; a large number of other commonly needed statistics have it as well, so that the achievement was indeed a major one.

The t distribution looks very much like the Z distribution; it is bell-shaped and symmetrical around a mean of 0. The main difference is that it has relatively more cases or area in the tails and relatively less area in the interior. In spite of the similarity in looks, it may be noted in passing that the formula for this frequency distribution is totally different from that of the normal distribution.

To say that the distribution of the statistic t is known is to say "If you give me the value of any t that you might calculate from a sample, I can tell you where, in terms of percentiles, that value is located in the sampling distribution." We have a table that makes these associations. Thus, if $(\overline{X} - \mu_X)/(s_X/\sqrt{n-1})$ has the t distribution, we let a particular $(\overline{X} - \mu_X)/(s_X/\sqrt{n-1})$ equal t and look up the percentile value for that number in the t table. If we knew that another, totally different statistic also was distributed as t, we could set a calculated value of that statistic equal to t and pursue the same process.

There is just one further complication to observe before we can accomplish the original task, it now being evident that we actually will be able to achieve the goal. The complication is that there is not just one t distribution, but many. The formula has a parameter in it called "the degrees of freedom," so that for every different value taken by the degrees of freedom, the whole table of associations is different. It is not enough, therefore, to say that a particular statistic has the t distribution; it is necessary to know that it has the t distribution with so many degrees of freedom. In our case, $(\overline{X} - \mu_X)/(s_X/\sqrt{n-1})$, it is known that this statistic has the t distribution with $n - 1$ degrees of freedom, or, in other words, the degrees of freedom are equal to one less than the sample size. When we calculate the value of t, therefore, we need to refer it to a table of t with $n - 1$ degrees of freedom to obtain the proper association between values of t and proportions of area under the curve. This would seem to involve the onerous necessity of printing a very large number of t tables in the backs of statistics books, but the problem is circumvented by printing only the most commonly used parts of such tables. That way, each "table" takes only one line, and all of them that one would ever need can be put onto one page. We will consult that page in a moment. First, let us see that we may accomplish our major task in the same pattern as before. For the sake of clarity in learning how to get about in the t tables, we will make just one change in the sampling situation we have in mind; let us now assume that our sample size is only 26 instead of 500.

The same seven steps proceed as follows:

t1. The t I will calculate once I draw my sample is an element located *somewhere* in *some* sampling distribution.

t2. That sampling distribution happens to be known; call it the "t distribution with 25 degrees of freedom." It has a mean of 0 (see Figure 4.4).

t3. Select a "worse-case" level in percentiles, for example, 5%. In other words, we will work with a confidence level of 95%.

t4. Working with that level, I recognize the following: The probability is .95 that the single t I will calculate will be within *some* certain distance of 0. Call that distance the *critical distance*.

t5. (Not relevant; standard-deviation units are not associated with percentiles in the t distribution as they are in the normal distribution.)

t6. Express the critical distance in terms of the value of the statistic on the horizontal axis: The probability is .95 that the single t I will calculate will be within 2.06 points of 0.

t7. Since the probability is .95 that t will be within the established critical distance of 0, then the probability is .95 that 0 will be within the established critical distance of t. This last statement is equivalent to a 95% interval estimate, as follows: With 95% confidence, the interval $t \pm 2.06$ includes 0.

It is clear that this series of steps is almost identical with the series in Z except that in steps 6 and 7 we find the value 2.06 instead of 1.96, as before. Turning to Table 4.2, we find that the left-hand column is headed "df," for degrees of freedom. Looking down that column for 25, which is one less than our illustrative sample size, and then looking across for the column headed .05 for a two-tailed test (to be explained below), we see the cell value of 2.06: that is, for 25 degrees of freedom, $t = 2.06$ is at the point where 2.5% of the cases are beyond that t value in each tail. Glancing down to the bottom of the table, we also see that if our illustrative sample size had been 500 again, the value of t associated with 5% of the cases would have been 1.96, just as it is in the Z distribution: for large samples, the t distribution tends toward the exact shape of the Z distribution. As before, however, the conclusion in step t7 is not of value in itself, but only as it will enable a conversion into a statement about $\overline{X}$ and μ_X instead of t. The algebra to accomplish this is identical with the algebra for converting from Z to $\overline{X}$, as follows:

t6. $\Pr\{-2.06 < t < 2.06\} = .95$

t6A. $\Pr\{-2.06 < [(\overline{X} - \mu_X)/(s_X/\sqrt{n-1})] < 2.06\} = .95$

t6B. $\Pr\{-2.06(s_X/\sqrt{n-1}) < (\overline{X} - \mu_X) < 2.06(s_X/\sqrt{n-1})\} = .95$

t6C. ($cf.\overline{X}$6). $\Pr\{\mu_X - 2.06(s_X/\sqrt{n} - 1) < \overline{X} < \mu_X + 2.06(s_X/\sqrt{n-1})\} = .95$

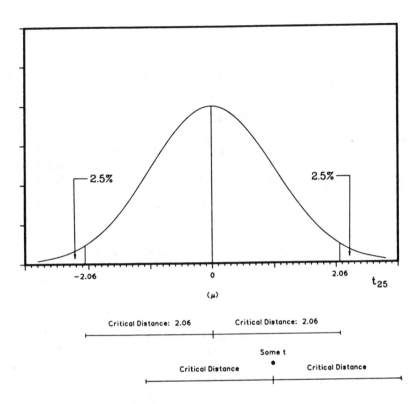

Figure 4.4. The t Distribution

Here, we arrive at a statement isolating $\bar{X}$ exactly as before, except that we started with the appropriate statement about t, rather than Z, and substituted accordingly in t6A. Having done so, the working expression is free of $\sigma_{\bar{X}}$. To move to the statement that isolates μ_X, we back up just as previously and finally arrive at the destination:

t6B. $\Pr\{-2.06(s_X/\sqrt{n-1}) < (\bar{X} - \mu_X) < 2.06(s_X/\sqrt{n-1})\} = .95$
t6B1. $\Pr\{-\bar{X} - 2.06(s_X/\sqrt{n-1}) < -\mu_X < -\bar{X} + 2.06(s_X/\sqrt{n-1})\} = .95$
t6D. $(cf.\overline{X}7).$ $\Pr\{\bar{X} + 2.06(s_X/\sqrt{n-1}) > \mu_X > \bar{X} - 2.06(s_X/\sqrt{n-1})\} = .95$
t6D1. $(cf.\overline{X}7A).$ $\Pr\{\bar{X} - 2.06(s_X/\sqrt{n-1}) < \mu_X < \bar{X} + 2.06(s_X/\sqrt{n-1})\} = .95$

Recall that before we assumed for illustrative purposes that the unknown parameter σ_X was equal to 14 tolerance points. Here we do

TABLE 4.2

Distribution of *t*

df	Level of significance for one-tailed test					
	.10	.05	.025	.01	.005	.0005
	Level of significance for two-tailed test					
	.20	.10	.05	.02	.01	.001
1	3.078	6.314	12.706	31.821	63.657	636.619
2	1.886	2.920	4.303	6.965	9.925	31.598
3	1.638	2.353	3.182	4.541	5.841	12.941
4	1.533	2.132	2.776	3.747	4.604	8.610
5	1.476	2.015	2.571	3.365	4.032	6.859
6	1.440	1.943	2.447	3.143	3.707	5.959
7	1.415	1.895	2.365	2.998	3.499	5.405
8	1.397	1.860	2.306	2.896	3.355	5.041
9	1.383	1.833	2.262	2.821	3.250	4.781
10	1.372	1.812	2.228	2.764	3.169	4.587
11	1.363	1.796	2.201	2.718	3.106	4.437
12	1.356	1.782	2.179	2.681	3.055	4.318
13	1.350	1.771	2.160	2.650	3.012	4.221
14	1.345	1.761	2.145	2.624	2.977	4.140
15	1.341	1.753	2.131	2.602	2.947	4.073
16	1.337	1.746	2.120	2.583	2.921	4.015
17	1.333	1.740	2.110	2.567	2.898	3.965
18	1.330	1.734	2.101	2.552	2.878	3.922
19	1.328	1.729	2.093	2.539	2.861	3.883
20	1.325	1.725	2.086	2.528	2.845	3.850
21	1.323	1.721	2.080	2.518	2.831	3.819
22	1.321	1.717	2.074	2.508	2.819	3.792
23	1.319	1.714	2.069	2.500	2.807	3.767
24	1.318	1.711	2.064	2.492	2.797	3.745
25	1.316	1.708	2.060	2.485	2.787	3.725
26	1.315	1.706	2.056	2.479	2.779	3.707
27	1.314	1.703	2.052	2.473	2.771	3.690
28	1.313	1.701	2.048	2.467	2.763	3.674
29	1.311	1.699	2.045	2.462	2.756	3.659
30	1.310	1.697	2.042	2.457	2.750	3.646
40	1.303	1.684	2.021	2.423	2.704	3.551
60	1.296	1.671	2.000	2.390	2.660	3.460
120	1.289	1.658	1.980	2.358	2.617	3.373
∞	1.282	1.645	1.960	2.326	2.576	3.291

SOURCE: Table 4.2 is abridged from Table III of Fisher and Yates (1948). Used by permission.

not have to make such assumptions. Statement t6D1 is a statement that can be made before any sampling is carried out, but now the time has come to draw the sample and, just as we will calculate $\overline{X}$, we will also calculate s_X, that is, we need both the mean and the standard deviation of the tolerance scores in the sample we draw in order to make our actual calculations. Let us suppose for illustration that the sample mean turned out to be 60 and the sample standard deviation 14.

We would then estimate that the unknown population mean tolerance score lies in the interval $60 \pm 2.06(14/\sqrt{25})$, or 60 ± 5.77. That is, we may say with 95% confidence that the population mean lies in the interval between 54.23 and 65.77.

Conclusion

Several observations should be made before transferring what has been learned about interval estimation to the question of tests of significance.

First, it is plain that we were able to accomplish what we did by having at our disposal the known sampling distribution of a statistic — in this case, $(\overline{X} - \mu_X)/(s_X/\sqrt{n-1})$ — that is a function of both the parameter (μ_X) and the statistic $(\overline{X})$ at issue. That seems plain enough, in fact, quite straightforward. It is a serious mistake, however, to think on the basis of that recognition that the idea of interval estimation is easy to comprehend. The apparent simplicity of the final step is deceptive. If in fact one were to ask the ordinary veteran scientist to explain the basis for an interval estimate, it is likely that it would take him or her hours or days of thought to be able to do so, and then only with pencil and paper in hand. Do not forget what we went through to arrive at the end point. One needs to know what a sampling distribution is and have that firmly in mind. Given that, one may indeed say, "I know that there is a statistic, $(\overline{X} - \mu_X)/(s_X/\sqrt{n-1})$, that has the t distribution with $n-1$ degrees of freedom, and from that I can derive the interval estimate required," but that sort of statement is strange, sudden, disembodied. How and why did anyone ever get to that? It seems to have no apparent rationale. It is a good place to begin an explanation, perhaps, once the basics have been learned, but then one has to back up to remember where it came from. Otherwise, one is dealing only in "cookbook statistics" — simply applying formulas to apparently relevant cases by virtue of rote learning. One needs to know about the form and parameters of the sampling distribution of the mean itself, the abstract relation between sample means and percentiles of that sampling distribution, the relation between standard deviation units and percentiles in that distribution, the crucial function of a worst-case assumption, the ability to convert from standard deviation units to the metric sought, the problem that the metric sought contains an unknown quantity, the relation between the distributions of Z and $\overline{X}$, and the insight that estimates may be made on the basis of functions of a statistic as well as the statistic itself. In short, the beginning student should not jump to the conclusion that the material has been mastered when the final step is understood, and should also not despair if it appears difficult to keep all of the background procedures and methods in mind. Most of us never can keep them in mind; we have to think the process through again and again.

Second, many readers no doubt observed with some consternation that the interval we ended up with in this illustration was a wide one: The mean tolerance score in the population, we may say with 95% confidence, is in the interval 60 ± 5.77, or 54.23 to 65.77. Perhaps that is good enough for one's particular purpose, but it is certainly possible that such a wide estimate is not good enough; we might need an estimate more on the order of sample mean plus or minus 2.5 points, let us say, or even 2 points. What determines how wide the interval estimate is, and what can be done to make it narrower and therefore probably more useful? A glance at the algebraic expression for the critical distance, $2.06(14/\sqrt{25})$, or, in abstract terms, $t_{n-1;.025} (s_X/\sqrt{n-1})$, makes it clear that three elements govern the width of the interval: the level selected for the worst-case t, the standard deviation of tolerance scores in the sample, and the sample size. Let us examine the importance of each of these in turn.

1. *The worst-case level.* It is clear from the t tables that if we had chosen a worst-case level closer to the center instead of so far out in the tails, the interval would have been smaller. For example, if we had chosen the 10% level instead of the 5% level, we would have been able to multiply by 1.708 instead of 2.06. It is just as clear, however, that in that case we would have been only 90% confident of our estimate instead of 95%. That is, step t6 would have read in part: "The probability is .90 that the single t I will calculate will be within 1.708 points of 0." There is therefore an inescapable trade-off. By tinkering just a little bit with the worst-case level selected, one may obtain either a relatively wide interval estimate in which one has a great deal of confidence, or a relatively narrow one in which one has only moderate confidence. As indicated earlier, the issue is one to be decided by the needs or feelings of the investigator in the individual case.

2. *The sample standard deviation.* Given the formula for the critical distance, the larger the sample standard deviation, the larger the interval estimate. The factor that governs the size of s_X is the standard deviation of tolerance scores in the population, σ_X. The first is a reflection of the second by virtue of deriving from a random sample. Of course, the investigator has no control over σ_X; it is what it is. We profit only by understanding that relatively narrow interval estimates must be considered difficult to achieve when the population standard deviation is, to the best of our knowledge, quite large.

3. *The sample size.* Being the denominator in the formula for the critical distance, it is clear that the larger the sample, the narrower the estimate. Recall how narrow our illustrative interval estimate was when we were thinking in terms of a sample of 500. Instead of 60 ± 5.77, as here, a sample size of 501, using the *t* distribution, would yield 60 ± 1.23, a very narrow and almost undoubtedly useful interval estimate indeed. This effect of sample size is intuitively reasonable because large samples yield very thin sampling distributions — almost every single large-sample mean in the infinite collection will be very accurately reflective of the population mean itself. Thus, if accuracy is important, a large sample is advised. The only sort of thing that stands in the way of using very large samples all of the time is expense.

Finally, it is desirable to note what might be considered a technicality about the sort of statement we make in presenting a statistical confidence interval. Although a technicality, it is worth reviewing for the sake of conceptual clarity. It is necessary to see that the statement, "The probability is .95 that the interval $\overline{X} \pm k$ includes μ_X," is not a statement about μ_X; μ_X is either in that interval or not; that is, it is in there either with probability 1.0 or with probability 0, and not anything in between. The magnitude of μ_X is a real, empirical fact, something that already exists. The classical statistican would no more attach probabilities to it than he or she would say that the probability is .4 that it rained yesterday. Instead, the statement in quotes is a statement about the *interval*: The probability is indeed .95 that this interval includes μ_X, since 95% of the time I will select a sample whose mean tolerance score is in the interior of the sampling distribution rather than in one of the 2.5% tails.

5. SIGNIFICANCE TESTING

I proposed earlier that one might entertain two tasks for classical inference in connection with an unobserved population parameter. One is to estimate what the magnitude of that parameter is. The previous section on Interval Estimation was concerned with that particular task. The second was to test specific claims about the parameter's magnitude. That process is called "hypothesis testing," or "significance testing." One might want at times to test a claim about a univariate parameter such as a population mean or variance. The great bulk of such tests by far, however, concern bivariate or multivariate parameters, that is, parameters that indicate relationships. Furthermore, most such claims are straw-man claims. We are interested in establishing that a certain relationship exists. If we can use statistics to *reject*, with substantial confidence, the straw-man claim that the relationship is zero, then we have discovered just the sort of thing we suspected and wanted to confirm. In that way, the straw-man claim becomes a very important logical device. To speak most usefully about significance tests, therefore, it will be well to frame the discussion in terms of statistics that indicate a relationship.

Two fundamental and simple bivariate statistics are the difference-of-means and the difference-of-proportions. To use the difference-of-proportions, both variables in question must be dichotomous, or two-valued. If tolerance were our result or outcome variable, for example, people might be scored somehow as either "tolerant" or "intolerant." Let us say that ambition was our presumed causal variable (although we will not yet deal with the question of demonstrating causality, only of relationship). Individuals might then somehow be scored also as either "ambitious" or "not ambitious." Thus, each individual has a score on two variables, ambition and tolerance. We might have the idea and therefore the research prediction that ambition (among other factors) determines tolerance in a given population. We would therefore suppose that ambition and tolerance are related in that population in such a way either that (1) ambitious people tend to be intolerant and unambitious people tolerant (negative relationship—the more ambitious, the less tolerant), or (2) the ambitious people tend to be the more tolerant (positive relationship). In either case, or even if we did not want to predict which category tended to be more tolerant, we could test the straw-man hypothesis, called the "null" hypothesis, that the relationship between ambition and tolerance is zero, with the research prediction that this hypothesis will in fact be rejected.

Having a measurement scale that assigns tolerance scores between zero and one hundred, we might want to take advantage of this finer discrimination rather than simply categorizing people as tolerant or intolerant. The finer scale encourages the calculation of mean tolerance scores. Ambition still being a dichotomy, we might then test a strawman null hypothesis about a difference-of-means, that is, the null hypothesis that the average tolerance score among ambitious people in the population is just the same as the average tolerance score among the unambitious.

In either case — difference-of-means or difference-of-proportions — note that the parameter is still only one number, albeit a more complicated one than in the case of the simple mean, as considered in prior sections. If we symbolize tolerance by Y, as is common for effect or outcome variables, then the difference-of-means might by symbolized as $(\mu_{Y2} - \mu_{Y1})$. If, say, the mean tolerance score among ambitious people in the population (group 2) was 45, and among the unambitious (group 1) it was 59, then the difference-of-means would be 45 − 59, or −14, one number still, but a number that is a bit more elaborate to calculate than a simple mean.

Let us continue to think in terms of the difference-of-means; almost everything we do will hold as a basic pattern for the difference-of-proportions, and in fact for all other bivariate statistics as well. The one number we use to express the relationship would have been arrived at by a different route and the relevant sampling distribution might be different, but the fundamental logic of the test is always the same.

The task, then, is to test the straw-man claim that the difference-of-means in the population, $(\mu_{Y2} - \mu_{Y1})$, is zero. Our vehicle will naturally be to draw a sample, split it into two subgroups by means of our measurement of ambition, and calculate the mean tolerance score in each subgroup. Then we can subtract one subsample mean from the other. The resulting difference-of-means in the sample might well be symbolized as $(\bar{Y}_2 - \bar{Y}_1)$, again one number. This sample difference might be −14, or −5, or 8, and so forth. In any case, we would use that sample value to make an inference about the population difference-of-means, that is, to infer whether or not $(\mu_{Y2} - \mu_{Y1})$ is zero.

The Indirect or Interval-Estimation Method

We already know one excellent method of accomplishing this. We may construct an interval estimate in exactly the way set out in the previous section, but using $(\mu_{Y2} - \mu_{Y1})$ and $(\bar{Y}_2 - \bar{Y}_1)$ in the place of μ_X and $\bar{X}$. *The test would consist simply in ascertaining whether the interval estimate, arrived at in the normal way, includes zero.* Our confidence interval conclusion would have the form: I can say with 95% confidence that $(\mu_{Y2} - \mu_{Y1})$ is in the interval $(\overline{Y}_2 - \overline{Y}_1) \pm$ some particular number (the critical distance). Putting that critical distance on either side of the observed sample value, the single number $(\overline{Y}_2 - \overline{Y}_1)$, I would then see if the resulting numerical interval includes zero or not. The interval estimate −3 to 9, for example, includes zero, whereas the interval estimate −11 to −3 does not. If the interval does not include zero, my interval estimate of $(\mu_{Y2} - \mu_{Y1})$ enables me to reject the claim that $(\mu_{Y2} - \mu_{Y1})$ is equal to zero with 95% confidence. The more conventional teminology would have us say that we can reject the claim that $(\mu_{Y2} - \mu_{Y1})$ is equal to zero at the 5% level of significance, that is, with only 5% chance of error.

All that is necessary to pursue this method is the known sampling distribution of the statistic "difference-of-means" plus a knowledge of where in that distribution the population parameter, $(\mu_{Y2} - \mu_{Y1})$, is located. Is the parameter located at the center of the sampling distribution, as was the case with μ_X and $\overline{X}$? Or, we might use a composite sort of statistic by which we can arrive at the goal using the algebraic steps of the previous section. In fact, for large samples the sampling distribution of $(\overline{Y}_2 - \overline{Y}_1)$ is normal, with mean $(\mu_{Y2} - \mu_{Y1})$ and standard deviation

$$\sqrt{(\sigma_1^2/n_1) + (\sigma_2^2/n_2)}.$$

(The symbols under the radical sign are translated as the variance of tolerance scores in subgroup 1, unambitious, divided by the number of unambitious people in the sample, plus the variance of tolerance scores in subgroup 2 divided by the number of ambitious people in the sample. The subscript Y indicating tolerance scores is simply omitted for convenience and considered understood.)

Clearly, however, we have the same difficulty here as before, namely, that the interval cannot be constructed without knowing the variance of tolerance scores among the ambitious and unambitious subgroups in the population. Fortunately, it turns out that the following statistic has the t distribution with $n_1 + n_2 - 2$ degrees of freedom:

$$t = \frac{(\overline{Y}_2 - \overline{Y}_1) - (\mu_{Y2} - \mu_{Y1})}{\sqrt{[s_1^2/(n_1 - 1)] + [s_2^2/(n_2 - 1)]}}$$

This statistic can be calculated using only sample data and isolating the one unknown quantity, $(\mu_{Y2} - \mu_{Y1})$, the quantity we want to estimate as a basis of the test of significance. Let us say, for example, that the mean tolerance score among the ambitious people in the sample turns out to be 45 and among the unambitious, 59. *Note that by this fact we see that there is a relationship, whose magnitude happens to be −14, between ambition and tolerance in the sample; we need no tests or estimates to arrive at this fact of observation.* Let us say as well that the variance of tolerance scores among the ambitious people in the sample was 196 and among the unambitious, 169, while the respective subsample sizes for the ambitious and unambitious were 58 and 64. Starting out with the above statistic having the t distribution with $n_1 + n_2 − 2$ degrees of freedom, and referring this to the algebraic steps involving the t distribution in the previous section, we would have the following statement, exactly comparable to t6D1:

$$\Pr\left\{(\overline{Y}_2 - \overline{Y}_{1)} - 1.98\sqrt{[s_1^2/(n_1 - 1)] + [s_2^2/(n_2 - 1)]} < (\mu_{Y2} - \mu_{Y1})\right.$$
$$\left. < (\overline{Y}_2 - \overline{Y}_1) + 1.98\sqrt{[s_1^2/(n_1 - 1)] + [s_2^2/(n_2 - 1)]} \right\} = .95$$

The number 1.98 comes from the t table for $n_1 + n_2 − 2$ or in this case $58 + 64 − 2 = 120$ degrees of freedom. Filling in the rest of the illustrative data just given, we have the estimate

$$\Pr\left\{(45 - 59) - 1.98\sqrt{169/63 + 196/57} < (\mu_{Y2} - \mu_{Y1})\right.$$
$$\left. < (45 - 59) + 1.98\sqrt{169/63 + 196/57} \right\} = .95$$

$$\Pr\left\{-14 - (1.98)(2.47) < (\mu_{Y2} - \mu_{Y1}) < -14 + (1.98)(2.47)\right\} = .95$$

$$\Pr\left\{-14 - 4.89 < (\mu_{Y2} - \mu_{Y1}) < -14 + 4.89\right\} = .95$$

In other words, we have the estimate that the parameter $(\mu_{Y2} - \mu_{Y1})$ — the difference in mean tolerance scores between ambitious and unambitious people in the population — is in the interval -14 ± 4.89, with 95% confidence. Clearly, this interval estimate of the population parameter, which runs from −18.89 to −9.11, does not include zero. By this indirect route, therefore, we may reject the hypothesis that $(\mu_{Y2} - \mu_{Y1}) = 0$ at the 5% level of significance. We reject the straw-man claim that there is no relationship between ambition and tolerance in the population; on the contrary, it appears from the sample data and the interval estimate that there probably is a relationship, and in fact a negative one, such that the unambitious are more tolerant than the ambitious.

In effect, then, the statement, "My sample result is significant at the 5% level," which is the sort of statement we will want to make in testing claims about relationships, can always be interpreted as meaning: "I put a 95% confidence interval around my sample relationship and it did not include zero." However, the interval-estimate logic is a bit elaborate to wade through and clumsy for some purposes. In particular it would be quite cumbersome to approach the very important procedure of one-tailed testing with the interval-estimate logic as the basis, as well as the concept of Type II errors, and these are both ideas that we will want to develop. Therefore, we will trace another but of course closely related logic in the next section.

The Direct Method of Significance Testing

Intuitively, the idea involved in the ordinary, direct significance test is quite simple. If a sample is a random sample from a certain population, then it ought to resemble that population pretty closely. Or, to say exactly the same thing the other way around, the population ought to resemble the sample. Consider an observed sample difference-of-means, say −14. If a claim about the population from which the sample was drawn is that the corresponding difference-of-means is some number very close to −14, it is believable that our observed sample could indeed have been drawn at random from a population with such a parameter, and there is no apparent basis for rejecting that particular claim about the population. The resemblance is strong. However, if the claimed population difference-of-means is some number that is very far from −14, then the truth of the claim would make our sample a very unrepresentative one. Since our sample is a random sample from the population in question, believing the claim would imply that our sample is an improbable one — possible, perhaps, but improbable. Why, in that case, would anyone believe the claim? The *sample* value, after all, is *real*; the population value is just somebody's guess. On this basis, *rejecting* the claim becomes a reasonable, and in fact the most reasonable, option. In short, we reject claims about population parameters if they are just too far away from the relevant observed sample statistic to make them believable.

The question, of course, is, "How far is too far? Just how far away is so far as to imply a highly improbable sample?" But this is an easy question to answer now. The answer is: "beyond the critical distance."

Furthermore we have all the tools and concepts needed to establish what that distance is and to understand how it functions.

Consider the straw-man claim that the population difference-of-means is 0. Can I reject that claim or not? Let me draw a sample from the population and see how close the resemblance is. Assume that the sample difference-of-means is –14. We know from the interval-estimation method that this value is *beyond the critical distance* away from 0; we know it because we put the critical distance on either side of –14 and 0 was not included in the resulting interval. Therefore, it seems, we should reject the hypothesis of 0. How can we understand this more directly, without recourse to the interval?

The answer is this: First, *assume* that the population from which we are about to draw our sample has, as in the straw-man claim, a difference of mean tolerance scores of zero between the ambitious and the unambitious subgroups. Zero, then, becomes the mean of our hypothetical sampling distribution of the difference-of-means. Here is a crucial step. We assume that the straw-man or other claim is true so that we can see how a real sample looks in comparison with this null hypothesis.

Second, decide on a definition of "improbable" for this case. For example, let us say that if the sample difference-of-means is so far from zero in the sampling distribution that a value so distant would occur less than 5% of the time under the above assumption about the population, then it is an improbable sample under that assumption. How do we decide on 5% rather that 10% or 1%, and so on? We will see that, as before, the decision should reflect the chance of error we are willing to risk in rejecting the straw-man claim when it is in fact true.

Third, establish the decision rule that if, and only if, the sample difference-of-means falls beyond the critical value corresponding to 5% probability, therefore appearing to be a highly improbable sample, then the null hypothesis is to be rejected (see Figure 5.1). After all, the sample value is real and the population value is only a claim.

Lastly, notice that one may sometimes fall into error in making such a rejection — the error of rejecting the null hypothesis when it is in fact true. This is called a "Type I" error. I have, in fact, a 5% likelihood of making a Type I error because, if the straw-man claim about the population is true, 5% of all sample differences-of-means will indeed have values more distant from zero than the critical value. Thus, the critical distance that I established translates into a probability of falling into error by rejecting the null hypothesis when it is true. Knowing this,

138

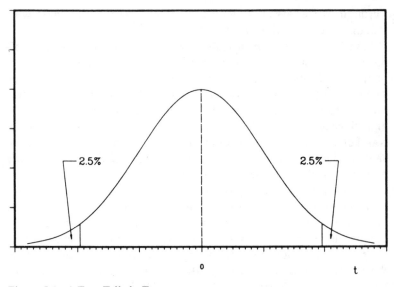

Figure 5.1. A Two-Tailed *t* Test

I should establish the critical distance on that basis, that is, set it at the 5% point if I am willing to risk 5% chance of error, and so forth.

All that now remains is to figure out what the critical value must be in research measurement terms (e.g., tolerance score terms) rather than probability terms. That is, we must answer the question, "What value is it such that sample differences-of-means farther than that distance from zero will occur less than 5% of the time, assuming that the population parameter is indeed zero?" Unfortunately, it is not possible to answer that question without knowing the population subsample variances. It is possible, however, to discover a proper critical value for the sample difference-of-means using the *t* distribution and a bit of algebra exactly comparable to the algebra we used before.

Before launching into that procedure, however, note that in resorting to the *t* distribution we abandon the nice, clean, clear sampling distribution of the difference-of-means. It is not practically useful to us because it has unknown parameters. Thus, we cannot determine *the* sample difference-of-means so distant that it and values farther out occur less than 5% of the time when sampling from this population. Instead, in using *t*, we must settle for a certain combination of a sample difference-of-means, subsample variances, and subsample sizes that is so distant that it and comparably calculated values farther out occur less than 5% of the time. Or, in other words, we settle for a sample difference-of-means so distant that it and values farther out occur less than 5% of the time when sampling from this population, *given* the subsample variances and sizes that we obtain in our actual sample, or *when* the subsample variances and sizes are what they actually turned out to be.

To proceed then, we know that the relevant statistic has as its sampling distribution the t distribution with $n_1 + n_2 - 2$ degrees of freedom, as follows:

$$t = \frac{(\overline{Y}_2 - \overline{Y}_1) - (\mu_{Y2} - \mu_{Y1})}{\sqrt{[s_1^2/(n_1 - 1)] + [s_2^2/(n_2 - 1)]}}$$

Knowing the t distribution with $n_1 + n_2 - 2 = 120$ degrees of freedom, we know that values of t near zero have high relative frequencies, whereas values of t out in the tails have low ones. In particular, we see from table 4.2 that the value -1.98 is at the 2.5th percentile and 1.98 is at the 97.5th. Thus, we know what critical value to use in terms of t. Now, we need only to convert this to tolerance-score terms. Starting from there and using the illustrative data from above, *plus the assumption that the population difference-of-means is zero,* we find the critical value for $(\overline{Y}_2 - \overline{Y}_1)$ as follows:

$$\Pr\{t < -1.98 \text{ or} > 1.98\} = .05$$

$$\Pr\{[(\overline{Y}_2 - \overline{Y}_1) - (\mu_{Y2} - \mu_{Y2})]/\sqrt{[s_1^2/(n_1 - 1)] + [s_2^2/(n_2 - 1)]}$$

$$< -1.98 \text{ or} > 1.98\} = .05$$

$$\Pr\{(\overline{Y}_2 - \overline{Y}_1) - (\mu_{Y2} - \mu_{Y1}) < -1.98\sqrt{[s_1^2/(n_1 - 1)] + [s_2^2/(n_2 - 1)]} \text{ or} >$$

$$1.98\sqrt{[s_1^2/(n_1 - 1)] + [s_2^2/(n_2 - 1)]} \} = .05$$

$$\Pr\{(\overline{Y}_2 - \overline{Y}_1) - 0 < (-1.98)(2.47) \text{ or} > (1.98)(2.47)\} = .05$$

$$\Pr\{(\overline{Y}_2 - \overline{Y}_1) < -4.89 \text{ or} > 4.89\} = .05$$

Thus, by starting with a critical value for t, we see that the critical value for the sample difference-of-means in our case (that is, given our subsample sizes and variances) is ± 4.89. This, of course, is what we earlier labeled the "critical distance," and we are in fact utilizing it in exactly the same way. The critical distance for t (at the 95% level) is simply the distance that, starting from the midpoint, covers 47.5% of the area under the curve, or 47.5% of all samples. Earlier, we converted that distance into real-variable terms, put it on either side of the observed sample value, and rejected the null hypothesis if the resulting interval did not reach as far as zero. Here, in the final algebraic step above, we reject the null hypothesis if the sample value is more than the critical distance away from 0. This shows that the interval-estimation approach and the direct approach to significance testing use precisely the same decision rule; they simply arrive at it by a different mode of thinking. The first approach establishes a 95% (or other) interval around the sample value and notes whether the hypothesized population parameter is inside that interval; the second establishes a not-to-be-exceeded distance between sample value and hypothesized population parameter on the basis of 5% (or other) risk of type I error.

It is conceptually reassuring to see that we can establish a critical value for $(\bar{Y}_2 - \bar{Y}_1)$, in this case ±4.89. That is, it is meaningful in the terms in which the research is framed to know that if the sample difference in mean tolerance scores between the two groups is greater than 4.89 in absolute magnitude, the hypothesis of no relationship in the population can be rejected at the 5% level. In truth, this is slightly more trouble than researchers usually take. It will do just as well to calculate t on the basis of the observed sample results and note whether it is beyond the critical value found from the table, in this case ±1.98. That is true because the above series of algebraic steps shows that if t is beyond ±1.98 (given our subsample sizes and variances), then $(\bar{Y}_2 - \bar{Y}_1)$ will automatically be beyond ±4.89, and vice versa. We can use the two bases interchangeably. In our illustrative example, the t that would be calculated from the sample data given, using the above definition of t, is $t = -14 / 2.47 = -5.67$, which surely far exceeds in absolute magnitude the required critical value of -1.98. On this basis, we would reject the hypothesis of a zero population parameter at the 5% level.

This approach is especially handy in the age of computers. Instead of outputting hundreds of *different* critical values (comparable to 4.89) for all the different relationships that might be under consideration, each of which must then be compared to the obtained sample values for those particular relationships, the computer merely gives the calculated values of t in each case, all of which, if the operative sample size does not change, are to be compared to the *same* criterion, or critical value, for example, ±1.98. In fact, investigators frequently simply become sensitive to the rounded value "2," and use it when there is reason to want to scan a large number of *t* values or *Z* values rather quickly for the interest they may hold.

As a final note in this section, let us consider the factors that determine whether a result will be statistically significant. We can do this best by considering the *t* statistic itself, keeping in mind that the larger the *t*, the smaller the significance level, that is, the more resoundingly the null hypothesis is rejected. The factors that determine significance duplicate those that determined the size of confidence intervals, with one important addition. There, we pointed first to the worst-case or error level selected. The same applies here; it is obviously easier to get a statistically significant result at the 10% or 20% level than at the 5% or 1% level. The calculated value of *t* would not change, but the critical value in the table with which we compare it would differ. In practice, the convention that centers on the 5% level as a maximum greatly restricts one's latitude for affecting the outcome of the test by manipulating the significance level. In addition, the next section will show that significance levels are often not selected ahead of time anyway.

Second, the subsample variances, and therefore the population subgroup variances, are clearly a factor: the larger the variances, the larger the denominator of *t*, and therefore the smaller the *t* statistic altogether. Significant results are thus more likely when variances are small. Surely, this makes sense. If the population variances are small, the samples will quite accurately reflect the population values. Thus, we can say with relatively great confidence (small chance of error) whether the population parameter is zero or not.

The third factor, again just as in the case of confidence intervals, is the sample sizes. The larger the subsample sizes, the smaller the denominator of *t*, and therefore the larger the *t* altogether. Again, this makes perfect sense: Large samples are very accurate ones, and one should be able to say on the basis of a very large sample, with little chance of error, just what the population parameter is, and in particular whether it is zero or not. Sample size is in fact crucial. Since one has little control over significance levels or population variances, sample size emerges once more as the most obvious way to affect the results of classical statistical inference. In fact, with sample sizes of 500 or 1,000, *almost any sample relationship will be statistically significant*, and the test loses its usefulness. True, with large samples that show a nonzero relationship, even if it be a very small one, we can be confident that the null hypothesis is not true, but it means little or nothing to reject the null hypothesis when the magnitude of the true population parameter may be very puny indeed. Who cares about puny relationships?

This brings us to the last of the factors that affect significance, and probably the most important. This is the magnitude of the relationship in the sample, which reflects the magnitude of the *true* population parameter. The larger the sample difference-of-means, for example, the larger the numerator of t, and therefore the larger the t altogether. Again, this makes perfect sense. It is in fact the direct mathematicization of the logic of significance testing: The more distant the sample value is from zero, the more confidence we have in rejecting the hypothesis that the population parameter is zero. Significance testing is made, in a sense, to reflect strength of relationship: We are pleased to be able to reject at the .01 or .001 level because it suggests that our sample relationship must really be strong. Of course, such results might only reflect a huge sample size, but if the sample size is moderate, we frequently look to significance testing to tell us something about strength. Obviously, interval estimation is a better way, and everybody knows and says that it should be used more, but it is more trouble. For better or worse, significance testing is vastly more common, at least outside of economics. The final section of the monograph will take up significance testing as an indicator of strength of relationship in greater detail.

The Textbook versus the Informal Approach

What has just been presented in this section is what might be called the "textbook" method of directly testing the significance of a sample value. One establishes a risk of error ahead of time; that is, one decides on the .05 level of significance, or the .01 level, or the .001, and so on. One then rejects the null hypothesis or not on the basis of whether the t value calculated with the sample data falls beyond the preestablished critical value of t corresponding to that probability. In our case, we rejected the null hypothesis at the .05 level because the sample t, -5.67, was beyond the critical t of -1.98.

There is a variant of the textbook method that is not really legitimate, strictly speaking, but that is in fact more common. In this variant, one looks at one's sample results first, before establishing a critical value. This would seem to be cheating, and, in a way, it is. In fact, in this variant a critical value is never really established. One merely notes a value of t that is exceeded by the sample result, usually the largest exceeded t value in the table for the relevant degrees of freedom

The column averages are recorded in row $\overline{X}$ of Table 10.3(b), and the square of the column averages in row $\overline{X}^2$; the average of the column averages (grand mean) is therefore GM $= 3.37$, and the sum of the squared column averages is $\Sigma\overline{X}^2 = 55.77$; the sum of squares of all 16 variances and covariances is $\Sigma\Sigma X^2 = 906.58$. In addition, the average of the four variances is $\overline{S}^2 = \frac{1}{4}(2.80 + 25.70 + 12.70 + 5.70) = 11.73$. The following three calculations are also required:

$$A \quad (\overline{S}^2 - GM)^2 = (11.73 - 3.37)^2 = 69.89$$

$$B \quad 2a\Sigma\overline{X}^2 = (2)(4)(55.77) = 446.16$$

$$C \quad a^2 GM^2 = (16)(3.37)^2 = 181.71$$

An estimated adjustment factor $(\hat{\epsilon})$, to be employed subsequently, is obtained as follows:

$$
\begin{aligned}
\hat{\epsilon} &= \frac{a^2 A}{(a-1)\left(\Sigma X^2 - B + C\right)} \\
&= \frac{(16)(69.89)}{(3)(906.58 - 446.16 + 181.71)} \qquad [10.1] \\
&= 0.58
\end{aligned}
$$

In the case of nonadditivity, the F test in Table 10.2 would still be an exact test so long as the sphericity requirement is met, in which case the adjustment factor would be $\hat{\epsilon} = 1.00$. To compensate for lack of sphericity, the degrees of freedom are modified as a function of $\hat{\epsilon}$. As shown in Table 10.2, $df_A = 3$ and $df_{SA} = 12$ are the numerator and denominator degrees of freedom, respectively, used in entering the F table (Appendix B), which indicates that the calculated F must exceed $F_{3,12} = 3.49$ in order to be significant at the $\alpha = .05$ level. Given that $\hat{\epsilon} = 0.58$, which reflects the magnitude of variance-covariance heterogeneity, the above degrees of freedom are adjusted as follows:

$$df'_A = \hat{\epsilon}(df_A) = 0.58(3) = 1.74 \simeq 2$$

$$df'_{SA} = \hat{\epsilon}(df_{SA}) = 0.58(12) = 6.97 \simeq 7$$

The adjusted df' are rounded to the nearest whole number (2 and 7, respectively), and the corrected values now indicate that the calculated F must exceed $F_{2,7} = 4.74$ in order to be significant at the $\alpha = .05$ level.

The Geisser-Greenhouse correction (Keppel, 1982: 470-471) always adopts an adjustment factor of $\hat{\epsilon} = 1/(a-1)$—in this case $1/3 = 0.33$—

that value to some small number generally forces an appropriately difficult criterion upon the investigator. We are forcing the investigator to be appropriately conservative. If we allowed the significance level to be commonly set at .50 instead of .05, we would be giving investigators a 50-50 chance of being able to reject the null hypothesis even if it were true. Generally speaking, we like to be more conservative than that; we want to allow ourselves to be persuaded that a relationship exists in a population only if the evidence is quite compelling, that is, if the sample value observed is quite distant from zero.

If the investigator were trying to persuade us that a relationship actually is zero or near zero, however, the opposite would be true. In such a case, the null hypothesis is not a straw-man claim, but a truly held hypothesis about the world. To demand conservatism and remain somewhat hard to persuade, one would want to minimize the probability of failing to reject the null hypothesis, which is what the investigator now wants us to do, when it is actually false. That is the definition of Type II error. Thus, Type I error means error committed by rejecting the null hypothesis (when it is true), whereas Type II error means error committed by accepting the null hypothesis (when it is false).

Concern for Type II error can arise in many sorts of cases — whenever there is a legitimate concern about missing a true relationship (or univariate value) by being too quick to accept a null hypothesis. One of the most common sorts of occasion in social research relates to program evaluation (Julnes and Mohr, 1989). Sometimes, one wants to show that a policy or program is unnecessary, or is not being effective, or would not be harmful. One might want to show, for example, that regular police patrols do not prevent crime, or that a negative income tax does not reduce work incentives, or that a certain food additive does not increase the risk of cancer in rats. In such cases, we might want to hold on to the notion that the programs or policies really do make an important difference unless the investigator can show us a sample value that is quite close to zero, that is, one that shows the policy as making very little difference indeed. We want to minimize the chance of accepting the null hypothesis in error.

Unfortunately, the statistics connected with hypothesis testing when the primary concern is with Type II error are more complicated, demanding extended treatment in themselves (see Cohen, 1987; Hays, 1981). The present monograph would exceed its stipulated length and level of difficulty by including such a treatment here. I say "unfortunately," however, because this topic is an important one and, for such reasons as I have just given, the typical course in statistics and many elementary textbooks also omit it altogether, or give it almost no emphasis.

One element may be noted, even though a thorough treatment is not possible here. In order to know the probability of error in failing to reject a null hypothesis (or any hypothesis) when it is false, it is necessary to have some assumption about what is true. Assume, for example, that the null hypothesis about the population is false. A sample difference-of-means that is nevertheless very small, thus perhaps leading to acceptance of the null hypothesis in error, is much more likely to occur when the true population difference is small than when it is very large. Thus, in worrying about the *probability* of Type II error, the investigator will in general have to decide on some *maximum tolerable relationship* and make a working assumption that such a relationship exists in the population. In this fashion, accepting a null hypothesis really becomes a matter of rejecting a population relationship of a certain magnitude or greater—a very healthy, meaningful procedure.

It is difficult to justify the lopsided emphasis on Type I error found in social research. This is true not only because a legitimate concern for Type II error is far more widespread than we tend to recognize in practice, but also because the above logic of dealing with Type II error can put a healthy perspective on dealing with Type I error, as well. In particular, this logic suggests that we should not always test the hypothesis of zero relationship when we want to establish that a relationship probably does exist. Rejecting a claim of precisely zero is, after all, not very informative. Instead, we should put ourselves in the position of saying, "I believe that there is a relationship in the population of at least such-and-such a magnitude," and then test and hope to reject the hypothesis that it is smaller. A statistically significant result in such a case would then be meaningful; it would tend to convey substantive significance, as well as statistical.

Technically speaking, such a procedure is only a minor modification of the one that is commonly used. Practically speaking, however, it would be a lot of trouble; it would force the investigator to think about and supply meaningful numbers to computer programs, and it would necessitate that computer programs *ask* the user for such numbers instead of automatically throwing zero into the formula for *t*. (In fact, the common practice long predated computers; I am only suggesting that the age of computers has reinforced it.) There is little likelihood that such an amount of trouble will be commonly taken in the near future. I have included this brief discussion nevertheless in the belief that an understanding of significance testing requires this particular perspective on its limitations.

One-Tailed Tests

The point just made provides a natural introduction to the subject of one- and two-tailed tests in that it raises the issue: "Which null hypothesis shall I test and try to reject?" Up to the previous paragraph, no mention was made of testing any null hypothesis for bivariate statistics except the hypothesis that a population parameter is zero. Yet, the null hypothesis of precisely zero is in fact not the only one that is commonly tested. A slight variant of it is also quite prevalent to accommodate one-tailed testing, and the t tables are generally modified a bit to allow for this option.

We have not up to now explored the general question of how one *decides* which hypothesis to test as the "null" hypothesis — zero, non-zero, or what have you. The proper answer is to test the hypothesis that is the opposite, or complement, of what one might call the "research" hypothesis — the hypothesis that the investigator is interested in supporting as a conclusion of the testing procedure. If the research hypothesis is that a relationship exists in the population, then the proper null hypothesis is that the population parameter is zero. That is the opposite of "exists." If the research hypothesis is that a relationship of less than –5 exists in the population, an example of the sort of procedure suggested at the end of the previous section, then the proper null hypothesis is that the population parameter is –5 or greater.

Tests of the null hypothesis that a parameter expressing a relationship is equal to some specific number other than zero are very rare. It is not so rare at all, however, to test the null hypothesis that the parameter is greater than or equal to zero, or less than or equal to zero, rather than precisely zero itself. Let us systematize that testing procedure a bit to show this by listing four steps:

1. Establish a "test" or "null" hypothesis, H_0, by taking the opposite, or complement, of the research hypothesis.

2. Select a percentage risk of error, call it "alpha %," of rejecting H_0 when it is true (Type I error).

3. Establish a "critical region" of the t (or other) distribution, bounded on the near side by the critical value(s). The region beyond the critical value(s) must

be such as to contain the least probable alpha % of all sample t, assuming the null hypothesis to be true.

4. Reject H_0 if the observed sample t falls in the critical region.

Up to now, we have conformed to the above steps in the following fashion. Let us assume a research hypothesis stating that some relationship between ambition and tolerance exists in the population. Step 1 directs us to establish the null hypothesis by taking the opposite. The opposite of "some relationship exists" is "no relationship exists," that is, the measure of the relationship is zero.

Proceeding to step 2, let us opt for a 5% risk of error in rejecting the null hypothesis when it is true. In step 3, we then establish a critical region containing the least probable t, given the truth of the null hypothesis, such that all together they amount to 5% of the total. No matter what value is assumed for the population parameter in calculating t from sample data, the *most* probable t under that assumption is always zero, since the most probable sample relationship would duplicate the population relationship, making the numerator of the t statistic zero. Thus, the least probable t are the furthest away from zero. At 120 degrees of freedom, the critical value is the double value ±1.98, since these t values mark off a critical region containing the most distant 2.5% in each tail (see Figure 5.1). Step 4 then directs us to reject H_0 if the sample t is greater than 1.98 or less than −1.98.

It would in fact be rare, however, to have a research hypothesis that is so noncommittal. If one suspects a relationship between two variables, one generally has some idea of why it would exist, and therefore would expect it to be either positive or negative, and not just nonzero. For example, if my thinking and prior research lead me to suspect a relationship between ambition and tolerance, that same thinking is likely to leave me with a belief about its direction. I might, for example, believe that ambition depresses tolerance, so that the expected relationship is negative (the higher the ambition, the lower the tolerance). Under these circumstances, it is still possible to follow through the above four steps, but the results are a bit different.

1: My research hypothesis now states that the population relationship is negative. The opposite of a negative relationship is a relationship of zero or greater. The latter, then, becomes the null hypothesis.

2: Let us again risk 5% chance of error.

3: What region contains the least probable 5% of all possible sample t, assuming the null hypothesis to be true? In this case, the null hypothesis is that the relationship is zero *or greater*. The trick in one-tailed testing is that we can work with the single *t* distribution in which the population parameter is assumed to be zero while testing the composite null hypothesis that it is zero or greater. If the population parameter is in reality zero, then the most probable sample relationship is zero. If we also *assume* the population parameter to be zero and plug that value into the formula for *t*, then the numerator of the most probable *t* statistic will be 0 − 0, or *t* = 0. If the population parameter is in reality greater than zero, however, then the most probable sample relationships will also be positive in sign. If we do not change the *assumption* in that circumstance, *the numerator of t would then most probably be positive* (some positive sample value minus the assumed zero). In the case of this composite null hypothesis, then, as long as zero is assumed and plugged in for the parameter, all positive values of *t* must be considered to be probable, and no positive values improbable. If the null hypothesis that the parameter is zero or greater were really true, the only really improbable *t* would be negative *t*, and 5% of all possible *t* that are the most improbable under these composite conditions are the 5% of all possible *t* that are the most negative (i.e., further to the left in the *t* distribution). In other words, the critical region is concentrated entirely in the negative tail, rather than being divided between the two tails (see Figure 5.2). This means that we would reject the null hypothesis (zero or positive) and accept our research notion that a negative relationship exists in the population only if the sample yields a strong negative relationship, which of course makes excellent sense.

How negative? That is, what value of *t* marks off the 5% negative tail? This may easily be read from the table (still assuming 120 degrees of freedom), where we see that, whereas *t* = − 1.98 would mark off the most negative 2.5%, it is *t* = −1.658 that marks off the most negative 5%. Our critical value at the 5% level for a one-tailed test of a hypothesis of negative relationship is therefore *t* = −1.658.

4: Any *t* that is less than −1.658 therefore directs rejection of the null hypothesis. If the hypothesized relationship had been positive in the first place, of course, then the null hypothesis would have stipulated zero or less, and the critical region would have been entirely concentrated in the positive tail.

Since most hypotheses by far are directional, most significance testing should be one-tailed testing, but in fact it is not. Investigators frequently (not always, by any means) use two-tailed testing, even when their idea is that the population relationship is positive (or negative).

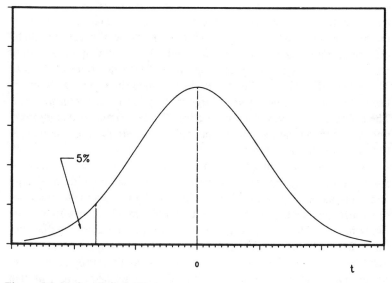

Figure 5.2. A One-Tailed *t* Test

What this means in effect is that they are being even more conservative than it seems; when testing at the 5% level, they are really testing at the 2.5% level, since values in only one of the tails would lead them to reject the null hypothesis and offer the sample results as support for their original beliefs. The same is true of the informal approach described above. One asterisk and a footnote indicating significance at the 5% level would truly mean, in many cases, "If I had used an a priori decision rule of 2.5% with a one-tailed test, this result would have been statistically significant." The claimed .05 level is therefore a show of modesty; the investigator could have claimed significance for the results at the .025 level.

6. THE FUNCTIONS OF THE TEST

Having probed the technical meaning of the significance test, it remains to explore its substantive meaning—what it tells us about the world. The univariate case is quite clear. We can test the null hypothesis that the mean income in a population is, say, $20,000, and either reject it or not on the basis of the mean income in a random sample. Significance testing is primarily used with bivariate and multivariate statistics, however; that is, it is used to say something about relationships. Here, the picture is not so clear; it is clouded by the issue of causality and by the use of ambiguous terms such as "real." I suggest that a measure of clarity can be introduced by consideration of four functions of the test. These are definitely not the only ways in which the significance test is used, but they do cover a very large proportion of common practice. The four are the survey-design function, the experimental-design function, the econometric-modeling function, and the strength-of-relationship function (see Mohr, 1988:90-96).

By the "function" of a test, I mean the kind of information that the significance test gives when interpreted in conjunction with the design and data-analysis operations employed. In order to discuss the functions of significance tests, it is important to keep in mind the meaning of the fundamental concept of a sampling distribution. The sampling distribution is valuable to know about because, under a given set of particular assumptions about the population, it tells us what the probabilities are of getting any specific value (or set of values) when sampling from that population. It is also important to bear in mind that the idea of known sampling distributions applies only under conditions of random sampling; statisticians have essentially nothing to say about the probability of one value or another when the sampling is not fundamentally random.

The first function of significance testing, and the one we have presumed all along, is called the *survey-design* function. It might also rather loosely be called the *population-inference* function to distinguish it from the causal-inference function, to be reviewed below. Here, the test yields the probability of getting a sample statistic — a difference between two means, let us say — beyond a certain magnitude when sampling at random from a population in which the comparable value (difference-of-means) is zero. For example, if we assume that the difference in mean tolerance is zero between those people in the population who are ambitious and those who are unambitious, the significance test informs us about the probability of getting a large difference of means, even so, in a random sample. If we do get an improbably large difference, we would then tentatively reject the notion that the population value is truly zero, since this was only a hypothesis and not an observation.

Note that we would not be in a position to say that the levels of ambition *caused* the levels of tolerance; many other explanations for the difference-of-means are possible. Here, the maxim that "correlation does not imply causation" becomes an important caveat. Variables can be correlated in the world without one causing the other at all. In particular, they may be correlated in a given population simply by coincidence. In a specific five-year period, for example, it may rain quite a bit toward the beginning of the week and hardly at all toward the end, but no causality is necessarily involved, that is, day of the week does not cause rain. Presumably, if we looked at a 100-year period the correlation would disappear. However, we do not always have the capability of observing such large chunks of time, or of space. Also, correlations may be "spurious," that is, they may be occasioned entirely, or at least partly, by extraneous forces. For example, the correlation between ambition and tolerance might be due in part to factors of childhood socialization summed up in the concept "birth order": First children may on the whole tend to become both ambitious and intolerant, whereas second or middle children become both less ambitious and more tolerant. To the extent that this spuriousness prevails, ambition itself is not the cause of degree of tolerance.

All we can infer from the test when using a random sample from a large population in this fashion is either that the relationship in the population is probably nonzero or that a zero relationship cannot be rejected. *Why* the population relationship is zero or nonzero is another question. Of course, if one thing causes another in the world, then the two are going to be related to one another somewhere. Thus, establishing that a relationship does or does not exist is at least relevant to the idea of causality. It is important to keep in mind, however, that the amount of causal information the test conveys in itself is quite limited. In short, we use the survey-design function when we have a true interest in the magnitude of relationships in a specific population and do not have the capability of observing the whole population. Typically, once that sort of fact is established the research task has barely begun; the tough and interesting part comes in figuring out why the relationship has the particular magnitude that was observed.

The second function of significance testing is called the *experimental-design* function, or the *causal-inference* function. Whereas one is not able to infer a causal connection in the first kind of case, one can do so in this one. The difference lies in the kind of design that backs up the test. Here, one selects a group, *all* of which is to be observed, and randomly subdivides it into subgroups. This process is generally called "randomization." For example, if we were vitally interested in the effect of a college education on tolerance, we might randomize a group of high school graduates into two subgroups and make one subgroup go through four years of college while not allowing the other to attend. Clearly, we would be very unlikely to be able to accomplish such a design in the world. I chose the example in order to illustrate the point that randomized experiments are not very available to social researchers in real-world settings. If we wish to know the effects of college on tolerance, we simply may not be able to use a design that permits a reliable causal inference. There are exceptions, however. Experimental designs are prevalent in program evaluation; they are also prevalent in laboratory research in psychology, although laboratory research does not always reflect the "real world" very well.

Let us assume for simplicity that the randomization subdivides the group into two subgroups, although one might randomize into more groups, as well. Note that, still thinking of tolerance as an outcome, the mean tolerance in the population from which both of the subsamples were drawn is clearly the same because each subsample was drawn at random from the same "population," namely, just the combined set of subjects before the randomization took place. The population difference-of-means, then, is already known and does not have to be inferred by significance testing or interval estimation; it is just plain zero. Thus, and this is the important implication, the two subgroups can differ in their mean tolerance levels just after the randomization only by the vagaries, generally quite small, of this random sampling process.

One then administers an experimental treatment to one of the two groups. Assume, for example, that one group is sent to college and kept there while the other — the control group — is prevented from attending. Now, we measure tolerance levels after four years of college. Knowing the details of the sampling distribution of the difference-of-means of two random samples from the same population, that is, when the null hypothesis is known to be true, one is now able to say how probable is a difference-of-means of a certain magnitude as a result of the vagaries of the randomization alone. *That is precisely the information communicated by a significance test.* Thus, we know just how probable it is that these two subgroups differed at the outset by any amount in their initial tolerance levels or in any other preexisting causes of later tolerance scores — *all such traits are randomized.* If the significance test tells us that the difference actually observed in the end is improbably large for a randomization vagary, then some of that difference, at least, may with substantial confidence be attributed to the treatment, *since that is the only nonrandomized difference between the two subgroups.* (Of course, it is not the only possible difference; some differences might have crept in after the randomization due to impurities in the way the experiment was conceptualized and carried out. Such "contamination" is always possible, but there are times when we are willing to consider it quite unlikely to be large.)

Note that the conclusion is possible only if there has been randomization, or, let us say, only if there has been an assignment procedure so close to random sampling that the statistical model becomes essentially relevant. The sampling distribution is known only for the case of random sampling, not for the selection of groups or subgroups in just any old way. We might compare two groups of high school graduates that seem to be pretty much the same, but that is not tantamount to randomization. There is in general very little basis for running a significance test on the emerging difference between such groups and making a causal inference; they could have differed in many undetected but important ways right from the beginning. The point is that if one has not randomized, one never knows. If one compared a college group and a noncollege group without randomization or random sampling of any sort, a significance test would have very little apparent relevance (it does rule out such factors as random measurement error). It does not permit a causal inference because of the absence of randomization and it does not permit inference to a larger population because no such population has been randomly sampled.

In the experiment, however, the combination of randomization, a postrandomization administration of the treatment conditions, and a known sampling distribution allows a *causal* inference to be made on the basis of the results of a significance test. The causal conclusion then holds at least for the subjects, times, and conditions observed. Even though one cannot generalize to other individuals and conditions, however, when the design is applicable, it is certainly very powerful. Unfortunately, as noted, most social researchers outside of experimental psychology cannot aspire to conduct randomized experiments on their social and behavioral questions.

The third function is loosely called the "econometric-modeling" function. It is not entirely rare or unusual outside of economics, but it is a common perspective primarily in that discipline. It gives the probability that a parameter estimate of a certain magnitude might be attributable to the random-disturbance component of a model rather than indicating a true causal effect. It is difficult to appreciate the econometric-modeling function without some reliance on the statistical technique called "regression analysis," but a skeletal outline may be provided here.

Consider, for example, that one has assumed that tolerance is caused only by a certain set of specified variables, including ambition among them, plus a random-disturbance component. In other words, we presume that any person's score on the outcome variable (tolerance) is fully determined by our set of causes, except that, for each individual, some positive or negative number picked at random out of a hat (that is, generated at random by other forces in life not included in the analysis) is added to this determined score.

We do not pick a random sample from a larger population nor do we implement any randomization process. We simply observe a collectivity. When one collects data on the variables and analyzes them, a certain relationship will show up between tolerance and ambition, as well as between tolerance and each of the other causes included. The point is that the disturbances meted out to any subgroup are assumed to be a random sample of the population of disturbances. Thus, if ambition itself has absolutely no effect on tolerance, the average tolerance scores of the ambitious and unambitious subgroups should differ only as the result of this random sampling of the disturbances. Do they differ by so much that two random samples from the same population of disturbance scores are unlikely to be responsible? The significance test gives us *precisely* that information. When one tests the relationship between tolerance and ambition for significance, one learns whether (a) it is so large that it probably could not be entirely the misleading result of the random disturbances but indicates, rather, a true causal impact, or (b) it is so small that it might well be due to the random-disturbance component, so that ambition may no longer be assumed to be causal.

Thus, there is a causal inference connected with this function. However, the validity of the causal inference based on the significance test does depend on the validity of the *model*; that is, if the assumption about the specified set of causes is wrong, and there is a cause of tolerance score that is not included in the analysis, then the basis for the causal inference evaporates. That is true because we can no longer pretend that all that is omitted is a *random* disturbance, one that is not related to any of the included predictors. An actual cause has been omitted, and if it is related to ambition, for example (as birth order would be), its absence will magnify the difference in tolerance scores between the ambitious and the unambitious subgroups. That ruins the basis for our causal inference about ambition. In order for the econometric-modeling function to apply, therefore, the model must be correct, that is, every true cause must be included, to the point where all that is left out is a random disturbance. Unfortunately, the models we deal with most are woefully far from this ideal; they leave a lot about the result or dependent variable to be explained, and there is no good basis for assuming that the large portion yet to be explained is random, that is, quite unrelated to the causes already included.

The fourth function is the *strength-of-relationship* function. Researchers hardly ever acknowlege that they are using a significance test in this manner, and this function is not commonly referred to in published material. Yet, it is probably the most common use of all. It is one way that almost all producers and consumers of statistical analyses alike have of assessing quickly, as a first impression, what to make of a reported relationship or a bit of computer output. What it does is to provide a metric of strength of relationship, one that is probably more broadly applicable than any other. It is appealing partly because some strength measures say little in their own voices. What, for example, does a difference-of-means of −14 mean in the case of ambition and tolerance — is this a strong relation, or a weak one, or is it moderate? Even when they do convey a message intrinsically, it is most convenient to be able to translate them all into a common language, whether originally expressed as correlation coefficients, regression coefficients, gammas, taus, chi-squares, or differences-of-means, or whether the measurement scales were dollars, pounds, attitude points, test scores, population densities, or anything else. The terminology for this common language is based in probability. No matter what design or nondesign has been employed, the results of the test give the probability that one would have obtained a statistic in a certain range of magnitude *if* one had actually implemented a randomization or random sampling procedure (given the sample size and variance estimates that were obtained). Any nonsignificant result means that the relationship tested is so small (no matter what its raw magnitude happens to be) that it could fairly easily occur through the vagaries of a randomization or random sampling process. Simple random assignment, for example, would yield a difference-of-means that great more than five times out of a hundred; such a difference-of-means, the test result tells us, is not a remarkably rare event even when looking at the difference between two random samples from the very same population. It therefore may be too small a relationship to bother about even if it were truly causal. In fact, any time, in any research, that a relationship turns out to be nonsignificant statistically, one might, with some caution, interpret it as indicating lack of importance. The basis for such a conclusion would be that if the magnitude of a relationship is such that it could easily occur by a random selection process, it is too puny to repay the time and effort necessary to think about or research it further (Blalock, 1960:270-271). The note of caution referred to is of course necessitated by the possibility that the relationship might be quite strong in some *other* group or subgroup — even a subgroup of the very group observed.

On the other hand, if a relationship is statistically significant, it means that it is so large that it could not easily have occurred as the result of random forces alone. Here, caution is necessary because of sample size; since almost any small relationship will still be statistically significant with very large samples, this interpretation of the test is helpful only with sample sizes in the small to moderate range. If not the result of a random process, why then did the observed magnitude occur? We do not know from the test alone. The relationship may be causal, but it may also be spurious or coincidental (see Mohr, 1988:178-182). We simply know that it is fairly large in this one universal metric. Or, one may compare two relationships with one another that are not otherwise directly comparable (a difference-of-means of 14 attitude points and 638 dollars, for example, or a difference-of-means of 14 and a correlation coefficient of .31). Given roughly similar sample sizes, if one result is barely significant at the .05 level and the other is significant beyond the .001 level, the second may be considered stronger than the first, at least as a starting point for further thought. Of course, there are pitfalls in such thinking; one cannot be a slave to significance tests. But as a first approximation to what is going on in a mass of data, it is difficult to beat this particular metric for communication and versatility.

Thus, common significance tests rank as a first-rate tool for detecting causality in conjunction with randomization designs. They are also convenient in surveys for noting whether population relationships are probably either zero or nonzero, although such information in itself is rather minimal. Survey-design functions and causal-inference do not apply, however, when one has simply observed one or more collectivities of interest — *without* true random sampling or random sampling assumptions — and such studies are probably the most common variety. In such cases, the strength-of-relationship function is the only one of the above that applies. It is a rough tool, but, for most of us, a welcome one.

REFERENCES

BLALOCK, H. (1960) Social Statistics. New York: McGraw-Hill.

COHEN, J. (1987) Statistical Power Analysis for the Behavioral Sciences (rev. ed.). New York: Academic Press.

FISHER, R.A. and YATES, F. (1948) Statistical Tables for Biological, Agricultural and Medical Research. Edinburgh and London: Oliver & Boyd.

HAYS, W. L. (1981) Statistics (3rd ed.). New York: CBS College Publishing.

JULNES, G. and MOHR, L. B. (1989) "Analysis of no-differences findings in evaluation research." Evaluation Review 13(6) pp. 499-525.

MOHR, L. B. (1988) Impact Analysis for Program Evaluation. Chicago: Dorsey.

RUGG, H. O. (1917) Statistical Methods Applied to Education. Boston: Houghton Mifflin.

PART III

ANALYSIS OF NOMINAL DATA

H. T. REYNOLDS

1. INTRODUCTION

Social scientists face a dilemma. On the one hand, they frequently have to analyze rather crudely measured data. Despite efforts to be as rigorous and precise as their colleagues in the natural sciences, they cannot quantify even some of the most important social and political concepts. Instead, they have to rely on rough and general category labels. On the other hand, they are called on to answer very sophisticated theoretical questions and to make exact predictions. It is as though a physicist were asked to construct a theory of heat but could only classify objects "hot" or "cold," instead of giving them a numerical temperature.

In response to this situation, political scientists, sociologists, statisticians, and others have developed a wide variety of techniques for analyzing categorical or nominal data. Indeed, so many methods have emerged that it is impossible to cover them in one place. Fortunately, however, once a few basic ideas have been grasped, understanding the different procedures becomes easier.

This paper describes methods for analyzing *nominal* variables, variables whose "scores" are category labels such as occupation, sex, or religion. It covers mostly two-way cross-classifications of such variables (e.g., Table 1), although toward the end more complicated situations are briefly discussed. Rather than describing every approach, the paper emphasizes a few fundamentals, including the special difficulties that arise in analyzing nominal data. Concentrating on the basics, one hopes, will make numerical results more meaningful.

TABLE 1

Party Identification and 1980 Presidential Vote

X: Party Identification

	Strong Democrat	Democrat	Independent Democrat	Independent	Independent Republican	Republican	Strong Republican	Totals
Reagan	11% 21	33% 66	29% 32	64% 54	76% 85	86% 131	92% 103	492
Carter	86% 168	60% 120	45% 49	22% 19	12% 13	5% 7	4% 5	381
Anderson	4% 7	7% 15	26% 28	14% 12	13% 14	10% 15	4% 4	95
Totals	196	201	109	85	112	153	112	968

Y: Presidential Vote 1980

SOURCE: These data, the 1980 American National Election Study, were made available by the Inter-university Consortium for Political Research through the Center for Political Studies, University of Michigan. The Consortium, of course, is not responsible for any errors or interpretation of these data.

Preliminaries

The analysis of nominal data is perhaps best illustrated by an example. The data in Table 1 consist of a sample of 968 adults cross-classified by their political party preference and their 1980 presidential vote.[1] Both variables are of course nominal or categorical because (a) each individual is assigned to one and only one class according to a particular trait or attribute; (b) the category labels are simply names that indicate how groups differ from one another; and (c) the labels say nothing about the magnitude of the differences—indeed, the appearance of the names in any particular order is arbitrary. (We will later rearrange the columns of the table to suit our needs at that time.)

Although the table seems simple enough—tables of this sort are probably familiar to most readers—it can be used to answer a startling variety of questions. One might ask, for example,

—Is there a relationship between party identification and candidate preferences? Alternatively, can knowledge of partisanship be used to predict how people will vote?

—Assuming that there is a relationship in the sample, can one infer that such a relationship holds for the population from which it was drawn?

—Do Democrats behave differently from Republicans? More specifically, which group votes more consistently along party lines and which deviates more?

—Similarly, do weak partisans differ from strong ones?

—Who did Anderson's candidacy hurt most, Carter or Reagan?

—How do independents vote, compared to party identifiers?

—One hears a lot these days about the decline of party; has the relationship weakened over the years?

—Is the relationship between party identification and vote the same among different subgroups in the population, such as college graduates or Southerners?

There are, in short, a host of questions that even a simple cross-classification like Table 1 can address. In fact, it is often self-defeating to limit oneself to a single question to be answered by a simple statistic. There is usually much more information than that in a cross-classification.

Nominal variables. A nominal scale consists of a set of categories representing different realizations of an underlying trait. Ideally, the individuals assigned to a category are homogeneous with respect to the attribute; mixing Democrats and Republicans in the category "Independent" only misinforms us about political behavior. The categories should also be *mutually exclusive* (no one is assigned to more than one category) and *exhaustive.*

The categories of a nominal variable can be arranged in any particular order that suits the needs of the investigator. As we will see, the columns of Table 1 can be rearranged without losing information. By contrast, the categories of an *ordinal* variable do have an implicit order: They measure not only qualitative but quantitative difference. The categories of a variable such as social status (low, medium, and high) cannot be arranged in another order (e.g., medium, low, high) without possibly throwing away valuable information. Hence, nominal and ordinal data are both categorical variables; the difference is that ordinal scales involve an ordering among the groups, whereas nominal variables do not.

Nominal scales may measure truly discrete phenomena such as race or sex, but in most instances they probably represent measurement error of one kind or another because the underlying traits are more or less quantitative. Attitudes, for instance, are not simply a matter of pro or con. Instead, people hold them with varying degrees of conviction. Thus, an attitude might really be considered a continuum running from Strongly Agree through Neutral to Strongly Disagree. Difficulties in measuring attitudes should not obscure this potential richness of information.

In particular, the number and quality of categories is extremely important in making correct inferences. One of the biggest mistakes in social and political research is to lump the respondents into a few categories. Dichotomizing data (putting everyone into one of two groups) for convenience or because everyone else does it is hardly ever justified. Poorly measured data will almost certainly produce misleading substantive conclusions, no matter what statistical technique is used.

Dependent versus independent variables. Most social scientists agree that a person's party identification, usually acquired by adolescence, partly determines his or her political preferences. In this sense, a vote in 1980 would "depend" on partisanship. A variable that depends on, is caused by, or temporally follows another variable is a "dependent variable." And naturally enough, the causal variable is called "independent." A change in the level of an independent variable changes the level of the dependent variable, but changing the dependent variable does not affect the independent variable.

Some of the techniques described here can be applied only when the investigator has a clearly defined dependent variable. Although other procedures make no assumptions about causal dependencies, one should think carefully about causal relationships among variables. It is possible to arbitrarily designate a variable as dependent or independent—this is occasionally necessary and there is nothing in any formula to prevent it—but the results may be wrong.

Of course, these decisions represent assumptions about the data, since it is not possible to prove that one variable causes another.

The number of categories. Since nominal variables are ordinarily organized into two-way or multi-way tables (see Tables 1 and 22, respectively, for examples), it is customary to construct them in such a way that each cell has as many cases as possible. This practice is understandable: Cross-classifications containing numerous zeros do not seem very reliable or impressive. Nevertheless, collapsing or combining categories to increase cell frequencies undoubtedly creates as many problems as it solves. There are two reasons for this.

First, the variation in a nominal variable depends in part on the number of its categories: the greater the number of classes, the greater the variation, other things being equal. Here, "variation" refers to the measured differences among individuals. If all of the cases are in a single category, there is no dispersion or variation among them; if, on the other hand, they are more or less evenly divided among several classes, there is greater variation. Classifying people as Democrats, Republicans, or Independents is simpler than assigning them to more precise groups like "strong Democrat," but there is less variation. And, as in regression analysis, the amount of variation, especially in independent variables, partly affects the magnitude of measures of association.

A second problem is that combining or reducing the number of categories often seriously affects observed interrelationships. Suppose, for example, an investigator has three variables, each having five categories. In order to simplify the presentation of the results, however, this person decides to collapse each variable into two categories. Yet it is likely that the results of most statistical methods based on the dichotomized data will differ from those that would be obtained from the uncollapsed variables, even though the same variables, sample, and techniques are used. One is apt to find associations in the $2 \times 2 \times 2$ table that did not occur in the $5 \times 5 \times 5$ cross-classification.

The lesson, then, is simple: Retain as many categories as possible and do not dichotomize or trichotomize variables without good reason and without attempting to ensure that substantive conclusions have not been affected.

Sampling. All of the techniques presented here apply to simple random samples drawn from a population. The marginal totals in such a sampling scheme are not fixed or predetermined by the investigator. (The column totals at the bottom of Table 1 are the "marginal totals" for party identification.) Referring to Table 1, for instance, 196 strong Democrats appeared in the sample by chance.[2] This number was *not* determined by the research design. Such a sample is sometimes called a "multinominal" sample, and variables generated in this way are sometimes called "responses."

Many of the methods can be applied to other types of samples. In particular, they can be often used when one or more marginal total is fixed before the research begins. For example, an investigator may decide to interview equal numbers of Democrats, Republicans, and Independents. Or he or she may include twice as many partisans as Independents. In either event, the marginal totals associated with party identification have been set ahead of time. Some statisticians call these variables "factors." Of course it is possible to have a mixture of responses and factors, as in a one-factor, one-response cross-classification. Responses are usually considered dependent and factors independent variables. Research designs involving only response variables occur most frequently in sample surveys, while designs involving factors as well as responses arise in laboratory experiments.

Notation. Possibly frightening at first, notation facilitates the presentation and explanation of statistical ideas. The principles are actually quite simple.

In cross-classifying subjects on the basis of two attributes (such as party identification and vote) one creates a "two-dimensional" table. The *dimensionality* of a cross-classification refers to the number of variables. Excluding the totals at the bottom, Table 1 has three rows and seven columns and is referred to as a 3×7 (read "3 by 7") table. If it has I rows and J columns, it is an $I \times J$ table, where I and J take any integer values.

TABLE 2
General Table with I Rows and J Columns

		X (Independent Variable)				
		1	2	j	J	
	1	n_{11}	n_{12} $\cdots$	n_{1j} $\cdots$	n_{1J}	n_{1+}
Y (Dependent Variable)	2	n_{21}	n_{22} $\cdots$	n_{2j} $\cdots$	n_{2J}	n_{2+}
	i	n_{i1}	n_{i2} $\cdots$	n_{ij} $\cdots$	n_{iJ}	n_{i+}
	I	n_{I1}	n_{I2} $\cdots$	n_{Ij} $\cdots$	n_{IJ}	n_{I+}
Totals		n_{+1}	n_{+2} $\cdots$	n_{+j} $\cdots$	n_{+J}	n

Cross-classifications of more than two variables are called "multidimensional" tables. An example might be a table showing the relationship between party identification and vote, controlling for education. (See Table 22.) By convention, the row variable (which is usually the dependent variable) appears first, then the column variable (usually independent), and the "layer" or "control" variable last. It is also convenient to let letters X, Y, and Z denote variables.

Table 2 shows a general I $\times$ J table, in which the independent variable is labeled X and the dependent variable is labeled Y. (This convention is used throughout the paper.) The row labels begin with 1 and go to I, which signifies the last category of Y and, similarly, column labels run from 1 to J, the last category of X.

A specific combination of row and column variables is designated by subscripts, the first letter indicating the row category and the second the column category. Small n's represent the cell frequencies of the number of cases in a particular row-column classification. The number of cases in the first row and first column of Table 2 is n_{11}. This is, of course, the number of people who are in the first category of each variable. (In Table 1, n_{11} corresponds to the 21 strong Democrats who voted for Reagan.) Likewise, n_{ij} represents the number of individuals in the ith row and j^{th} column. The subscripts i and j can take on any values from 1 to I and 1 to J respectively.

The totals at the bottom and side $(n_{1+}, n_{2+} \ldots ; n_{+1}, n_{+2} \ldots ;$ etc.) constitute the *marginal distributions* of X and Y. Looking at the first row, note that n_{1+} means the sum of all the observations in the first row. The plus sign in the subscript indicates that all the entries in the first row have been added over the J columns. By the same token, n_{+1} is the total of all the cases in the first column. In Table 1, for example, $n_{1+} = 21 + 66 + \ldots + 103 = 492$ and $n_{+1} = 21 + 168 + 7 = 196$.

The total number of observations is n. This quantity is found by summing all the n's in the table or by summing the marginal totals of either variable.

Besides working with tables of frequencies, it is often necessary or useful to deal with probabilities. Let $P(Y_iX_j)$ denote the probability that an individual is in the ith class of Y *and* j^{th} class of X in an I × J population cross-classification. $P(Y_1X_1)$ in other words, represents the probability of having characteristic 1 on variable Y (that is, voting for Reagan) *and* characteristic 1 on variable X (that is, being a strong Democrat). To simplify the notation, P_{ij} often replaces $P(Y_iX_j)$.

The layout of probability tables follows the same guidelines as contingency tables. P_{i+}, for instance, means the marginal probability of being in the ith category of Y. It is obtained by adding the probabilities in the ith row:

$$P_{i+} = P_{i1} + P_{i2} + \ldots + P_{iJ}$$

assuming the table has J columns. It gives the probability of being in the ith category of Y, irrespective of X.

Analyzing Nominal Data

The analysis of nominal data normally begins with a two-variable cross-classification. An investigator identifies a pair of variables that on theoretical grounds are assumed to be related in one way or another. Several questions arise in the study of such a relationship:

I. Are the variables statistically independent in the population? This question is usually answered with the familiar chi-square test, described next.

IIa. If the variables are related, what particular combination of categories explains their association? Chapter 2 illustrates two methods for answering this question.

IIb. Again assuming a statistically significant association, what is the magnitude or strength of the relationship? Section 3 presents a few common indices of association, together with a discussion of their properties and interpretations.

III. Finally, is the observed relationship part of a more complex system of interrelationships involving three or more variables? This problem, perhaps the most important of all, leads to multivariate analysis. Although this topic cannot be treated in detail here, some preliminary ideas will be presented in Chapter 4 that may make the more advanced techniques easier to comprehend.

2. CHI SQUARE TEST

The chi square test for independence provides a standard for deciding whether two variables are statistically independent. The test consists of four parts: (1) the null hypothesis (H_o) that the variables are statistically independent; (2) expected frequencies derived under the assumption that the null hypothesis is true; (3) a comparison of these expected values with the corresponding observed frequencies; and (4) a judgment about whether or not the differences between expected and observed frequencies could have arisen by chance.

The chi-square test actually has the same logic as more advanced multivariate procedures: One first states a model or hypothesis. *If* the model is true for a population, then, except for sampling error, one would expect that a sample drawn from it would exhibit certain characteristics. These expected results can be compared with what actually occurs. If the differences between the expected and observed results are small, the conclusion is that they could have arisen by chance, hence, the model is acceptable. On the other hand, if the discrepancies between what is expected and observed are large, one might decide to reject the model in favor of an alternative.

The null hypothesis. The null hypothesis is that in a population the two variables in a cross-classification are statistically independent. More formally, statistical independence holds if:

$$P_{ij} = P_{i+} P_{+j} \text{ for all } i, j \qquad [1]$$

where P_{ij} is the probability of being in the ith category of Y (the row variable) *and* the jth category of **X (the column variable)**; P_{i+} is the *marginal* probability of being in the ith category of Y; and P_{+j} is the marginal probability of being in the jth category of X. Returning to the example, the probability of having a particular party identification *and* voting for a particular candidate is the product of the corresponding marginal probabilities. If, on the other hand, Democrats, say, are more likely to vote for Carter than are Republicans, then equation 1 would not hold and the variables would be statistically related.

Deriving expected values. The next step is the determination of cell frequencies expected in a sample table if the null hypothesis is true. In a sample of 968, for example, how many cases would we expect to find in the cells of Table 1 if equation 1 were true for the population?

To make these calculations, consider this reasoning: If there is no association between party and vote, the proportion of Reagan voters should be the same in all seven categories of partisanship. If the proportion of Reagan voters overall is .5 and statistical independence holds, then 50 percent of strong Democrats, 50 percent of Democrats, and so on down the line should have voted for Reagan. The true proportion of Reagan voters is unknown, but it can be estimated from the sample as

$$\frac{492}{968} = .508$$

Consequently, under the hypothesis of independence, one would expect 50.8 percent of the 196 strong Democrats to have voted for Reagan. In other words, the first cell of the table should contain

$$\frac{492}{968} \times 196 = .508 \times 196 = 99.62$$

cases. That is, there should be about 99 to 100 cases in the first cell if the null hypothesis is true.

Other expected frequencies are found in a similar way. Assuming independence, one would expect about 50.8 percent of, say, the 112 weak Republicans to have voted for Reagan, or

$$\frac{492}{968} \times 112 = 56.93$$

These considerations lead to the following formula for estimating the expected frequencies under the null hypothesis:

$$\hat{n}_{ij} = \frac{(n_{i+})(n_{+j})}{n} \qquad [2]$$

where $\hat{n}_{ij}$ is the estimated expected frequency and n_{i+} and n_{+j} are the ith and j^{th} row and column marginal frequency, respectively.

Applying formula 2 to each of the row and column totals gives the expected frequencies shown in Table 3.

Comparing observed and expected frequencies. As one can tell from even a cursory glance at Table 3, there are large discrepancies between observed and expected values. In the first cell, for example (i.e., strong Democrats who voted for Reagan), the observed frequency is 21, whereas, if the null hypothesis were true, we would expect to find about 99 or 100 cases. The differences between observed and expected values are just as large in many other cells of the table, leading one to wonder if the null hypothesis is tenable. After all, if partisanship and vote were statistically independent in the population, should not there be more observations in the first cell?

Still, the agreement is relatively close in other parts (among weak Democrats who voted for Carter, for example), suggesting the need for a systematic method for comparing observed and expected frequencies among all cells of the table. A useful statistic for making this overall comparison is the *goodness-of-fit chi square*:

$$X^2 = \sum_i \sum_j \frac{(n_{ij} - \hat{n}_{ij})^2}{\hat{n}_{ij}} = \sum_i \sum_j \frac{n_{ij}^2}{\hat{n}_{ij}} - n \qquad [3]$$

TABLE 3
Observed and Expected Frequencies and Components
of Chi Square for Table 1

	SD	D	ID	I	IR	R	SR
			Party Identification				
Reagan	21	66	32	54	85	131	103
	99.62	102.16	55.40	43.20	56.93	77.76	56.93
	62.05	12.80	9.88	2.70	13.85	36.44	37.29
Carter	168	120	49	19	13	7	5
	77.14	79.11	42.90	33.46	44.08	60.22	44.08
	107.00	21.13	.87	6.25	21.92	47.03	34.65
Anderson	7	15	28	12	14	15	4
	19.24	19.73	10.70	8.34	10.99	15.01	10.99
	7.78	1.13	27.99	1.60	.82	0.0	4.45

KEY: SD = strong Democrat; D = Democrat; ID = Independent, leaning Democrat; I = Independent; IR = Independent, leaning Republican; R = Republican; SR = strong Republican

NOTE: Row 1 contains raw or original frequencies; row 2 expected frequencies, $\hat{n}_{ij}$; and row 3 the components of the chi-square statistic, e_{ij}.

where n_{ij} and $\hat{n}_{ij}$ are the observed and expected frequencies in the ij^{th} cell; n is the table total; and the summation is over all I rows and J columns. For the data in Table 3, goodness-of-fit chi square is

$$X^2 = \left[\frac{(21)^2}{99.62} + \frac{(66)^2}{102.16} + \ldots + \frac{(4)^2}{10.99} \right] - 968 = 457.63$$

An alternative statistic, which for large enough samples will lead to the same conclusion as X^2, is the *likelihood ratio chi square*. Since it is useful for dissecting a cross-classification, one ought to note its formula:

$$L^2 = 2 \sum_i \sum_j n_{ij} \left[\log \left(\frac{n_{ij}}{\hat{n}_{ij}} \right) \right] \qquad [4]$$

where n_{ij} and $\hat{n}_{ij}$ are defined as before and log denotes the natural logarithm. Returning once again on Table 3, we have

$$L^2 = 2\left\{21\left[\log\left(\frac{21}{99.62}\right)\right] + 66\left[\log\left(\frac{66}{102.16}\right)\right] + \ldots + 4\left[\log\left(\frac{4}{10.99}\right)\right]\right\}$$

$$= 2\left\{21\ [-1.5568] + 66\ [-.4369] + \ldots + 4\ [-1.0107]\right\}$$

$$= 501.12$$

Although X^2 and L^2 are not equal (as is usually the case), they both lead to the same conclusion about the variables.

Decision. These observed values of X^2 and L^2 are quite large, but since they are computed from a sample one can fairly ask if they could have arisen by chance from a population in which the variables were really independent. Fortunately, if certain conditions are satisfied, one can determine the probability of observing a chi square as large or larger than the one actually observed. The conditions or assumptions are relatively straightforward:

(1) a random sample of n observations;

(2) mutually exclusive and exhaustive categories such that each observation is placed in one and only one cell;

(3) most (e.g., more than 80 percent) of the estimated expected frequencies are larger than 5.

If these conditions hold, one can compare the observed chi square statistic (either X^2 or L^2) with a so-called critical chi square, $x^2\alpha$ to decide whether or not the observed value arose by chance. If X^2 (or L^2) is less than the critical value, one accepts the null hypothesis (H_o) that the variables are independent; if, on the other hand, X^2 (or L^2) equals or exceeds $x^2\alpha$, then the null hypothesis is rejected, and one would conclude that the variables probably are related. The decision, then, rests on a comparison of an observed chi square with a standard that has been determined beforehand—that is, before the data have been examined.

All that remains is the selection of the critical value, $\chi^2\alpha$. The choice depends on two additional considerations: the *degrees of freedom* in the table and the desired level of significance. The degrees of freedom associated with any two-way cross-classfication table are easily computed from the following formula:

$$df = (I - 1)(J - 1) \qquad [5]$$

where I and J are the total number of rows and columns, respectively. For Table 1, df = (3 - 1)(7 - 1) = 12.

The desired level of significance, α, which should be established prior to seeing the data, determines the specific critical value. In order to find it one refers to a tabulated distribution of chi square such as ones found in Blalock (1979) or Reynolds (1977a). These tabulations give critical values for different levels of probability and degrees of freedom. (The degrees of freedom are read down the side of the table, while levels of significance are read across the top.) Given 12 degrees of freedom, for example, the critical values at the .05, .01, and .001 levels are, respectively, 21.026, 26.217, and 32.909. Since both X^2 and L^2 clearly exceed these values, one would reject the null hypothesis of independence between voting and party preference.

There are times when a chi square test is not appropriate. Given a 2×2 table where n is small (say less than 20), Fisher's test, which gives exact rather than approximate probabilities for the observed table, should be used. (See Blalock, 1979: 292-297.) Furthermore, the X^2 statistic only approximates the theoretical chi square. In order to ensure the reasonableness of the approximation, many statisticians recommend computing X^2 only if most *expected* cell frequencies (say 80 percent) are greater than or equal to five. Although there is considerable controversy about the topic, this seems to be a safe rule that can be met in most situations where n is relatively large.

Interpreting the Chi Square Test

When we are told one baseball team defeated another, we usually want to know much more, such as the score, the winning and losing pitchers, and so forth. Likewise, a "significant" chi square tells us that two variables are probably related in the population, but by itself, it reveals little else. What is worse, if used uncritically, the test can mislead as much as it informs.

As with any statistical test, the sample size affects its magnitude. Large samples frequently produce significant chi squares even if the variables are weakly related. Consequently, we may decide to reject the hypothesis of independence when in fact the variables have little or no practical or substantively interesting relationship.

Following an example given in Blalock (1979), the data in Table 4 illustrate the point. The nonsignificant goodness-of-fit chi square in Table 4a reflects the trivial relationship between X and Y. The distributions in columns 1 and 2 are the same and differ only slightly from the third. Hence, scores on X do not reveal much about Y values and vice versa.

Furthermore, this conclusion is not changed by multiplying every frequency by 10, as in Table 4b. Since the *proportions* remain exactly the same, the X-Y relationship has not changed at all. Yet, the chi square is now significant. If we looked at only this value without paying attention to the distribution of the cases in the table, we would conclude X and Y are strongly related. These tables illustrate a well-known principle: If all the frequencies in a cross-classification are multiplied by a constant, K, the magnitude of chi square increases K times. Therefore, in order to interpret meaningfully chi square, we have to look at more than its numerical value. Assessing the "practical" or "theoretical" significnce of a chi square requires that we measure the strength of the relationship.

TABLE 4
Sample Size Affects the Numerical Magnitude of Chi Square

(Hypothetical Data)

	a						b			
		X		Totals				X		Totals
	30	30	30	90			300	300	300	900
Y	30	30	36	96		Y	300	300	360	960
	40	40	34	114			400	400	340	1140
Totals	100	100	100	300		Totals	1000	1000	1000	3000

$X^2 = 1.38$ with 4 df $X^2 = 13.82$ with 4 df

$\phi^2 = .005$ $\phi^2 = .005$

NOTE: Table entries are frequencies.

The conventional chi square test presents another problem of interpretation. As normally applied, it is not directed at any specific alternative hypothesis. An alternative hypothesis might be, for example, that the variables are related in a particular way. Since the X^2 measures only departures of expected from observed values (i.e., $n_{ij} - \hat{n}_{ij}$), it does not call attention to any "pattern of deviations . . . that may hold if the null hypothesis of independence is false" (Cochran, 1954: 417). If we can specify the form of a possible relationship *before* making the test, we can sometimes improve the efficiency and sensitivity of the procedure.

Thus, once an investigator finds a significant chi square, the work has just begun. Since one often knows ahead of time that two variables are statistically related, not much information is gained from a significance test alone. Instead, it is possible and desirable to further analyze data by specifying more precisely how the variables are related. There are at least two quick and simple methods for doing so: examining the components of the chi square statistic and partitioning the original table into subtables, each pertaining to a particular subhypothesis or question.

Components of the chi square. An easy yet effective procedure is to examine each component of the chi square statistic:

$$e_{ij} = \frac{(n_{ij} - \hat{n}_{ij})^2}{n_{ij}} \qquad [6]$$

These numbers, which are analogous to residuals in regression analysis, indicate which cells contribute most to the chi square and, hence, which categories of variables are most closely related. Table 3 shows, for example, that the cells pertaining to strong partisans (both Democrat and Republican) in the Carter and Reagan rows contribute the most to the relationship, categories involving Independents and Anderson the least. What makes the relationship so strong, apparently, is the differential behavior of Democrats and Republicans toward the main candidates. Over half of the total X^2 is due to just four cells: (1,1), (2,1), (1,7), (2,7). Although this finding makes intuititive sense, in a more complex table such an analysis might reveal less obvious insights.

Some authors recommend computing standardized residuals ($r_{ij} = ((n_{ij} - \hat{n}_{ij})/\sqrt{\hat{n}_{ij}})$ or adjusted residuals, which can be interpreted as standard normal deviates. These statistics make the detection of extreme cases or outliers particularly easy. The interest reader should consult Haberman (1973) and Reynolds (1977) for further details.

Partitioning chi square. Partitioning offers another simple method for more precisely analyzing a cross-classification. It is especially useful because we can test various subhypotheses. In other words, a complex table such as Table 1 may contain a wealth of information that the overall chi square masks.

The basic idea is simple: A table with $(I - 1)(J - 1)$ degrees of freedom can be divided into various subtables. Each subtable is analyzed as though it were a separate cross-classification. Therefore, one can calculate a series of sub-chi squares, each with appropriate degrees of freedom. Many of these subtables can be further divided into still more subtables, each having a chi square and degrees of freedom. In particular, an original $I \times J$ table can ultimately be partitioned into $(I - 1)(J - 1)$ 2×2 subtables, each with one degree of freedom.

These subtables are formed from the original tables in such a way that specific questions and hypotheses are addressed. Table 1, for instance, will be partitioned so that we can assess, among other things, the impact of strong partisanship. The total chi square is thus divided into parts, each pertaining to a separate table and hypothesis. If we calculate L^2 instead of X^2, the sum of the component chi squares will equal the total, as will the degrees of freedom.

Of course, the subtables cannot be formed arbitrarily. Certain rules have to be followed to ensure that the tables are independent and do not contain redundant information.

Professor Gudmund Iversen (1979) provides a simple algorithm for finding suitable subtables. He first divides the frequencies in a contingency table into two types:

A frequencies are either cell frequencies (n_{ij}) or the table total (n). In Table 1, for example, A frequencies are (21, 66, 32 . . . 14, 15, 4) and the table total, 968.

B frequencies are row and column marginal totals, n_{i+} and n_{+j}. In Table 1, B frequencies are the marginal totals (196, 201 . . . 112) and (492, 381, 95).

Iversen's rules for partitioning rely on these two types of frequencies:

Rule 1: Each frequency (whether *A* or *B*) in the original table must appear once and only once as a frequency of the *same* type in one of the subtables. (For example, n must appear in one of the

TABLE 5
Table of Party Identification by Vote in 1980 Rearranged

		Party Identification						
		Partisans				Independents		
		SD	SR	D	R	ID	IR	I
1980 Vote	Reagan	21	103	66	131	32	85	54
	Carter	168	5	120	7	49	13	19
	Anderson	7	4	15	15	28	14	12
	Totals	196	112	201	153	109	112	85

KEY: (See Table 3).

NOTE: $L^2 = 501.1230$; 12 df.

subtotals as a total; similarly, each n_{i+} and n_{+j} must appear as a row and column total, respectively.)

Rule 2: Each frequency that is in a component or subtable but not in the original table must appear as a frequency of the other type in another subtable. In other words, subtables contain some frequencies, like marginal totals, that do not appear in the original table; these "new" frequencies have to be used again, so to speak, but as frequencies of a different type.

As with many statistical methods, it is perhaps easier to illustrate the procedure than to describe it verbally. Table 5 shows a simple rearrangement of Table 1 in which partisans (both Democratic and Republican) have been grouped together. This new arrangement is of course legitimate since category labels are arbitrary. Rewriting the columns in this fashion makes it easier to explore various subhypotheses.

Tables 6, 7, and 8 show one of many possible partitions of Table 5. Formed from the first four columns of Table 5, Table 6, for example, explores the voting behavior of partisans. As one can see, $L^2 = 398.240$, suggesting that about 80 percent (398.240/501.123 = 79.47) of the

TABLE 6
Voting Behavior Among Partisans

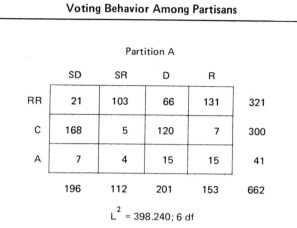

Partition A

	SD	SR	D	R	
RR	21	103	66	131	321
C	168	5	120	7	300
A	7	4	15	15	41
	196	112	201	153	662

$L^2 = 398.240$; 6 df

Further Partitioning of A

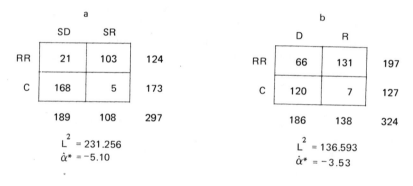

a

	SD	SR	
RR	21	103	124
C	168	5	173
	189	108	297

$L^2 = 231.256$
$\hat{\alpha}^* = -5.10$

b

	D	R	
RR	66	131	197
C	120	7	127
	186	138	324

$L^2 = 136.593$
$\hat{\alpha}^* = -3.53$

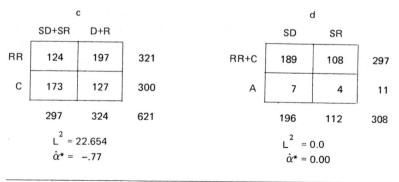

c

	SD+SR	D+R	
RR	124	197	321
C	173	127	300
	297	324	621

$L^2 = 22.654$
$\hat{\alpha}^* = -.77$

d

	SD	SR	
RR+C	189	108	297
A	7	4	11
	196	112	308

$L^2 = 0.0$
$\hat{\alpha}^* = 0.00$

(continued)

Table 6 (Continued)

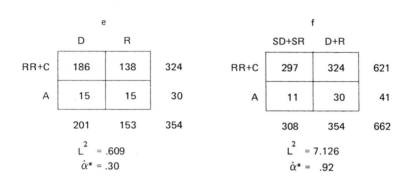

	e				f		
	D	R			SD+SR	D+R	
RR+C	186	138	324	RR+C	297	324	621
A	15	15	30	A	11	30	41
	201	153	354		308	354	662

$$L^2 = .609$$
$$\hat{\alpha}^* = .30$$

$$L^2 = 7.126$$
$$\hat{\alpha}^* = .92$$

KEY: RR = Ronald Reagan; C = Carter; A = Anderson (also see Table 3).

original chi square is due to the differential behavior of Democrats and Republicans.

In addition, Table 6, with six degrees of freedom, has itself been partitioned into six more tables, each with one degree of freedom. Also note that all of these partitions follow the two rules above. Each of the frequencies in Table 6, for instance, appear in one of the component tables (Tables 6a to 6f) as a frequency of the same type (Rule 1) and each "new" frequency (a frequency that was not in Table 6 to start with) appears twice, once as an A frequency and once as a B frequency. (The row marginal total of 124 in Table 6a—a B type frequency—appears as an A type frequency in the first cell of Table 6c). The reader can quickly verify that both rules have been followed in making this partition.

The decomposition of Table 6 leads to further insights. An enormous part of the relationship in Table 6 (and indeed in the original table as well) is due to differences between strong Democrats and strong Republicans in their votes for Reagan and Carter; similarly, the differences between plain Democrats and Republicans are large (Table 6b). Together these two chi squares account for the lion's share of the relationship in Table 6. Anderson's candidacy had relatively little effect on partisans because they mostly stayed with their party's candidate; the two chi squares total only .609.

Table 7, formed from Table 4 according to the two rules, shows the political behavior of Independents and weak partisans. It and the

TABLE 7
Voting Behavior Among Independents

Partition B

	ID	IR	I	
RR	32	85	54	171
C	49	13	19	81
A	28	14	12	54
	109	112	85	306

$$L^2 = 54.744; \ 4 \ df$$

Further Partitioning of B

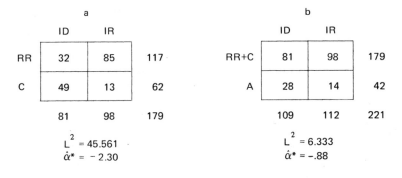

a

	ID	IR	
RR	32	85	117
C	49	13	62
	81	98	179

$$L^2 = 45.561$$
$$\hat{\alpha}^* = -2.30$$

b

	ID	IR	
RR+C	81	98	179
A	28	14	42
	109	112	221

$$L^2 = 6.333$$
$$\hat{\alpha}^* = -.88$$

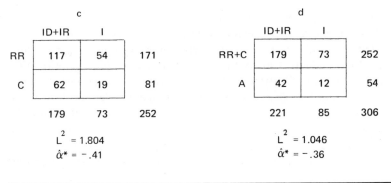

c

	ID+IR	I	
RR	117	54	171
C	62	19	81
	179	73	252

$$L^2 = 1.804$$
$$\hat{\alpha}^* = -.41$$

d

	ID+IR	I	
RR+C	179	73	252
A	42	12	54
	221	85	306

$$L^2 = 1.046$$
$$\hat{\alpha}^* = -.36$$

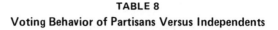

TABLE 8
Voting Behavior of Partisans Versus Independents

Partition C

	Partisans (SD+SR+D+R)	Independents (ID+IR+I)	
RR	321	171	492
C	300	81	381
A	41	54	95
	662	306	968

$$L^2 = 48.138;\ 2df$$

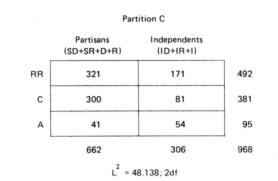

Further Partitioning of C

a

	Partisans (SD+SR+D+R)	Independents (ID+IR+I)	
RR	321	171	492
C	300	81	381
	621	252	873

$$L^2 = 19.422$$
$$\hat{\alpha}^* = -.68$$

b

	Partisans (SD+SR+D+R)	Independents (ID+IR+I)	
RR+C	621	252	873
A	41	54	95
	662	306	968

$$L^2 = 28.716$$
$$\hat{\alpha}^* = 1.18$$

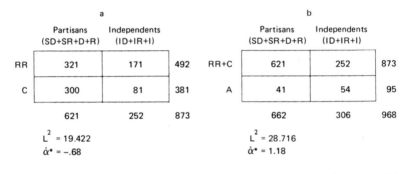

KEY: (See Tables 3 and 6).

subsequent partition (Tables 7a to 7d) illustrate that even among weak partisans, people tend to follow their party identification, but Anderson did better among weak Democrats than among Republicans.

Table 8 finally completes the partitioning by comparing partisans with Independents. Clearly the relationships are smaller here than in Table 6, but they illustrate that partisans vote a more consistent party line (see Table 8b). These findings suggest that party identification is still an important determinant (or at least codeterminant) of voting. If partisanship has become less influential, as many claim, the decline is probably due to fewer people identifying with a party than to a weakening of the relationship. As an interesting exercise, the reader

TABLE 9
Summary of the Partition of Table 5

Source	L^2	df	Sig.	Log Odds $(\hat{\alpha}*)$
Partisans (Table 6)				
a SD/SR v. Reagan/Carter	231.256	1	.001	−5.10
b D/R v. Reagan/Carter	136.593	1	.001	−3.53
c SD+SR/D+R v. Reagan/Carter	22.654	1	.001	−.77
d SD/SR v. Major/Anderson	0.000	1	NS	0.0
e D/R v. Major/Anderson	.609	1	NS	.30
f SD+SR/D+R v. Major/Anderson	7.126	1	.01	.92
	398.240	6		
Independents (Table 7)				
a ID/IR v. Reagan/Carter	45.561	1	.001	−2.30
b ID/IR v. Major/Anderson	6.333	1	.001	−.88
c ID+IR/I v. Reagan/Carter	1.804	1	NS	−.41
d ID+IR/I v. Major/Anderson	1.046	1	NS	−.36
	54.744	4		
Partisans v. Independents (Table 8)				
a Partisans and Independents v. Reagan/Carter	19.422	1	.001	−.68
b Partisans and Independents v. Major/Anderson	28.716	1	.001	−1.18
Total	48.138	2		
Total	501.123	12		

KEY: (See Table 3).

could compare the strength of the relationship across time, using the partitioning described above.

Table 9 summarizes the partitioning of Table 4. It shows once again that out of a total chi square of 501.123, the vast majority (231.256 + 136.593 + 45.561 = 413.410, or 82 percent) is due to 12 out of 21 cells: those pertaining to strong and weak partisans and Reagan and Carter votes. Although these findings are consistent with existing theory and common sense, partitioning a complex cross-tabulations may lead to new and unexpected results. It should also be emphasized here that the partitioning given in Tables 6, 7, and 8 is not the only one possible. Others based on different substantive questions and lines of reasoning might be worth pursuing. The only constraints are the two rules described by Iversen. For further information and examples, the reader should consult Reynolds (1977a), Iversen (1979), and Goodman (1969).

3. MEASURES OF ASSOCIATION

Introduction

Since the usual goodness-of-fit chi square test says only whether two variables may or may not be statistically independent, and by itself it does not give the strength or form of the relationship, one usually calculates a *measure of association* as the next step in the analysis.

A measure of association is a numerical index summarizing the strength or degree of relationship in a two-dimensional cross-classification. Depending on its meaning, it may also reveal how the variables are related to each other. There are literally dozens of measures from which to choose. Three considerations guide the choice of a measure: whether it is symmetric or asymmetric, its interpretation, and its sensitivity to confounding influences.

Symmetric versus asymmetric measures. If a theory or common sense indicate that one variable causes another, then it is usually necessary to predict values of the dependent variable from knowledge of the causal or independent variable. In this case the most appropriate measure would be *asymmetric*. The calculation and interpretation of asymmetric measures depend on which variable is considered dependent. There are thus two versions—one when X is considered independent, the other when it is considered dependent—and the versions do not normally equal each other. With a *symmetric* index, by contrast, either variable can be considered dependent.

The interpretation of measures of association. Since a measure of association—a single number—supposedly summarizes the information in a table, it should have a clear interpretation. The numerical value of most measures lie between 0 and 1.0—zero if the variables are completely unrelated according to some definition of a nil relationship, and 1.0 if the variables are perfectly associated, again according to some criterion of "perfect." The meaning of intermediate values depends on how the measure is operationally defined.

Nil associations. To say that the association between two variables is "nil" usually—but not always—implies that they are statistically independent. As noted above, statistical independence means that the probability of the joint occurrence of two events—that is, for example, the probability of being *both* a Democrat *and* a Reagan voter—equals the product of the probabilities of their separate occurrences. If independence holds for a population table, most measures of association are defined so that they will be zero. For samples drawn from that population, the measures will equal zero subject to sampling error. Thus, values close to zero typically indicate a weak to nil relationship.

A few measures of association are zero even in the absence of statistical independence. Lambda, an index described later, frequently equals zero when the marginal totals are highly skewed—that is, most cases fall into one category—but the variables are not independent. Many social scientists view this property as an inherent weakness in the measure. On the other hand, one can define "nil" to mean something besides independence (Weisberg, 1974). Such definitions are rare, however, and throughout this paper statistical independence is the definition of nil association.

Perfect associations. Having only rough classifications, an investigator may not worry about defining or measuring perfect association. After all, classified variables often represent measurement error where individuals are lumped together into categories out of convenience or necessity. Were more refined divisions available, the observed pattern of relationship might be different. Hence, defining perfect association for nominal data might be premature; if nothing else, it assumes the meaningfulness of the observed classifications. Nevertheless, it is common to conceptualize perfect association even for categorical variables. There are at least three different ways of doing so.

(1) *Strict Perfect Association.* Under strict perfect association, each value of one variable is uniquely associated with a value of the other. Table 10a presents an example. Note that for this condition to hold, the numbers of categories of Y and X must be equal. Here knowledge of a person's X category implies perfect prediction of his or her score on Y. Under this relationship, "normed" measures of association equal 1.0.

(2) *Implicit Perfect Association.* Since one variable frequently has more classes than another (that is, the rows and columns are not

TABLE 10
Models of Perfect Association for Nominal Variables

	a Strict Perfect Association				b Implicit Perfect Association			
	X					X		
	50	0	0		0	50	0	50
Y	0	0	50	Y	50	0	0	0
	0	50	0		0	0	50	0
Totals	50	50	50	Totals	50	50	50	50

	c Weak Perfect Association		
	X		
	50	0	0
Y	50	0	0
	50	50	50
Totals	150	50	50

NOTE: Table entries are the number of cases.

equal), the definition of perfect association has to be modified. In Table 10b, for example, a column category completely specifies a row category. In other words, the members of a column classification are as homogeneous as possible with respect to Y in the sense that there is only one nonzero row entry per column. Different X categories are generally associated with different Y categories, but since the classes on X outnumber those on Y, the association is not unique.

Not every measure of association achieves its maximum values here. Hence, if one feels this type of table represents a perfect association, the choice should be a measure that does attain its maximum.

(3) *Weak Perfect Association.* Table 10c illustrates a relationship that a few social scientists consider perfect. Here, the categories of, say, X are as homogeneous as possible with respect to Y, given the differences in the variables' marginal totals.

Most measures do not attain their maxima for relationships of this sort. In Table 10c the problem lies in the first column and last row, which contain the preponderance of cases. Knowing an individual's score on one of these classes does not help predict his or her classification on the other variable. Furthermore, if more refined classifications could be obtained, one still has no assurance that the association would be perfect in any of the above senses. Nonetheless, if it seems that these data exhibit perfect association, one should choose an appropriate measure. Unfortunately, the only strictly nominal measures that attain their maximums in this case are applicable solely for 2×2 tables. (If the variables are both ordinal—that is, they have ordered classes—then other indices are available.)

Intermediate values. Since most indices are normed so that they have intelligible lower and upper bounds, one has some basis for choosing among them. He or she simply selects the one based on the definitions of nil and perfect relationships most in agreement with research needs.

The rub lies in interpreting intermediate values. Suppose that an investigator wants statistical independence and strict association to define nil and perfect association. The choice of measures is narrowed somewhat but the investigator still has to make sense of values lying between 0 and 1.0. Suppose the value of an index is .45. What does he or she conclude about the strength and form of the relationship?

The answer naturally turns on the measure's operational definition. Some, like measures based on chi square, do not have intuitively appealing interpretations. Others, proportional-reeducation-in-error indices, for example, are more easily understood but depend on looking at a cross-classification in a particular way. Thus, each measure has to be examined separately in order to grasp its underlying logic and meaning.

Confounding factors. A problem common to all indices is that extraneous factors frequently confuse their interpretation. It is well known that the number of cases affects the magnitude of the chi square statistic: the greater the sample size, the larger the value of chi square, other things being equal. Almost all measures of association eliminate the effects of sample sizes—this is one reason for calculating them in the first place—but similar types of factors can influence their numerical values. The two most common problems are skewed marginal distributions and unequal numbers of rows and columns.

Skewed marginal distributions. Marginal distributions affect the numerical values of many measures of association. In the first panel of Table 11a, most of the cases fall in the middle column, whereas in Table 11b, they are more evenly distributed among the categories of X. Clearly, the second data set involves more variation on X. But also notice that the column percentages (or relative frequencies) are the same in both tables.

In spite of the equivalence in the relationships (at least as measured by percentages), many measures do not give the same value for both tables. A researcher who computes an index for the second set of data might report a strong relationship, while someone analyzing the first table might find a much weaker association, even though they both use the same statistic.

TABLE 11
Categorical Data with Different Marginal Distributions
but the Same Inherent Relationship

		a					b		
		X		Totals			X		Totals
	60% (60)	20% (200)	10% (10)	270		60% (180)	20% (120)	10% (30)	330
Y	30 (30)	60 (600)	30 (30)	660	Y	30 (90)	60 (360)	30 (90)	540
	10 (10)	20 (200)	60 (60)	270		10 (30)	20 (120)	60 (180)	330
Totals	100% (100)	100% (1000)	100% (100)	1200	Totals	100% (300)	100% (600)	100% (300)	1200

NOTE: Numbers in parentheses are the number of cases.

Only a few indices are impervious to marginal distributions. As a result, an investigator has to pay particular attention to marginal totals. When one or both variables are highly skewed, it should be decided whether or not the relative absence of variation is substantively meaningful. If one wants to know what more even distributions would produce, the observed data can be adjusted (using a method described shortly) or a less sensitive measure selected. On the other hand, the lack of variation may itself be theoretically important, and in that case one would want to preserve the original marginal distributions. The point is simply that it is necessary to be aware of the possible confounding effects of marginal distributions.

Nonsquare tables. The number of rows and columns frequently are not equal. Tabular asymmetry usually occurs by happenstance and ought not to disturb the inherent relationship between two variables. Yet a surprisingly large number of measures are affected by it.

The difficulty arises because some measures cannot attain their maximums if the rows do not equal the columns. Suppose interest lies in the hypothesis that two variables are "implicitly" perfectly correlated. In order to test this proposition, one requires an appropriate measure that can attain its maximum in nonsquare tables.

Measures of Association for 2×2 Tables

Perhaps the best-known and most extensively studied type of cross-classification is the 2×2 table. Formulas and calculations are usually much simpler in the 2×2 case than in larger tables. In addition to their simplicity, they have interesting and useful properties. Many seemingly different measures of associations equal each other in these tables and, as will become apparent, many concepts applicable in the dichotomous case readily generalize to higher dimensional tables.

Nevertheless, there is little advantage in "collapsing" or reducing a larger array into a 2×2 table. Collapsed data frequently introduce distortions. What might be a weak relationship in and I X J table where I and J are both greater than 2 could turn out to be a large association if the variables have been dichotomized. The observed relationship would then be more an artifact of one's measurement than a reflection of the true state of affairs. Of course, if the variables really have only two categories or no other measurement is available, a researcher has little choice. But the widespread practice of uncritically dichotomizing variables risks throwing away valuable information and producing misleading results (Reynolds, 1977b).

Percentages. Regardless of the size of a table, one of the easiest ways to measure a relationship between two variables, especially if one is clearly dependent, is to calculate percentages. After all, one wants to compare how people in different categories of one variable behave with respect to the classes of another. If the distribution of responses changes from one category to another, there is evidence for a relationship.

Table 1 illustrates the point. Comparing Democrats, Independents, and Republicans, one sees a steady decline in the percentage or proportion of support for Reagan. Thus, percentages permit one to detect patterns of departure from independence. That is, besides seeing that two variables are not independent (as chi square test would indicate), one can see *how* the variables are related. If Democrats tended to vote for Reagan instead of Carter, and Republicans for Carter instead of Reagan, the variables would still be related, but in a different fashion. Hence, percentages help one distinguish different forms of association.

Percentages are particularly useful in 2 × 2 tables. A difference in percentages (or proportions) can be interpretated as a regression coefficient between two dichotomous variables. (A regression coefficient gives the magnitude of a change in Y, considered the dependent variable, for a unit change in the independent variable.) Consider this very simple 2 × 2 table of proportions, where raw frequencies are in parentheses:

X

		.9	.4
		(45)	(20)
Y			
		.1	.6
		(5)	(30)
		1.0	1.0
		(50)	(50)

Here the difference in proportions (with respect to the first row) between the two columns of X is .5. The same quantity would be obtained if the categories of X and Y were coded 0 and 1 and the data substituted into familiar regression formulas. A change in one unit of X (from 0 to 1)

TABLE 12
Relationship Between Party Identification and Candidate
Preference When the Variables Are Dichotomized

Y: Presidential Vote, 1982	X: Party Identification		
	Democrats	Republicans	Total
Reagan	87	234	321
Carter	288	12	300
Totals	375	246	621

NOTE: Table entries are the number of cases. Independents and Anderson voters have been excluded. "Democrats" include both strong and regular Democrats. Likewise, "Republicans" include both strong and regular Republicans.

produces a change of .5 in Y. Given the range of possible values (0 to 1), this result indicates a substantial relationship.

Thus, a difference in percentages or proportions has a clear interpretation as a measure of association in a 2×2 table. Furthermore, by virtue of its definition, it is not sensitive to imbalances in the marginal distribution of X.

Being asymmetric, the calculation and meaning of a difference in percentages assume that the dependent and independent variables have been unambiguously specified. And, of course, one needs a sufficiently large number of cases in each category of X (usually 20 or more) in order to obtain a reasonable estimate of its value, a remark that applies to the computation of percentages in general.

Cross-product ratio. The cross-product ratio, often called the odds ratio, is surprisingly little known in the social sciences—surprisingly because it actually underlies two popular measures of association and has several useful properties. A thoroughly researched statistic, the ratio also provides a very helpful heuristic device for understanding log-linear analysis, a categorical multivariate technique (see Knoke and Burke, 1980).

A simplified version of the voting data (see Table 12) illustrates its meaning and computation. (An investigator would not normally analyze these data in this manner; it is done here for convenience.) The new table shows the relationship between two dichotomies: party identification (Democrats and Republicans) and vote. The marginal totals are considered fixed.

Obviously the variables are related; but the question is, how strongly? One answer is given by comparing the *odds* of voting for Reagan. For Democrats these odds are 87 to 288, or about .3 to 1. (More precisely, 87/288 = .302.) Now compare these odds to the odds of voting for Reagan among Republicans. If partisanship were unrelated to ideology, the odds of being a Reagan voter should be the same for both Democrats and Republicans. If, on the other hand, party identification affects people's preferences, then the odds among Republicans will be different. As it turns out, the odds of voting for Reagan among Republicans is considerably greater than 1, namely 234/12 = 19.500.

Although the odds for the two groups obviously differ, it is useful to compare them more explicitly by calculating their ratio:

$$\hat{\alpha} = \frac{\dfrac{n_{11}}{n_{21}}}{\dfrac{n_{12}}{n_{22}}} = \frac{n_{11}n_{22}}{n_{21}n_{12}} = \frac{\dfrac{87}{288}}{\dfrac{234}{12}} = \frac{.302}{19.500} = .02$$

The ratio of the odds (denoted $\hat{\alpha}$) has a simple interpretation. If the odds are the same in both categories of party identification, their ratio will equal 1.0. As an example, the ratio for the hypothetical data

$$X$$

		45	90
Y		15	30

is 45/15/90/30 = 3/3 = 1.0. Hence, 1.0 indicates no relationship. This definition has intuitive appeal because if the odds of being for Reagan are the same in both classes of party identification, it (partisanship) provides very little insight into how people will vote.

Departures in either direction from 1.0 suggest association: the greater the departure, the stronger the relationship. The small value of $\hat{\alpha}$ in the example reflects the very great difference in the odds of voting for Reagan: Among Democrats, the odds are virtually nil, whereas among Republicans, they are quite large.

This interpretation implicitly assumes fixed marginal totals. But $\hat{\alpha}$ can actually be calculated when none, one, or both sets of marginals are fixed. This is the one measure for which a nil association is 1.0, rather than the customary 0.

Properties of the odds ratio. The odds ratio ranges from 0 to ∞ with 1.0 indicating statistical independence. Values less than 1.0 imply a "negative" association, while values greater than 1.0 mean a positive relationship. In order to see this point, examine these two seemingly different 2×2 tables:

	a			b
100	50		25	100
25	200		200	50
125	250		225	150

The odds ratios for Tables a and b are 16.0 and .0625, respectively. But notice the similarities: The second table is obtained from the first by simply rotating the frequencies while maintaining the same underlying strength of association. Most observations in Table a lie in the diagonal running from the upper left to the lower right; in the other table they tend to be in the opposite diagonal. In this sense, the two tables reflect similarity in the magnitude but not in the *direction* of the relationship.

Also note that $\hat{\alpha}_b = 1/\hat{\alpha}_a$ (that is, .0625 = 1/16). The upshot is that departures in either direction from 1.0 imply essentially the same thing but are measured on different scales. Negative relationships are measured on the interval 0 to 1.0 and positive relationships on the interval 1.0 to plus infinity. Not being symmetric about 1.0 means that two tables with the same degree of association, but in opposite directions, have different $\hat{\alpha}$'s.

The lack of symmetry[3] is easily removed by calculating the natural logarithm of $\hat{\alpha}$:

$$\hat{\alpha}^* = \log \hat{\alpha} = \log \left(\frac{n_{11} n_{22}}{n_{21} n_{12}} \right)$$

$$= \log n_{11} + \log n_{22} - \log n_{21} - \log n_{12} \qquad [7]$$

The measure $\hat{\alpha}^*$, called the log odds, varies from $-\infty$ to ∞ with 0 indicating independence. In the two previous tables, $\hat{\alpha}^*_a = 2.77$ and

TABLE 13
Effect of Changes in Marginal Distributions on Measures of Association

	a First Investigator X			b Second Investigator X	
	75	15		750	15
Y			Y		
	10	100		100	100
Totals	85	115	Totals	850	115

$$\hat{\alpha} = 50 \qquad\qquad\qquad \hat{\alpha} = 50$$
$$\hat{\alpha}^* = 3.91 \qquad\qquad\qquad \hat{\alpha}^* = 3.91$$
$$\hat{Q} = .96 \qquad\qquad\qquad \hat{Q} = .96$$
$$\hat{Y} = .75 \qquad\qquad\qquad \hat{Y} = .75$$
$$X^2 = 111.65 \qquad\qquad\qquad X^2 = 348.57$$
$$\hat{\Phi}^2 = .56 \qquad\qquad\qquad \hat{\Phi}^2 = .36$$
$$r = .75 \qquad\qquad\qquad r = .60$$

SOURCE: Reynolds (1977: Table 2.4).
NOTE: Table entries are the number of cases.

$\hat{\alpha}^*_b = -2.77$. Although $\hat{\alpha}^*$ has the appeal of being symmetric, it is perhaps more difficult to interpret than the simple odds ratio.

Both the odds ratio and its logarithm have several important properties. They are invariant under row and column multiplications. To appreciate this feature, consider two hypothetical investigators working on the same problem. Even though their variables are identical, they sample different populations at different rates and thus obtain different marginal distributions (see Table 13).

Not only does the first investigator have a smaller sample (200 versus 965), but the cases are relatively more dispersed on X: The proportions in the first column of each table are .44 and .88, respectively. Yet in spite of these differences, the odds ratio and its logarithm are the same in both tables, namely $\hat{\alpha} = 50$ and $\hat{\alpha}^* = 3.91$. Most social scientists find this stability—a trait not found in many other measures of association— quite useful because the inherent relationships appear essentially equivalent. Indeed, the second table has been obtained from the first simply by multiplying the entries in the first column of Table 13a by 10. As a practical matter, this property allows one to compare relationships across tables drawn from different samples. If the basic form of the association is the same in different populations, the $\hat{\alpha}$'s and $\hat{\alpha}^*$'s will be the same (except for sampling error) no matter how much the marginal distributions vary.

The odds ratio is also invariant under interchanges of rows *and* columns. (Switching only the rows *or* columns changes $\hat{\alpha}$ to $1/\hat{\alpha}$.) In this sense, the odds ratio is a symmetric index.

The odds ratio attains its upper bound under weak perfect association, a fact some statisticians consider a virtue, others a vice. Certainly the form of association exhibited in the two subtables of Table 14 differs substantially.

Letting Y and X denote the row and column variables, respectively, one sees that in the first table, values of Y never occur in the absence of a given value of X, a pattern that does not hold in Table b. There the first column of X is not a good predictor of Y; one can only conclude that a person who is in the second column of X will also be in the second category of Y. In this sense the relationship seems weak.

Yet in the two tables, $\hat{\alpha}$ (and $\hat{\alpha}^*$) equals plus infinity, suggesting an equivalence in relationships. The observed odds ratio equals infinity whenever n_{12} or n_{21} (or both) equal zero. (It equals zero whenever n_{11} or n_{22} or both equal zero.) A similar principle applies whenever one frequency is very small. Changing the 0 in the second table to 1 means $\hat{\alpha}$ = 200, a value many social scientists would still consider misleading.

Yule's Q. One of the best-known measures of association in the social sciences, Yule's Q is a function of the odds ratio and consequently shares most of its strengths and weaknesses. Its definition is

$$\hat{Q} = \frac{n_{11}n_{22} - n_{12}n_{21}}{n_{11}n_{22} + n_{12}n_{21}} = \frac{\hat{\alpha} - 1}{\hat{\alpha} + 1} \qquad [8]$$

For the data in Table 12,

$$\hat{Q} = \frac{(87)(12) - (234)(288)}{(87)(12) + (234)(288)} = -.97$$

Unlike α, Q lies between -1.0 and 1.0 with 0 implying statistical independence. But like the odds ratio, Q attains its upper limit under strict, implicit, *or* weak perfect association. Thus, as was true of $\hat{\alpha}$, $\hat{Q}$ reaches its maximum, 1.0, in both subtables of Table 14. (One readily sees from the appropriate formula that Q is 1.0 whenever n_{12} or n_{21} or both are zero; it is -1.0 whenever n_{11} or n_{22} or both are zero.) For this reason many investigators feel it overstates the strength of an association. Certainly it gives the largest numerical value of all the normed indices usually computed for 2×2 tables, but whether it overstates a relationship depends on one's model of perfect association (Weisberg, 1974). In any event, values close to $|1.0|$ indicate a strong relationship.

Q is invariant under row and column multiplications (see Table 13), and is symmetric.

Yule's Y. Yule's Y, sometimes called the coefficient of "colligation," is also a simple function of the odds ratio:

$$\hat{Y} = \frac{\sqrt{n_{11}n_{22}} - \sqrt{n_{12}n_{21}}}{\sqrt{n_{11}n_{22}} + \sqrt{n_{12}n_{21}}} \qquad [9]$$

For Table 12 the estimate is

$$\hat{Y} = \frac{\sqrt{(87)(12)} - \sqrt{(234)(288)}}{\sqrt{(87)(12)} + \sqrt{(234)(288)}} = -.78$$

Y has the same properties as Q though they are by no means equal in most 2×2 tables. In fact, the absolute value of Y is less than the absolute value of Q except when X and Y are independent or completely associated.

A measure based on chi square, Φ^2. One reason for not using the goodness-of-fit chi square as a measure of association is that its numerical magnitude depends partly on the size of the sample. Dividing chi square by n corrects for n and leads to a popular measure of association—phi squared:

$$\hat{\Phi}^2 = X^2/n$$

where X^2 is the observed goodness-of-fit chi square.[4]

Φ^2 for Table 12 is

$$\hat{\Phi}^2 = \frac{307.719}{621}$$

$$= .50$$

In a 2×2 table, Φ^2 varies between 0 and 1, obviously equaling zero when the variables are statistically independent. It attains its maximum only under strict perfect association. In Table 14, for instance, Φ^2 equals 1.0 in the first subtable but not in the second, where it is only .25.

On the other hand, the marginal variation in X or Y affects its magnitude. As one sees in Table 13 above, the greater the imbalance in the marginal distributions, the lower its value, other things being equal. Using either percentages or the odds ratio as the criterion, the form and strength of association are the same in both tables, but Φ_b^2 is considerably smaller than Φ^2_a. Where one or both marginals are highly skewed, a less sensitive measure may be preferred. Finally, the computation of Φ^2, a symmetric index, does not depend on which variable is considered dependent. The interpretation of Φ^2 can be further facilitated by realizing that it is equivalent to r^2, the square of the product-moment correlation coefficient, applied to a 2×2 table.

The correlation coefficient, r. The categories of dichotomous variables can be coded 0 and 1 and used in the (Pearson) product-moment correlation formula. In a 2×2 table, the calculations reduce to

$$r = \frac{n_{11}n_{22} - n_{12}n_{21}}{\sqrt{n_{1+}n_{2+}n_{+1}n_{+2}}} \qquad [10]$$

Although a symmetric measure, the square of the correlation coefficient is commonly interpreted as the percentage of variation in the dependent variable that is "explained" by the independent variable. The estimate for Table 12 is

$$r = \frac{(87)(12) - (234)(288)}{\sqrt{(321)(300)(375)(246)}} = -.70$$

TABLE 14
Behavior of Measures of Association Under Different
Models of Perfect Relationship

	a			b	
	X			X	
	50	0		50	0
Y			Y		
	0	50		50	50
Totals	50	50	Totals	100	50

$\hat{\alpha}$ $= +\infty$	$\hat{\alpha}$ $= +\infty$
$\hat{\alpha}^* = +\infty$	$\hat{\alpha}^* = +\infty$
$\hat{Q}$ $= 1.0$	$\hat{Q}$ $= 1.0$
$\hat{Y}$ $= 1.0$	$\hat{Y}$ $= 1.0$
$\hat{\Phi}^2 = 1.0$	$\hat{\Phi}^2 = .25$
r $= 1.0$	r $= .50$

NOTE: Table entries are the number of cases.

Since $r^2 = .495$, about 49 percent of the variance in voting is accounted for by party identification. Thus, remembering that statistical explanation is not equivalent to theoretical understanding, r has a clear interpretation.

Because r^2 is equivalent to Φ^2 in 2 × 2 tables, they share the same properties. The correlation coefficient is sensitive to skewed marginal distribution (see Table 13), but is invariant under interchanges of *both* rows and columns. (It changes sign only when the rows or columns are switched.) It is an appropriate measure when one's definition of perfect is strict perfect association (see Table 14).

As is well known, r varies between –1.0 and 1.0. It equals zero if the row and column variables are independent. (It can also equal zero when the variables are *nonlinearly* related.) From the formula it is apparent that r = 1.0 if $n_{12} = n_{21} = 0$ and r = –1.0 if $n_{11} = n_{22} = 0$. In this sense, the correlation coefficient gives both the direction and strength of association. In a standardized 2 × 2 table, where each marginal probability equals ½, r = Y; otherwise $|r| < |Y|$ except when the variables are independent or completely related. Consequently, its numerical value will usually be less than either Y or Q.

Measures of Association for I × J Tables

Measuring association in I × J tables involves many of the same concepts and problems found in the analysis of 2 × 2 tables. The objective is to find clearly understandable measures, ones that are not confounded by marginal distributions or table dimensions. Although innumerable approaches exist, many of them can be grouped under three headings:

(1) generalizations of the odds ratio,
(2) measures based on chi square, and
(3) "proportional-reduction-in-error" measures.

The odds ratio in I × J tables. The odds ratio or its logarithm readily generalizes to larger tables. An I × J table, where either I or J or both are greater than 2, contains subsets of 2 × 2 tables, and an $\hat{\alpha}$ or $\hat{\alpha}*$ can be calculated for each. Looking at several individual odds ratios instead of a single summary index permits one to examine various subhypotheses of interest and, in many instances, to locate the precise source of an association.

Let P_{ij} denote the probability that an observation is in the ij^{th} cell of an I × J population table. Then a *basic set* of odds ratios is:

$$\hat{\alpha}_{ij} = \frac{P_{ij} P_{IJ}}{P_{iJ} P_{Ij}} , \quad i = 1, 2, \ldots, I\text{--}1; j = 1, 2, \ldots, J\text{--}1 \qquad [11]$$

Notice that the last (the bottom right hand) cell of the table is the reference point. (Actually, any cell could serve this purpose.) Viewed from this perspective, there are t = $(I - 1)(J - 1)$ 2 × 2 tables in an I × J table, each composed of probabilities from the ith and I^{th} rows and the jth and J^{th} columns.[5] Corresponding to each such subtable is an odds ratio that can be estimated from a sample by

$$\hat{\alpha}_{ij} = \frac{n_{ij} n_{IJ}}{n_{iJ} n_{Ij}} \qquad [12]$$

where n_{ij} represents the frequency in the ij^{th} cell. Of course, the $\hat{\alpha}$'s (or their logarithms), have the same interpretation as odds ratio (or its logarithm) presented earlier.

Using odds ratio to analyze a cross-classification means an investigator must examine a set of coefficients. In a large table the number of possible $\hat{\alpha}$'s will be sizable. Partly for this reason and because it is not a normed index, social scientists have been reluctant to employ this technique in contingency table analysis.

But there are several advantages. As already noted, one can partition a cross-classfication in order to examine various "subhypotheses." In addition to calculating L^2, the likelihood ratio chi square, it is of course possible to compute $\hat{\alpha}$ (or $\hat{\alpha}*$) for each component table. Table 9 illustrates the point. Predictably, the strongest relationships as measured by $\hat{\alpha}*$ involve differences between Democrats and Republicans. Notice also that although several L^2's are statistically significant, the strength of the corresponding relationships is relatively small; indeed, only in Tables 6a, 6b, and 7a are the log odds much different than zero. Once again these findings may be obvious, but they demonstrate how odds ratios can be used to pinpoint relationships in a complex table.

Learning to use odds ratios has two other advantages. First, there is a well-developed sampling theory for them so that one can calculate their "simultaneous" confidence intervals. Whenever one makes several significance tests or—what is the same—constructs several confidence intervals on the same set of data, it is necessary to adjust the significance level to take account of the fact that several hypotheses are being tested. Simultaneous inference procedures allow one to make the necessary adjustment. See Reynolds (1977a) or Goodman (1964, 1969) for further details. The second advantage is that the odds ratio lends itself very nicely to the interpretation of log-linear models, a relatively new and important technique for analyzing multidimensional nominal data. (See Knoke and Burke, 1980.)

Measures based on chi square. As in the 2×2 case, chi square alone is not a good indicator of the form or strength of a relationship in a general table, for its magnitude depends partially on n. Standardizing it by dividing by the sample size is an obvious solution. But the resulting measure, $\hat{\Phi}^2$, does not have an upper bound except in 2×2 tables. Not being bounded, the measure is difficult to interpret. In Table 1, where the goodness-of-fit chi square is 457.634 with 12 degrees of freedom,

$$\hat{\Phi}^2 = 457.634/968 = .47$$

How should this number be interpreted? Since Φ^2 equals zero if the variables are independent, the observed value implies a weak relationship. Without more information, however, one cannot say precisely what .43 means. It is just as hard to do so in tables showing stronger relationships (see Table 15, for example).

Partly for these reasons, a number of normed variations of Φ^2 have been proposed. All of them are symmetric and equal zero when the variables are statistically independent. Two shortcomings are, however, that they frequently cannot attain their maximums, and values lying between 0 and 1.0 are hard to interpret.

The *contingency coefficient*, C, theoretically lies between 0 and 1. For sample data it is estimated by

$$\hat{C} = \sqrt{\frac{\hat{\Phi}^2}{\hat{\Phi}^2 + 1}} = \sqrt{\frac{X^2}{X^2 + n}} \qquad [13]$$

In Table 1,

$$\hat{C} = \sqrt{\frac{457.634}{457.634 + 968}}$$

$$= .57$$

C does not always reach 1.0, even when the variables seem completely associated. In square tables (such as $I = J$), for instance, its maximum value is $\sqrt{(I-1)/I}$. In this instance one can obtain an "adjusted" C by computing $C_{adj} = C/C_{max}$, where C_{max} is the maximum value C for a particular table.

In asymmetric tables, such an adjustment is less feasible. As an example, Table 15 shows that C is less than 1.0 even though there is an implicit perfect association. Some investigators, furthermore, recommend that C not be used for tables smaller than 5×5 (Garson, 1976).

Another version of Φ^2, Tschuprow's T, varies between 0 (for independence) and 1.0 but can attain its maximum only in square tables. When I does not equal J, T will be less than 1.0 (see Table 15). The sample estimate of T is

$$\hat{T} = \sqrt{\frac{\Phi^2}{\sqrt{(I-1)(J-1)}}} = \sqrt{\frac{X^2}{n\sqrt{(I-1)(J-1)}}} \qquad [14]$$

TABLE 15

**Behavior of Measures of Association Under Model
of Implicit Perfect Association**

	X				Totals
	0	50	0	50	100
Y	50	0	0	0	50
	0	0	50	0	50
Totals	50	50	50	50	200

$$x^2 = 400$$
$$\hat{\Phi}^2 = 2.000$$
$$\dot{C} = .816$$
$$\hat{T} = .816$$
$$\dot{V} = 1.0$$
$$\lambda_y = 1.0$$
$$\hat{\tau}_y = 1.0$$

NOTE: Table entries are the number of cases.

In Table 1, T is

$$\hat{T} = \sqrt{\frac{457.634}{(968)\sqrt{(2)\,(6)}}} = .37$$

Cramer's V corrects for some of the deficiencies in C and T—it achieves its maximum in asymmetric arrays as in Table 15—but is still rather difficult to interpret. The sample estimate is

$$\hat{V} = \sqrt{\frac{\Phi^2}{m}} = \sqrt{\frac{X^2}{nm}} \qquad [15]$$

where m equals the smaller of $(I - 1)$ or $(J - 1)$. In Table 1, V is

$$\hat{V} = \sqrt{\frac{457.634}{(968)\,(2)}} = .49$$

Note that V is always at least as large as T.

Besides their sensitivity to table dimensions and marginal distributions, chi-square-based measures do not have intuitively appealing interpretations. Even though they lie between 0 and 1.0 it is hard to understand a value of, say, .49. Presumably the relationship is weak but there is no operational standard for judging its magnitude. These measures were originally intended as crude approximations of the usual correlation coefficient and have been supplemented (if not replaced) by more easily interpreted measures.

Proportional-reduction-in-error measures. To avoid the weaknesses of indices based on chi square, statisticians have developed a variety of other approaches. Perhaps the most popular alternative is proportional-reduction-in-error (PRE) logic.

PRE measures rest on a simple conception of association. Imagine a game in which one randomly draws people from a population and guesses their scores on Y, the dependent variable. The predictions can be made in either of two ways: first, (1) knowing nothing at all about the individuals or (2) knowing their scores on another, independent, variable, X. Whatever rule is followed, one will surely misguess at least some of the time. But if Y depends on X, then knowledge of X categories should reduce the errors.

Each rule has its own probability of error. Under the first rule no information is used to predict scores on Y; the guesses are, in a sense, blind. Denote the probability of misclassifying subjects on this basis by P (A). According to the second rule, one examines each individual's X category and then, based on that information, predicts the value on Y. If each category of X corresponds to one and only one category of Y, then knowing an X category permits guessing the Y category exactly. If, on the other hand, the variables lack perfect correspondence but are related to some degree, the probability of misclassification, P(B), will still be less than under the first rule.

It seems natural to compare the probabilities of making errors under the two rules. To the extent that X is related to Y, the probability of error under the second rule will be less than under the first. The amount of reduction is a criterion for measuring association. Dividing this magnitude by the probability of an error by the first rule gives the *proportional reduction in error*:

$$\text{PRE Measure of Association} = \frac{(\text{Probability of Error by Rule 1}) - (\text{Probability of Error by Rule 2})}{(\text{Probability of Error by Rule 1})}$$

$$= \frac{P(A) - P(B)}{P(A)}$$

Suppose, for example, the probability of misclassifying people under Rule 1 on vote in 1980 is .6 but that once information about their party identification is taken into account the probability of making an error drops to .3. The proportional reduction in error is

$$\text{PRE} = \frac{(.6) - (.3)}{(.6)} = .5$$

meaning that knowledge of the independent variable leads to a 50 percent reduction in the expected number of errors that would have been made had party identification not been used.

Properties of PRE measures. Notice first of all that $P(A)$ is always greater than or equal to $P(B)$.[6] If the variables are statistically independent, the categories of X do not supply any information about the Y categories, and $P(A) = P(B)$. In this situation, the PRE measure is zero, as it should be. Unfortunately, there are instances where the measure will be zero though the variables are *not* statistically independent. This problem usually arises when the distribution on Y is highly skewed.

For perfect association, the probability of error under the second rule, $P(B)$, is zero and the measure reduces to

$$\text{PRE Measure} = \frac{P(A) - 0}{P(A)} = 1.0$$

The limits are thus 0 and 1.0—zero when X and Y are independent, 1.0 when they are completely related. The principal advantage is that intermediate values have a clear interpretation as the proportional-reduction-in-error in predicting classes of the dependent variable.

TABLE 16
Example of a Table of Probabilities (hypothetical data)

		X		
		c	d	Totals
Y	a	.3	.1	.4
	b	.2	.4	.6
	Totals	.5	.5	1.0

NOTE: Entries are probabilities. a, b, c, and d are category labels.

At first glance the definition appears somewhat awkward. But the operations are really quite compatible with social science research. After all, most investigators want to predict scores on dependent variables.

Finally, it is clear that one variable must be treated as dependent on the other. Predicting categories of X instead of Y will normally lead to different error rates and hence different values for the PRE measure. In this sense PRE measures are asymmetric: Their numerical value depends on the dependent variable. For the instances when the designation of the dependent variable is arbitrary, one can compute both versions (that is, PRE_Y and PRE_X, where the subscript indicates the dependent variable) or a symmetric version. Because PRE logic is quite broad, numerous nominal measures of association are based on it. Their meaning and computation stem from the precise definition of errors.

Goodman and Kruskal's lambda. Goodman and Kruskal's (1954) lambda rests on very straightforward definitions of prediction error. Referring to the hypothetical population probabilities or proportions presented in Table 16, one sees that the first entry, .3, is the probability of having both characteristic *a* on Y and characteristic *c* on X. The marginal probability, .4 indicates that a member of this population has a four-in-ten chance of being in category *a, regardless of the value on X.*

According to the first rule, one predicts a randomly selected individual's Y class without knowledge of his or her classification on X. How should the prediction be made? The marginal probability of category *b*, .6, is larger than the marginal probability of category *a*, .4.

With no other information available, it would be sensible to guess *b*. Guessing that class *each* time, of course, leads to errors, since not everyone belongs in it. But the probability of *b* is .6, and over the long run 60 percent of the choices should be correct. The proportion of successful predictions by this method exceeds the proportion of successes obtained by predicting *a*. Hence, the first rule is as follows: Always guess the modal class of Y (here *b*) with the probability of error being simply one minus the probability of a success, or

$$1. - .6 = .4.$$

For an I $\times$ J table, let P_{m+} denote the *maximum* marginal row probability. Without knowledge of X, one should always guess the category corresponding to the probability P_{m+}. The probability of making accurate predictions is P_{m+}, while the probability of error is

$$P(A) = 1 - P_{m+}$$

According to the second rule, the investigator selects an individual at random, examines that individual's classification on X, and then predicts the Y category. Again, exactly how should the prediction be made? Continuing with the example, suppose an individual happens to belong to the first category of X in Table 16. The largest cell probability in that column, .3, implies that if a person belongs to category *c* on X he or she is slightly more likely to belong to category *a* than *b* on variable Y. The difference in probabilities suggests predicting category *a* for each individual who has characteristic *c*. Once it is known that a person is in the first column, the best guess is category *a* instead of *b*. Knowledge of the independent variable has altered the prediction made under the first rule. Once again mistakes will be made, because some members of column *c* do not belong in row *a*. Nevertheless, within a given column the errors can be minimized by guessing the most probable row category.

Consider a member of the second column. In what row does the member most likely belong? The largest cell probability in this column, 4, lies in the second row. If the individual's X characteristic is *d,* one would suspect that he or she has characteristic *b*. Predicting *b* for each member of the second column d results in a number of errors, but fewer than if a is chosen.

Finally, to calculate the number of errors under the second rule, add the probability of making errors in each column and subtract from 1.0. Since the probabilities of successful prediction in the two columns are .3 and .4, the probability of error is simply

$$1 - (.3 + .4) = .3$$

(Or conversely, the probability of errors is simply .2 + .1 = .3.)

In an I $\times$ J table, the symbol P_{mj} denotes the *maximum* cell probability in the jth column, (In Table 16, P_{m1} and P_{m2} are .3 and .4, respectively.) The probability of error under the second rule, P(B), is

$$P(B) = 1 - \sum_{j=1}^{J} P_{mj}$$

These steps define a PRE measure, lambda:

$$\lambda_y = \frac{(1 - P_{m+}) - \left(1 - \sum_{j=1}^{J} P_{mj}\right)}{(1 - P_{m+})} = \frac{\left(\sum_{j=1}^{J} P_{mj}\right) - P_{m+}}{(1 - P_{m+})} \qquad [16]$$

The subscript Y indicates that categories of Y are being predicted from information about X.

Hence, λ_y and λ_x for the population in Table 16 are

$$\lambda_y = \frac{(.3 + .4) - .6}{(1 - .6)} = .25$$

$$\lambda_x = \frac{(.3 + .4) - .5}{(1 - .5)} = .40$$

Using X as the predictor leads to a 25 percent reduction in error in predicting categories of Y. This reduction suggests a moderately strong relationship between X and Y, at least as the term "relationship" has been defined here. Knowing an individual's X classification does improve predictions of the Y categories. Similarly, in predicting X categories on the basis of Y, the percentage reduction in error decreases by 40 percent.

The data also illustrate the asymmetry of the measures: λ_y does not equal λ_x. One should therefore rely on substantive knowledge to determine the most appropriate index. If, for instance, the aim of a study is the explanation of variation in Y by reference to other variables, λ_y should be computed.

Sample estimates can be calculated by replacing the population probabilities with estimated probabilities. It is simpler, though, to use raw frequencies and compute the estimate of λ_y from the following formula:

$$\hat{\lambda}_y = \frac{\left(\sum_{j=1}^{J} n_{mj} \right) - n_{m+}}{(n - n_{m+})} \qquad [17]$$

where n_{m+} represents the largest marginal row total, n_{mj} represents the largest frequency in the jth column, and n is the sample size. These quantities correspond to the probabilities in the previous expression, and the underlying logic remains the same. The estimate, $\hat{\lambda}_y$, gives the proportional reduction in error for a sample of n observations.

Returning to Table 1, it is easy to estimate the reduction in error in predicting vote based on knowledge of party identification. Since the first row contains the largest marginal total, $n_{m+} = 492$. The sum of the largest cell frequencies in the successive columns is

$$\sum_{j=1}^{7} n_{mj} = 168 + 120 + 49 + 54 + 85 + 131 + 103 = 710$$

Substituting into the previous formula, the estimate for Table 1 is

$$\hat{\lambda}_y = \frac{710 - 492}{968 - 492} = .46$$

Hence, by taking party identification into account, about a 46 percent reduction in error is achieved in predicting candidate preference.

Using an analogous formula, the estimate of λ_x is

$$\hat{\lambda}_x = \frac{(131+168+28) - 201}{(968-201)} = \frac{327 - 201}{968 - 201} = .16$$

From this point of view, the reduction in error is about 16 percent.

Symmetric version of lambda. Whether an investigator wants $\hat{\lambda}_y$ or $\hat{\lambda}_x$ depends on his or her understanding of the variables: if Y depends on X, then $\hat{\lambda}_y$ is appropriate; otherwise $\hat{\lambda}_x$. Occasionally, however, investigators do not know or are unwilling to assume any dependency among the variables. In this case they might prefer a "symmetric" coefficient. Fortunately, slightly modifying the PRE logic, a symmetric version of lambda can easily be defined.

The definition of this measure, denoted simply λ, requires the imaginary process of using the two rules to predict people's classifications. This guessing game, as noted before, is a purely heuristic device designed to clarify the meaning of the measure. One does not actually make any predictions, but only pretends to in order to define association.

Symmetric lambda combines the logic of computing both λ_y and λ_x. Suppose, for example, individuals are randomly selected, and half are assigned to Y classes and half to X categories. According to the first rule, these predictions are made without any additional knowledge. In guessing Y categories, one would always place individuals in the most probable Y class, the one pertaining to P_{m+}, if one wished to minimize the number of errors. On the other hand, when predicting X categories, he would pick the one associated with P_{+m}. During the time Y classes are guessed, the probability of a successful prediction is $\frac{1}{2} P_{m+}$, and during the time X categories are assigned, it is $\frac{1}{2} P_{+m}$. A little thought shows that the probability of an incorrect guess is

$$P(A) = 1 - \frac{1}{2} P_{m+} + \frac{1}{2} P_{+m} = 1 - \frac{P_{m+} + P_{+m}}{2}$$

where p_{m+} and p_{+m} are, respectively, maximum row and column marginal probabilities. (In Table 16, these numbers are .6 and .5.) The factor $\frac{1}{2}$ enters because each probability applies to half of the guesses.

Knowledge of both variables is taken into account under the second rule. For those individuals whose Y classes are being guessed, the investigator uses information about their scores on X. As with λ_y, the probability of a successful guess is a function of the p_{mj}'s. In particular, it is

$$\frac{1}{2} \sum_{j=1}^{J} P_{mj}$$

This is the same probability as before, except that since Y classes are being predicted only half of the time, it is multiplied by one half. For the other individuals—the ones whose X class is being guessed—the probability of a correct prediction knowing Y is

$$\frac{1}{2} \sum_{i=1}^{I} P_{im}$$

The logic is the same as in the calculation of λ_y and λ_x, except that one effectively computes one measure half of the time and the other measure the rest of the time. The probability of error under Rule 2 is then

$$P(B) = 1 - \frac{1}{2} \sum_{j=1}^{J} P_{mj} + \frac{1}{2} \sum_{i=1}^{I} P_{im} = 1 - \frac{\sum_{j=1}^{J} P_{mj} + \sum_{i=1}^{I} P_{im}}{2}$$

PRE logic measures the proportional reduction in error using Rule 2 instead of Rule 1. Hence, symmetric lambda is defined as after algebraic manipulation:

$$\lambda = \frac{\sum_{j=1}^{J} P_{mj} + \sum_{i=1}^{I} P_{im} - P_{m+} - P_{+m}}{2 - P_{m+} - P_{+m}} \qquad [18]$$

For Table 16, symmetric lambda is

$$\lambda = \frac{(.3 + .4) + (.3 + .4) - .6 - .5}{2 - .6 - .5} = \frac{.30}{.90} = .33$$

The sample estimate, computed from observed frequencies, is

$$\hat{\lambda} = \frac{\sum\limits_{j=1}^{J} n_{mj} + \sum\limits_{i=1}^{I} n_{im} - n_{m+} - n_{+m}}{2n - n_{m+} - n_{+m}} \tag{19}$$

The estimated lambda between party identification and vote in 1980 (Table 1) is thus

$$\hat{\lambda} = \frac{[(168 + 120 + 49 + 54 + 85 + 131 + 103) + (131 + 168 + 28)] - 492 - 201}{2(968) - 492 - 201}$$

$$= .28$$

Goodman and Kruskal's tau. Another PRE measure, Goodman and Kruskal's tau, represents a modification of the hypothetical guessing game. As before, randomly selected individuals are assigned Y scores with and without knowledge of the independent variable. But this time the assignments preserve the original distributions.

Preserving a distribution means that the distribution of guesses is the same as the original distribution. If, for example, n_{1+} and n_{2+} individuals are in the first two categories of Y, then the assignment process will keep exactly n_{1+} and n_{2+} people in those categories. When calculating lambda, everyone is assigned to Y's modal category, thus the pattern of guesses is not the same as the observed distribution. For some purposes it is useful to have a measure based on maintaining the original distribution.

Instead of developing an explicit formula for tau, it is easier to illustrate its computation on the data in Table 1. Suppose 492 individuals are randomly selected from the table and labeled "Reagan voters." Since many of them are not Reagan backers at all, classifying these people in this fashion creates a number of expected errors. How many? Out of 968 respondents, $381 + 95 = 476$ (or $476/968 = .492$) do not belong in that category. Thus the proportion of incorrectly assigned individuals would be .492 or $(.492)(492) = 241.93$ cases.

Now suppose a sample of 381 is drawn from the table and assigned to the "Carter" category. Once again, misclassification would result since

492 + 95 = 587 are not Carter voters, but how many? The probability of error is 587/968 = .606; hence, of the 381 assignments, we would expect about (.606) (381) = 231.04 cases to be incorrectly assigned.

Continuing in this manner, the total number of expected errors under Rule 1—preserving the marginal distribution but not using X to make the predictions—would be

$$= (.492) (492) + (.606) (381) + (.902) (95)$$

$$= 241.93 + 231.04 + 85.68$$

$$= 558.65$$

Notice that in making these guesses the marginal totals have been preserved because 492 cases were classified "Reagan," 381 "Carter," and 95 "Anderson." More generally, to compute the expected errors under Rule 1, subject to the constraint that the marginal totals be maintained, proceed as follows: for each category of the dependent variable, count the number of observations not belonging in it, divide by n, and multiply by the category total. Then sum these totals.

To compute the errors under Rule 2, one continues in exactly the same manner except that it is necessary to work within categories of the independent variable. This amounts to guessing a person's vote preference while knowing his or her party affiliation, but again subject to the constraint of preserving the original distribution, this time within categories.

Consider, for example, the 196 strong Democrats. We have to assign 21 of them to the Reagan category, 168 to Carter, and 7 to Anderson. Suppose we pick 21 of these strong Democrats at random. A few might be Reagan voters, but most will not. Hence, in classifying all of them as Reagan voters, we will surely be making some errors. To find the expected number of errors, first count the number of non-Reagan voters among the strong Democrats: 168 + 7 = 175. Since 175 is about 89 percent of 196, we would expect that of the 21 cases assigned to the Reagan category, about 89 percent or 18.75 cases would be erroneously classified. But next classify 168 of the 196 as Carter voters. Although we will still make a few errors, we will do much better because only 21 + 7 = 28 of the 196 strong Democrats did not vote for Carter. That turns out to be about 14 percent (28/196 = .143) so only about 14 percent of the 168 assignments or (168) (.143) = 24.02 cases will be wrong. And finally, of the 7 people assigned to Anderson,

$$(21 + 168/196) \times 7 = 6.74$$

will be incorrectly classified. Thus, the errors made in assigning the 196 strong Democrats to the three classes of voting total

$$18.75 + 24.02 + 6.74 = 49.51$$

The expected number of errors for the remaining 6 categories of partisanship are found in the same way. The *total* number of errors expected by following the second rule is thus

$$49.51 + 106.57 + 70.39 + 44.75 + 42.98 + 39.05 + 16.91 = 370.16$$

More generally, expected errors from following the second rule are found by taking each level of the independent variable in turn. Working within categories, say the jth, one counts the number of cases not belonging to a specific category of the dependent variable, say the ith, divides this total by n_{+j} and then multiplies by n_{ij}.

The two sets of expected errors are substituted into the PRE formula to obtain an estimate of the proportional reduction in error subject to the constraint that the marginal totals be kept. For Table 1, the estimate is

$$\hat{\tau}_y = \frac{558.65 - 370.16}{558.65} = .34$$

Hence, knowledge of party identification leads to about a 34 percent reduction in error.

A computing formula for sample data is:

$$\hat{\tau}_y = \frac{\sum\limits_{i} n_{i+}\left[\dfrac{\sum\limits_{\substack{i' \\ i' \neq i}} n_{i'+}}{n}\right] - \sum\limits_{j}\left[\sum\limits_{i} n_{ij}\left(\dfrac{\sum\limits_{\substack{i' \\ i'=i}} n_{i'j}}{n_{+j}}\right)\right]}{\sum\limits_{i} n_{i+}\left[\dfrac{\sum\limits_{\substack{i' \\ i' \neq i}} n_{i'+}}{n}\right]} \qquad [20]$$

Here the notation $\displaystyle\sum_{\substack{i' \\ i' \neq i}}$ means that the summation

is taken over each row except the ith. A little reflection will show that this formula simply makes explicit the preceding logic.

Like λ, Goodman and Kruskal's tau lies between 0 and 1: It equals zero if the variables are statistically independent and equals 1.0 under complete association. "Complete" in this concept means "strict" or "implied" perfect association. That is, $\tau = 1$ if for each category of the independent variable, j, there is a category of the dependent variable, i, not necessarily unique, such that $p_{ij} = p_{+j}$. It is also an asymmetric index since $\tau_y \neq \tau_x$ in most cases, as the reader can verify by treating party identification as the dependent variable and calculating tau.

Comparing Measures of Association

A measure of association purportedly describes the type and strength of a relationship between two variables. Ideally, the index tells us how the variables are related in the population, but at the least it should have an unambiguous meaning when applied to observed data. Unfortunately, however, various factors that are not directly related to the nature of the association can affect a measure's numerical value, thereby clouding its interpretation. Perhaps the most important of these factors is the way the variables have been categorized.

Categorization partly affects marginal distributions. The actual distribution of adults in terms of party identification only partially determines their distribution in a sample cross-classification. Question wording and the definition of category boundaries are also important. Suppose, for example, an investigator simply classified people as Democrat, Independent, or Republican, omitting the gradations "strong" and "weak." The resulting variable and marginal distribution would be quite different than what appears in Table 1. Decisions about category boundaries and the like are to some extent arbitrary, because they represent choices rather than the inexorable determination of nature. Consequently, two individuals studying the same phenomenon can obtain different observed marginal distributions. Even if they follow exactly the same operational procedures, they might still get different distributions if they sample populations with different variances. Since measures of association are affected by these distributions, it is entirely possible that their substantive conclusions about the underlying relationship would differ, even though in fact they are the same.

It is important, then, to think carefully about categorization process and marginal distributions.

Indices of dispersion for nominal data.[7] A measure of dispersion or variation indicates the degree of differences among observations on a variable. As opposed to a measure of central tendency, like the mode, it tells how much variation exists among the cases. A useful and simple measure of marginal variation for nominal data is the *index of diversity*:

$$\hat{D} = 1 - \sum_i (n_{i+}/n)^2 \qquad [21]$$

where n_{i+} is the ith marginal total in the ith class and $n = \sum_i n_{i+}$ is the sample size.

The index of diversity gives the probability that a pair of randomly selected observations will be in different categories. If, for example, $\hat{D} = .8$, then the probability that two randomly chosen individuals will have different party identifications is .8. If there is no variation—that is, if all the cases fall in a single category—then $\hat{D} = 0$. If, on the other hand, the variable has I categories, the maximum possible value of $\hat{D}$ is $(I - 1)/I$, which occurs if equal proportions appear in each category. Hence, $\hat{D}$ lies between 0 and $(I - 1)/I$.

Potential variation, it ought to be pointed out, increases as the number of categories increases. Classifying a population into seven groups leads to greater potential variation than simply dichotomizing it: $6/7 = .87$ is of course greater than $1/2 = .5$.

The index of diversity for party identification is

$$\hat{D}_{Party} = 1 - [(196/968)^2 + (201/968)^2 + \ldots + (112/968)^2]$$

$$= .84$$

A related measure is the *index of qualitative variation*:

$$IQV = [I/(I-1)]\hat{D} = [I/(I-1)] \ [1 - \sum(n_{i+}/n)^2] \qquad [22]$$

where I is the total number of categories. The index of qualitative variation, which is a "standardized" version of D because it takes into account the number of categories, has the same interpretation (it is the probability that a randomly selected pair of observations will be in different categories) except that its maximum possible value is 1.0. Thus, $0.0 \leq IQV \leq 1.0$. IQV is appropriate and useful when comparing the variation of distributions based on different numbers of categories. As an example, suppose that a questionnaire administered in the 1950s classified respondents as liberal, conservative, or moderate, whereas a more recent survey used a seven-point scale. It would be preferable to calculate IQV rather than $\hat{D}$ when comparing variation because the number of categories differs.

For Table 1, the index of qualitative variation is

$$IQV = (7/6)(.844) = .98$$

Hence, there is about as much variation (in this sense) as possible, given the nature of categorization.

These measures obviously do not have the same interpretation and mathematical utility as the standard deviation (or variance) calculated on quantitative data. Nevertheless, they can be quite useful in the analysis of nominal scales, as seen below and in later sections.

There has been considerable discussion recently about the decline of political parties. One might suppose among other things that the proportion of the population identifying with a party has decreased while the number of independents has increased. Showing the distribution of partisanship over the last thirty years, Table 17 permits one to examine that supposition. Both $\hat{D}$ and IQV clearly suggest that variation in party identification has changed hardly at all: The probability of two people having the same affiliation is about the same in 1980 as in 1952.

It is also apparent from the table that the way variables are categorized affects the magnitudes of variation. Suppose we decided to collapse party identification into just three categories. The index $\hat{D}$ shows the effect. (Since IQV is a standardized measure—that is, it adjusts for the number of categories—it does not change very much.) For reasons to be seen in a moment, decreasing variation can confuse the interpretation of measures of association, and it is advisable to keep as many categories as possible.

TABLE 17
Distribution of Party Identification, 1952-1980

a

Seven Categories

	1952		1960		1972		1980	
	%	n_{i+}	%	n_{i+}	%	n_{i+}	%	n_{i+}
SD	22	392	20	382	15	404	17	228
D	26	446	26	478	26	700	24	326
ID	10	178	6	115	11	296	11	150
I	6	107	10	191	13	350	12	171
IR	7	125	7	134	11	296	12	171
I	14	250	14	268	13	350	14	193
SR	14	250	16	306	10	269	10	137
Totals:	99	1748	99	1874	99	2665	100	1376
$\hat{D}$:	.82		.83		.84		.84	
IQV:	.96		.96		.98		.98	
$\hat{\sigma}$:	2.20		2.22		1.97		2.00	

b

Three Categories

	1952		1960		1972		1980	
	%	n_{i+}	%	n_{i+}	%	n_{i+}	%	n_{i+}
Democrats	48	838	46	860	41	1104	40	554
Independents	23	410	23	440	35	942	36	492
Republicans	29	500	31	574	23	619	24	330
Totals:	100	1748	100	1874	99	2665	100	1376
$\hat{D}$:	.63		.64		.65		.65	
IQV:	.95		.96		.97		.98	
$\hat{\sigma}$:	.85		.86		.78		.78	

SOURCE: Miller, Miller, and Schneider (1980), Table 2.1, p. 81; 1980 American National Election Study (see Table 1 for complete citation).

KEY: (See Table 3). In Table b, "Democrats" consist of SD and D; "Independents" consist of ID, I, and IR; and "Republicans" of R and SR. Percentages do not add to 100% because of rounding errors.

Finally, note a major difference between these indices and the usual standard deviation, $\hat{\sigma}$. The standard deviation describes the dispersion about a central point, the mean, and one can see that by this definition there has been a very slight decrease in variation. The explanation is, of course, that people are "migrating" from the extreme categories into the middle ones, but the movements are rather even, so that no single category dominates the others. In any event, the change in partisanship is perhaps not so dramatic as commonly supposed, although even marginal changes can greatly affect a party's fortunes at the polls.

How variation and categorization affect measures of association. Generally speaking, the higher the variation, the larger a measure of association *can* be, other things being equal. And as might be expected, if variation is limited by, for example, combining adjacent classes or eliminating categories altogether, an index might be smaller than it would otherwise be. Hypothetical data illustrate these points.

According to most definitions, the variation in a categorical variable is greatest when all categories have equal numbers of cases, as in Table 18a. Combining the last two rows in each table reduces the variation in Y without substantially changing the relationship as measured by percentages. Notice, for example, that 75 percent of the cases lie in the second category of Y in Table 18c, but that the joint percentages are about the same as in Table 18a.

For every decline in Y's variation, each measure except $\hat{\tau}$ also declines. Lambda as well as the indices based on chi square are highest in the symmetric table where variation in Y is greatest and lowest where variation is less. Only tau remains stable through the three tables.

In some tables, in fact, lambda equals zero even if the variables are not statistically independent. This problem arises when the modal class of Y is so large relative to the others that all n_{mj} lie in the same row (see Table 19). As $\hat{\tau}_y$ indicates, X and Y are related, but since the maximum cell frequencies in each column are in the same row,

$$\sum_{j=1}^{J} n_{mj} = n_{m+} \quad \text{and} \quad \hat{\lambda}_y = 0$$

In other tables having a preponderance of cases in one category of Y, lambda may be quite close to zero, suggesting little or no relationship. Tau is less sensitive in this respect and might be used when the dependent variable is highly uneven.

TABLE 18
Effects of Decreasing Variation in the Dependent Variable

a

Cases Distributed Evenly
Among Four Categories of Y
$(\hat{D}_y^* = .75)$

	X				Totals
	80% (800)	10% (100)	5% (50)	5% (50)	1000
	10 (100)	80 (800)	5 (50)	5 (50)	1000
Y	5 (50)	5 (50)	80 (800)	10 (100)	1000
	5 (50)	5 (50)	10 (100)	80 (800)	1000
Totals	100% (1000)	100% (1000)	100% (1000)	100% (1000)	4000

$X^2 = 6480 \quad \hat{C} = .79 \quad \hat{T} = .90 \quad \hat{\tau}_y = .54$

$\hat{\Phi}^2 = 1.62 \quad \hat{V} = .90 \quad \hat{\lambda}_y = .73$

b

Cases are Unevenly Distributed
$(\hat{D}_y = .62)$

	X				Totals
	80% (800)	10% (100)	5% (50)	5% (50)	1000
Y	10 (100)	80 (800)	5 (50)	5 (50)	1000
	10 (100)	10 (100)	90 (900)	90 (900)	2000
Totals	100% (1000)	100% (1000)	100% (1000)	100% (1000)	4000

$X^2 = 4520 \quad \hat{C} = .531 \quad \hat{T} = .68 \quad \hat{\tau}_y = .58$

$\hat{\Phi}^2 = 1.13 \quad \hat{V} = .75 \quad \hat{\lambda}_y = .70$

(continued)

Table 18 (Continued)

c

Marginal Distribution in Y is Skewed
$(\dot{D}_y = .37)$

	X				Totals
	80%	10%	5%	5%	
	(800)	(100)	(50)	(50)	1000
Y					
	20	90	95	95	
	(200)	(900)	(950)	(950)	3000
	100%	100%	100%	100%	
	(1000)	(1000)	(1000)	(1000)	4000

$$X^2 = 2160 \quad \hat{C} = .35 \quad \dot{T} = .56 \quad \hat{\tau}_y = .54$$
$$\dot{\Phi}^2 = .54 \quad \dot{V} = .73 \quad \dot{\lambda}_y = .60$$

NOTE: Numbers in parentheses are the number of cases. $\dot{D}_y$ is the index of diversity for Y.

TABLE 19

λ_y **Equals Zero Even Though There Is a Significant Relationship Between X and Y**

	X			Totals
	45%	10%	5%	
	(45)	(10)	(5)	60
Y	50	70	60	
	(50)	(70)	(60)	180
	5	20	35	
	(5)	(20)	(35)	60
Totals	100%	100%	100%	
	(100)	(100)	(100)	300

$$\hat{\lambda}_y = 0.0$$
$$\hat{\lambda}_x = .25$$
$$\hat{\tau}_y = .095$$

NOTE: Figures in parentheses are the number of cases.

The same principle applies to changes in the variation of the independent variable. In general, as the variation in X decreases (that is, as its marginal distribution becomes increasingly uneven), most measures decrease, other things being equal. Looking at Table 20, one sees that the basic relationship, as measured by percentages, stays the same in all three subtables. Indeed, the tables are generated by simply halving the frequencies in the first and last columns while keeping the middle column constant. Although hypothetical, the data could represent three samples drawn from populations having different amounts of variation in X.

Whatever the case, the underlying relationship remains the same. But both PRE and chi square measures decline, indicating that the numerical values depend partly on how the cases are distributed. Note, on the other hand, that the basic sets of odds ratios remain constant. (That is, for example, $\hat{\alpha}_{21} = 2.25$ in all three tables.)

Problems of this sort are particularly acute when one is trying to compare tables with unequal marginals. As in the previous section, suppose two investigators who are studying the relationship between X and Y base their analyses on samples from different populations. Calculating either lambda or tau, the first investigator—whose data appear in Table 21a—finds a weak relationship as measured by lambda and tau. The other investigator finds a moderately strong relationship. At first, the results seem incompatible. Yet closer inspection reveals that the relative proportions are exactly the same. (In fact, the entries in the first column of Table 21b have been multiplied by 10 to produce the other data.)

Standardizing a table can often solve problems like this. Standardization is a method for adjusting frequencies to conform to any desired set of marginal totals. An observer may wonder, for example, what the relationship would be if each category of X had the same number of cases. The easiest method is to compute percentages, treating the percentages as though they were raw frequencies. In percentaging on the independent variable, one pretends that each category of X contains exactly 100 cases.

Table 21c is a standardized table. (Since the proportions in both a and b are the same, they generate the same standardized frequencies.) Now the nature of the relationship seems clearer. The first investigator's findings appear somewhat misleading because of the skewed marginals, while results in the second table agree with the standardized data.

TABLE 20
Effects of Decreasing Variation in the Independent Variable

a
Cases Evenly Distributed
Among X Categories
$(\dot{D}_x = .67)$

		X		Totals
	600	300	100	1000
Y	300	400	300	1000
	100	300	600	1000
Totals	1000	1000	1000	3000

$x^2 = 780$ $\dot{V} = .36$ $\dot{T}_y = .13$ $\dot{\alpha}_{12} = 6.0$

$\dot{\phi}^2 = .26$ $\dot{T} = .36$ $\dot{\alpha}_{11} = 36$ $\dot{\alpha}_{22} = 2.67$

$\dot{C} = .45$ $\dot{\lambda}_y = .30$ $\dot{\alpha}_{21} = 6.0$

b
Uneven Distribution
Among X Categories
$(\dot{D}_x = .75)$

		X		Totals
	300	300	50	650
Y	150	400	150	700
	50	300	300	650
Totals	500	1000	500	2000

$x^2 = 406.59$ $\dot{V} = .32$ $\dot{T}_y = .10$ $\dot{\alpha}_{12} = 6.0$

$\dot{\phi}^2 = .20$ $\dot{T} = .32$ $\dot{\alpha}_{11} = 36$ $\dot{\alpha}_{22} = 2.67$

$\dot{C} = .41$ $\dot{\lambda}_y = .23$ $\dot{\alpha}_{21} = 6.0$

(continued)

Table 20 (Continued)

c

Extremely Uneven Distribution
Among X Categories
($\dot{D}_x = .50$)

	X			Totals
	150	300	25	475
Y	75	400	75	550
	25	300	150	475
Totals	250	1000	250	1500

$$X^2 = 211.72 \quad \dot{V} = .27 \quad \dot{\tau}_y = .07 \quad \dot{\alpha}_{12} = 6.0$$

$$\dot{\Phi}^2 = .14 \quad \dot{T} = .27 \quad \dot{\alpha}_{11} = 36 \quad \dot{\alpha}_{22} = 2.67$$

$$\dot{C} = .35 \quad \dot{\lambda}_y = .16 \quad \dot{\alpha}_{21} = 6.0$$

NOTE: Table entries are frequencies. The relative proportions remain the same in every table. D_x is the index of diversity for X.

In general, when comparing tables or when variables are skewed, it will be useful to recompute measures of association on standardized data. This should eliminate to a degree the vagaries of marginal totals. Of course, variation itself may have substantive interest and should also be reported.

It is possible to standardize data so that they conform to any desired set of marginals. Suppose, in particular, that one wanted to know what the relationship between X and Y would be if there were an equal number of cases in the categories of *both* X and Y. A procedure called iterative proportional fitting allows one to adjust the observed frequencies in such a way as to produce the desired marginals *without* changing the nature of the relationship as measured by $\hat{\alpha}$ (or $\hat{\alpha}^*$). Since the calculations are a bit cumbersome, we will not describe them here. (The interested reader should consult Reynolds [1977a: 31-33].) Nevertheless, if one is interested only in the marginal distribution of X, the independent variable, it is sufficient to compute percentages as in Table 21c and treat the percentages as frequencies.

Finally, these remarks suggest two generalizations. First, it usually pays to look at a relationship from several points of view, as each

222

TABLE 21
Standardizing a Table Helps Remove Effects
of Unequal Marginal Totals

a

First Investigator's Data
$(\hat{D}_x = .28)$

		X		Totals
	350	10	5	365
Y	150	30	15	195
	50	10	35	95
Totals	550	50	55	655

$$\hat{\lambda}_y = .17 \qquad \hat{\tau}_y = .11$$

b

Second Investigator's Data
$(\hat{D}_x = .67)$

		X		Totals
	35	10	5	50
Y	15	30	15	60
	5	10	35	50
Totals	55	50	55	160

$$\hat{\lambda}_y = .40 \qquad \hat{\tau}_y = .21$$

c

Standardized Table
$(\hat{D}_x = .67)$

		X		Totals
	64	20	9	93
Y	27	60	27	114
	9	20	64	93
Totals	100	100	100	300

$$\hat{\lambda}_y = .40 \qquad \hat{\tau}_y = .21$$

NOTE: $\hat{D}_x$ is index of diversity for X.

measure rests on a slightly different definition of association. Unless a theory explicitly assumes a particular definition, which is at most never the case, one may overlook important aspects of the data by relying on a single index.

Second, measures of association by themselves do not prove the relative explanatory power of variables. Social scientists commonly ask for the most important explanation of a given dependent variable. After computing a series of coefficients, it is tempting to take the variable whose index has the largest numerical value as the best predictor or explanation. But since the coefficients are susceptible to extraneous factors like marginal distributions and since they each represent a certain conception of association, these comparisons could be very misleading. In addition, the impact of one variable on another depends partly on its relationship to still other variables, many of which may be unmeasured. For these reasons, using a coefficient of association alone to show explanatory importance seems questionable.

4. INTRODUCTION TO
MULTIVARIATE DATA ANALYSIS

Having found a connection between party identification and voting, one wonders if introducing additional variables will further the understanding of the relationship. The simultaneous examination of more than two variables, called multivariate analysis, raises two general questions. Although it is not possible to explore these problems in detail, a brief introduction may be a useful guide to the more advanced methods.

One may ask in the first place if additional variables improve predictions about the dependent variable. Suppose, for example, that the respondents in Table 1 have been classified by their level of education as well as their partisanship and vote. Does the extra information lead to a better understanding of political preferences?

A second general question concerns changes in a relationship caused by controlling for a third variable. How, for instance, is the association between party identification and vote affected by holding education constant? Table 22 contains three contingency tables, each displaying the association between partisanship and vote *within* a particular level of education. The first table shows the cross-classification among respondents with less than a high school education, the second the relationship among high school graduates, and the third among people with at least some college training. Looking at the data from this perspective, one can ask the following questions:

—Is the nature and strength of the relationship the same in each subtable? If the form of the association varies from one level of the control variable to another, then *interaction* exists. "Interaction" means that the relationship between X and Y is not the same in each category of Z, a control variable (or set of control variables). X and Y might be strongly related in the first level of Z, weakly related in the second, and so forth.

—Assuming no interaction (that is, the relationships are essentially the same in each contingency table), are the variables statistically independent? If so, the *partial association* between X and Y is zero. If, on the other hand, the variables are statistically related and the strength of the relationship is the same across categories of Z, the partial association is constant but not nil.

—If interaction is present, in which subtable is the relationship strongest? In which is it weakest? Is the relationship nil at some levels of Z and not others? The answers *specify* the conditions under which a relationship holds.

Detecting interaction, measuring partial associations, and specifying relationships lie at the heart of many multivariate techniques. As mentioned above, a description of these methods lies beyond the scope of this paper, but the underlying objectives and logic can be outlined.

The Causal Analysis of Nominal Data

In the past, many social scientists recommended "explicating" an original relationship between two variables by holding control or "test" variables constant, thereby creating a series of contingency tables (Hyman, 1955; Rosenberg, 1968). In Table 22, the test factor—education—is the control variable. The objective is to examine the original relationship within levels of the test factor.

What does one look for? The answer depends on what are believed to be the underlying causal mechanisms. A social scientist can never prove causality or even the direction of causation. But if various simplifying assumptions are made, it is at least possible to eliminate models that are inconsistent with the data.

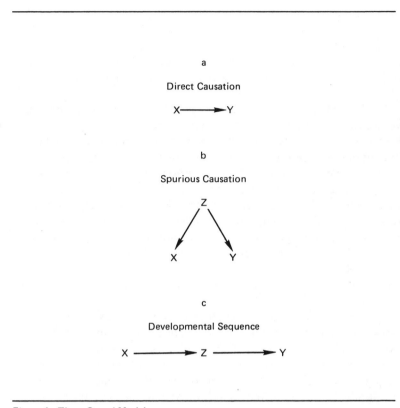

Figure 1: Three Causal Models

Consider the three models in Figure 1. In the first, X directly causes Y. Changing X will presumably change Y. By contrast, X and Y are "spuriously" related in the second model. A change in X has no effect on Y since both variables are causally dependent on Z. Finally, in the third model, a developmental sequence, X is indirectly linked to Y through Z. Changing X causes Z to change, which in turn produces a change in X.

The second and third models can be distinguished from the first by controlling for Z, the test factor. If the contingent associations between Y and X are nil or at least very much weaker than the original relationships (except for sampling error), then one infers that the relationship is either spurious or a developmental sequence; otherwise the variables are directly related. (Whether it is a spurious or developmental sequence depends on whether Z causally or temporally precedes X—a matter that must be decided on substantive, not statistical grounds.) Even if Y and X are directly related, the nature or form of the association might be affected by Z. With such interaction present, one has to specify the relationship by describing it for each level of Z.

To illustrate these ideas, consider again Table 22. Suppose someone wished to develop a theory explaining variations in political preferences. Past research suggests that party identification is an important determinant but the investigator wants to be sure that the relationship is not spurious, due to education. If it is spurious, the partial associations between candidate preference and partisanship should be zero, except for sampling error. Or, suspecting interaction, one may believe that the relationship will be stronger among high school graduates than college graduates. Assuming that other variables are not confusing the matter, one ought therefore to control for education. Hence, with the proper simplifying assumptions, test factor stratification permits a choice among alternative causal models. There are several ways of carrying out the analysis.

Perhaps the easiest is to "eyeball" each subtable, relying on percentages as a guide. To check for interaction in Table 22, for example, one compares the percentages in all three subtables. In both cases, Democrats are most likely to vote for Carter, and Republicans are more apt to support Reagan. Since the pattern of the relationship seems to be essentially the same, at first sight, interaction does not appear to be present.

It is also clear from an inspection of the tables that controlling for education does not eliminate the basic relationship. The partial correlation, in other words, is not zero. One can determine this by noting the statistically significant chi squares in each table. Thus, neither a spurious relationship nor a developmental sequence seems to hold for these data. (Of course, had another test factor been used, the results might have been different.)

Although these techniques for detecting spuriousness, interaction, and other models have been used for years, they have several shortcomings. One must scan a series of contingency tables. If the control factor has a large number of categories, the number of contingent relationships is quite large. More important, in looking at percentages, particularly in tables with numerous cells, an investigator often has trouble deciding systematically and objectively to what extent the

TABLE 22

Vote by Party Identification by Education

a

Less Than 9 Years

Vote in 1980	Party Identification							Total
	SD	D	ID	I	IR	R	SR	
RR	6% (2)	33% (8)	33% (2)	50% (4)	100% (4)	100% (6)	75% (6)	32
C	94 (32)	67 (16)	50 (3)	50 (4)	0.0 (0)	0.0 (0)	2 (1)	56
A	0.0 (0)	0.0 (0)	17 (1)	0.0 (0)	0.0 (0)	0.0 (0)	13 (1)	2
	100% (34)	100% (24)	100% (6)	100% (8)	100% (4)	100% (6)	100% (8)	90

$X^2 = 50.61$; 12 df

b

9 to 12 Years

Vote in 1980	Party Identification							Total
	SD	D	ID	I	IR	R	SR	
RR	12% (12)	36% (33)	33% (13)	71% (34)	69% (34)	84% (54)	89% (41)	221
C	85 (84)	59 (54)	55 (22)	18 (9)	16 (8)	5 (3)	9 (4)	184
A	3 (3)	4 (4)	12 (5)	10 (5)	14 (7)	11 (7)	2 (1)	32
	100% (99)	99% (91)	100% (40)	99% (48)	100% (49)	100% (64)	100% (46)	437

$X^2 = 180.60$

(continued)

Table 22 (Continued)

c

More Than 12 Years

Vote in 1980	SD	D	ID	I	IR	R	SR	Total
RR	11%	29%	27%	55%	80%	85%	97%	
	(7)	(25)	(17)	(16)	(47)	(70)	(56)	238
C	82	58	38	21	9	5	0.0	
	(50)	(49)	(24)	(6)	(5)	(4)	(0)	138
A	7	13	35	24	12	10	3	
	(4)	(17)	(22)	(7)	(7)	(8)	(2)	67
	100%	100%	100%	100%	101%	100%	100%	
	(61)	(91)	(63)	(29)	(59)	(82)	(58)	443

Party Identification column spans SD through SR.

$$x^2 = 225.68$$

SOURCE: See Table 1.
KEY: (See Table 3).

relationships are nil or to what extent they differ among themselves. The connections between vote and party in the two subtables seem to be the same, but are they? Since the chi squares are so different, one wonders if the percentages are not misleading.

A quick but somewhat more objective way to answer these questions is to compute a coefficient of partial association, proceeding as follows:

(1) stratify the sample by the control variable to create a series of contingency tables (as in Table 22);

(2) compute an index of association for each contingent relationship; and

(3) average the separate indices, the average being interpreted as a measure of partial association.

Either a simple or weighted average can be used. (A weighted average is computed by multiplying each coefficient by the number of cases used in its calculations, adding these multiplications, and dividing the sum by the total number of cases.) Since the two types of averages frequently vary, especially if the numbers of observations in the subtables differ substantially from one another, it is preferable to compute a weighted average whenever the cases are not evenly distributed on the control variable.

In Table 22, for example, where the bulk of the cases are in the subtables b and c, one can compute a weighted average of the lambdas or taus. These averages are interpreted as measures of partial association: They show the "typical" correlation between vote and partisanship after education has been controlled. If the original, uncontrolled relationship is really spurious, then the partial relationships, as measured by lambda or tau, should be approximately zero. Hence, if the average is close to zero, this is evidence of a spurious relationship.

The data, however, do not conform to these expectations, because the estimated partial associations are $\bar{\hat{\lambda}}_y = .42$ and $\bar{\hat{\tau}}_y = .42$, where the bar symbol denotes a weighted average. These values do not differ much from the corresponding uncontrolled measures. Within each subtable, there remains an association between vote and party identification, although it is stronger in Tables b and c, suggesting the presence of interaction.

A partial coefficient of this sort has to be interpreted carefully, for these measures—like all indices—are sensitive to how the variables have been categorized. Only if the observed cutpoints closely reflect the variables' true categories can the partials be expected to produce valid and consistent conclusions. Underlying variables are often really continuous or interval-scale, but are dichotomized or trichotomized because the investigator lacks sufficient knowledge to measure them more precisely.

In addition to these rather ad hoc procedures, one can compute more formal partial correlation coefficients for nominal data. Goodman and Kruskal (1954), for example, propose a partial lambda

$$\hat{\lambda}_{yx.z} = \frac{\sum\limits_{k=1}^{K} \sum\limits_{j=1}^{J} n_{mjk} - \sum\limits_{k=1}^{K} n_{m+k}}{n - \sum\limits_{k=1}^{K} n_{m+k}} \qquad [23]$$

where n_{m+k} is the largest row marginal total in the kth subtable and n is the total number of cases in all K subtables. For Table 22 partial lambda is

$$\hat{\lambda}_{yx.z} = \frac{706 - 518}{970 - 518} = .42$$

Other measures of partial association for categorical data are available, but I shall not examine them here. (The interested reader should consult Reynolds [1977].) The difficulty is that even these more sophisticated indices have to be interpreted cautiously.

Unfortunately, crude measurement makes it difficult if not impossible to detect the real underlying model. If Z creates a spurious relationship between X and Y, then the partial association ought to be close to zero or at least substantially smaller than the original, uncontrolled relationship. Yet measures of partial association usually do not behave predictably unless the categorizations represent the true state of affairs.

As a consequence, the investigator cannot be sure that the correct model has been detected. It is imperative, therefore, to think carefully about the level of measurement. Crude measurement usually yields misleading, even erroneous conclusions no matter how sophisticated the technique.

5. CONCLUSIONS

The procedures described in this paper have been greatly augmented by recent developments in the analysis of categorical data. Two are worth mentioning.

Log-linear models allow one to express the logarithm of cell frequencies (or some other function of these frequencies) as a function of a linear model. The parameters (or absence of parameters) of such models often have interesting substantive interpretations. Consider as an example the data in Table 22. One might postulate the following model:

$$\log (F_{ijk}) = \mu + \mu_i^V + \mu_j^P + \mu_k^E \qquad [24]$$

where F_{ijk} is the *expected* frequency in the ijk[th] cell and log refers to the natural logarithm. The specific definition of these terms is not important, however. What is worth noting is that models of this sort have a particular theoretical interpretation. Equation 24, for instance, asserts that the three variables vote, partisanship, and education are all mutually independent; that is, each pair of variables is statistically unrelated.

Presumably this model would not fit the data. To be sure, one could obtain estimated expected frequencies under the model ($\hat{F}_{ijk}$) and compare them with the corresponding observed counts (n_{ijk}), using the usual goodness-of-fit chi square. (If X^2 is large, the model would be rejected.) An alternative might be

$$\log (F_{ijk}) = \mu + \mu_i^V + \mu_j^P + \mu_k^E + \mu_{ij}^{VP} + \mu_{ik}^{VE} + \mu_{jk}^{PE} \qquad [25]$$

In other words, this model asserts that although all three variables are related, there is no "interaction"; that is, the nature of the relationship between, say, voting and party identification, is the same in all levels of education. (See the discussion in the preceding section.)

Under the right circumstances, log-linear models lead to a more thorough understanding of the data than can be gained from simple measures of association. Unfortunately, we cannot go into the details here. Suffice it to say that a good place to begin to understand them is the material presented earlier on odds ratios and on the multivariate analysis of nominal data. For further references see Reynolds (1977) and Knoke and Burke (1980).

The second general approach worth mentioning, however briefly, applies mainly to two-way tables but can be applied to multi-way tables as well. It is sometimes possible and desirable to estimate "association" models for a table. Consider once more the data in Table 1, which consists of 3 rows and 7 columns. One can compute a set of $(I - 1)(J - 1) = (3 - 1)(7 - 1) = 12$ basic odds ratios as follows:

$$\alpha_{ij} = \frac{F_{ij} \, F_{i+1,j+1}}{F_{i+1,j} \, F_{i,j+1}} \qquad \begin{array}{l} i = 1, 2 \ldots I - 1 \\ j = 1, 2 \ldots J - 1 \end{array} \qquad [26]$$

(See Goodman, 1979.)

These odds ratios define the relationship between vote and partisanship for a specific 2×2 subtable formed by considering rows i and i+1 and columns j and j+1. The set of α's pertaining to the 12 subtables thoroughly describes the relationship between the two variables. (Actually, we could consider other basic sets of tables; see Goodman [1969].)

Indeed, it is possible to express α's themselves as functions of various parameters. One possibility is

$$\alpha_{ij} = \theta \tag{27}$$

This model asserts that the relationship between the two variables is the same or uniform throughout the table. An alternative model might be that the nature of the relationship depends on the nature of the particular rows and columns; that is, $\alpha_{ij} = \Theta_{i+}\Theta_{+j}$.

Once again, it is not possible to go into this approach in detail. Yet, since it promises to provide rich insights into categorical data, particularly ordinal variables, the reader is encouraged to pursue the matter in greater detail. (See Goodman, 1979, 1981.)

NOTES

1. The data, the 1980 American National Election Study, were made available by the Inter-university Consortium for Political Research of the Institute for Social Research, University of Michigan. The consortium is not responsible for any errors or interpretation of these data.

2. Actually, the data in Table 1 and in the other tables in this paper do not come from a simple random sample. They were generated by a more complex sampling procedure. But since they only illustrate various statistics, they are treated as if they were a random sample.

3. Note that the term "symmetry" does not have the same meaning as in Chapter 2. The earlier discussion of symmetry referred to whether or not a measure of association depended on defining a dependent variable.

4. The formula for chi square in a 2×2 table is

$$X^2 = \frac{n(n_{11}n_{22} - n_{12}n_{21})^2}{n_{1+}n_{2+}n_{+1}n_{+2}}$$

where n_{i+} and n_{+j} are marginal totals ($i = 1,2; j = 1,2$).

5. There are actually more than t subtables, but the remainder can be generated from this basic set (see Goodman, 1969).

6. A PRE measure is undefined whenever $p(A) = 0$. This contingency will not arise, however, because if there is no possibility of misclassification, the subjects must all occupy the same Y category and data in this form—a $1 \times J$ table—would not be analyzed by these methods.

7. This discussion is based on Agresti and Agresti (1977).

234

REFERENCES

AGRESTI, A. and B. F. AGRESTI (1977) "Statistical analysis of qualitative variation," in K. F. Schuessler (ed.) Sociological Methodology 1978. San Francisco: Jossey-Bass.

BLALOCK, H. M., Jr. (1979) Social Statistics. New York: McGraw-Hill.

COCHRAN, W. G. (1954) "Some methods of strengthening the common χ^2 tests." Biometrics 10: 417-451.

GARSON, G. C. (1976) Political Science Methods. Boston: Holbrook.

GOODMAN, L. A. (1981) "Three elementary views of log linear models for the analysis of cross-classification having ordered categories," in S. Leinhardt (ed.) Sociological Methodology 1981. San Francisco: Jossey-Bass.

———(1979) "Simple models for the analysis of association in cross-classification having ordered categories." Journal of the American Statistical Association 74 (September): 537-552.

———(1969) "How to ransack social mobility tables and other kinds of cross-classification tables." American Journal of Sociology 75 (July): 1-40.

———(1964) "Simultaneous confidence limits for cross-product ratios in contingency tables." Journal of the Royal Statistical Society (Series B) 26: 86-102.

———and W. H. KRUSKAL (1954) "Measures of association for cross-classifications." Journal of the American Statistical Association 49 (December): 732-764.

HABERMAN, S. J. (1973) "The analysis of residuals in cross-classified tables." Biometrics 29: 205-220.

HYMAN, H. H. (1955) Survey Design and Analysis. Glencoe, IL: Free Press.

IVERSON, G. R. (1979) "Decomposing chi square." Sociological Methods and Research 8: 143-157.

KNOKE, D. and P. BURKE (1980) Log-Linear Models. Beverly Hills, CA: Sage.

MILLER, W. E., A. H. MILLER, and E. J. SCHNEIDER (1980) American National Election Studies Data Sourcebook, 1952-1978. Cambridge, MA: Harvard University Press.

REYNOLDS, H. T. (1977a) The Analysis of Cross-Classifications. New York: Free Press.

———(1977b) "Some comments on the causal analysis of surveys with log-linear models." American Journal of Sociology 83 (March): 127-143.

ROSENBERG, M. (1968) The Logic of Survey Analysis. New York: Basic Books.

WEISBERG, H. (1974) "Models of statistical relationships." American Political Science Review 68 (December): 1638-1655.

PART IV

ANALYSIS OF
ORDINAL DATA

DAVID K. HILDEBRAND

JAMES D. LAING

HOWARD ROSENTHAL

1. ORDINAL MEASUREMENT

Propositions stated in the form, "the more of this, the more of that," are common in social science. Another prediction style is illustrated by the statement, "If any observation is rated *high* on the first variable, then it tends to be *medium* or *high* on the other." Both of these statements illustrate propositions relating ordinal variables. This paper discusses ways to evaluate such propositions with scientific data.

In the following sections we discuss the ordinal measurement of variables, identify alternative types of propositions relating ordinal variables, and present methods for using data to evaluate how successfully such propositions predict observed events.

The basic strategy of this paper is to develop a general prediction framework and a related statistical measure, ∇_ρ. This general framework is then used to explain the most widely used measures of bivariate association for ordinal variables, including gamma and the various d and tau measures. These measures were designed to evaluate "the more of this, the more of that" type of proposition. Many other types of propositions can be evaluated with the general framework. After dealing extensively with bivariate propositions, we briefly consider the

AUTHORS' NOTE: *We thank our research assistant, Richard Gunsaulus, for a careful and critical reading of the manuscript. We have also benefitted from comments by the series editor and a referee.*

evaluation of multivariate predictions. The general framework not only provides a common perspective for interpreting standard measures of association. When a research application arises where no standard measure is appropriate to evaluate the specific proposition of interest, the framework permits custom-designing of a measure.

Many types of variables are used in science. We can distinguish between *quantitative* and *qualitative* variables. The particular value (amount, degree, or intensity) that an observation exhibits on a quantitative variable is expressed as a (real) number. Examples of quantitative variables include temperature measured in degrees Celsius, material wealth in dollars, and a candidate's electoral support in votes. However—whether as an inherent property of the concept being measured, inadequacies in measurement techniques, or the investigator's research goals—many important concepts are measured only qualitatively.

There are two basic types of qualitative variables: nominal and ordinal. A *nominal* variable consists of a set of alternative and mutually exclusive categories or states, so that each observation is assigned to just one state. For example, a voter's home region might be described by one of the categories: *East, Midwest, South,* or *West.* The states of a nominal variable may be listed in any arbitrary order. (On analysis of nominal data, see Hildebrand, Laing, and Rosenthal, 1974a, 1974b, 1975, 1976, 1977; Reynolds, 1977.) An *ordinal* variable also has a set of mutually exclusive states. Unlike a nominal variable, however, an ordinal variable's states are ordered or ranked in terms of the alternative amounts or degrees of intensity that the states represent. For example, Aberbach and Rockman (1976) classified each member of a sample of top-level Washington bureaucrats in terms of their support for a greater government role in the provision of social services. The ordered categories or states they used were: *left* (the highest degree of support), *left-center, center, right-center,* and *right.*

For certain sets of categories, investigators impose order for theoretical reasons. Consider, for example, the three categories, *Democrat, Republican,* and *Independent.* For some purposes of analysis, these categories might be viewed as nominal. Social scientists, however, frequently impose an order, viewing *Independent* as the middle category—presumably because party affiliation is an index of preferences on the liberal-conservative dimension. One could go even further and assign numerical values to the categories, letting Democrat be 1, Independent 0, and Republican −1, or, as another possibility, Democrat 2, Independent .625, Republican 0. Typically social scientists don't go this far; although they operate as if the categories were ordered, social scientists are generally unwilling to assert that they can measure numerically the amounts of the variable represented by these categories. In fact, the Aberbach and Rockman research illustrates the typical approach; they used party affiliation as an ordinal independent (predictor) variable in the analysis of support for social services as a dependent (predicted) variable.

Ordinal variables are important for several reasons. First, at least in some situations certain concepts can only (or, at least, readily and economically) be measured at the ordinal level. For example, in grading essays, the teacher may feel confident that the quality of any essay graded A is better than any graded B, that B is better than C, and C is better than D. Yet he may be unwilling to make such quantitative judgments as, "An A paper is six times better than a C paper." Luke may be able to tell Sue with confidence that the bath water feels *hot*, *warm, cool,* or *cold,* but be unable to judge the water temperature accurately in degrees Celsius. (In fact, Sue might think Luke is a little strange if he gives a quantitative judgment in this situation.) Similarly, in coding interview data, researchers might believe that their judgmental capacities are only fine enough to justify using a small number of ordered categories. Again the Aberbach and Rockman study is representative: they used five ordered categories of support for social services (*left, left-center, center, right-center,* and *right*).

Second, in some situations only the ordering of observations on a quantitative variable matters; specific numerical values have no importance. For example, in professional baseball, and in many other social processes as well, relative—rather than absolute—performance is what counts. A baseball team's share of post-season monies does not depend directly on the percentage of games the team won. Rather, it depends on how the team performed relative to the other teams in the same division. Players on the first-place team get a large amount of money, those on the second-place team much less, those on the third-place team still less, and the fourth-, fifth-, and sixth-place teams get nothing. Similarly, the traditional French *agrégation* exam divided a fixed number of available teaching slots among the highest scorers on the exam, the best plums going to the best finishers. In Congress, seniority is not measured by the number of years of consecutive service but by the relative ranking of members in this regard. These examples indicate that ordinal data do not always contain less relevant information than related quantitative data. If we are told that the Phillies finished first in the National League East, we know that they won more games than any of the other five teams in that division; we would not know this if we had been told, instead, that the Phillies won 75 percent of their games. On the other hand, of course, knowing that a team finished first does not tell us what percent of games it won.

In this paper, an ordinal variable is defined simply as a set of mutually exclusive states that are ordered in terms of the characteristic of interest. Although various refinements to ordinal measurement are possible, such as ranking the distances between various states as well as ranking the states themselves, we do not consider such complications here. At times, it will be useful to give numerical names to states of an ordinal variable such as (1) high, (2) medium, (3) low. Note that, when the ordering is a rating or ranking, we use low numbers to indicate high ratings. This conforms to a cultural convention that "high ranks" are assigned "low numbers": the team winning the greatest number of games is "number one." Thus, the lower the number used to index the state, the greater the "amount" of the variable that the state represents. It is important to recognize that the purpose of these numeric names is only to indicate the rank of the variable state in the ordering; no additional significance should be attached to these numbers. In fact, any set of numeric state labels that assigns the same order to the states will serve equally well. For example, suppose that no two teams in the National League East had identical won-lost records. Then we may use the numbers [1, 2, 3, 4, 5, 6] to indicate the ranking of the six teams in the final division standings. These particular numbers are convenient, since "3" means "finished in third place," and so on. Despite this convenience, any order-preserving transformation of these numbers could also be used to index the states: for example, multiplying the original numbers by any positive constant (say, 2) preserves the ordering with a new set of indices, [2, 4, 6, 8, 10, 12], as does using the set of their natural logarithms, [0, .69, 1.10, 1.39, 1.61, 1.79]. In any order-preserving scale, lower number still mean a higher rank. The [1, 2, 3, ...] ranking is easier to read, and it is convenient to imply by "number one" that the team finished first, by "number two" that it finished second, and so on. However, the particular set of ordered numerical names to be used is arbitrary. Any order-preserving relabelling of these names conveys the same ordinal information.

Three Issues in the Analysis of Ordinal Variables

Issue 1: Tied Observations. In the baseball example, no two teams had the same won-lost record; consequently, no two teams were tied in the final standings. Two observations are *tied* on an ordinal variable if they are assigned to the same variable state. Whether in baseball or statistics, rules should be specified as to what should be done with ties.

To be generally useful in social science, measures must be able to deal appropriately with ties. Going back to the Aberbach and Rockman bureaucrat sample, we have only three categories of party affiliation and five of support for social services. As an example, we will consider a subsample of 31 bureaucrats from three social services agencies, HEW, HUD, and OEO. Since, for both variables, there are far more bureaucrats than categories, we are guaranteed to have ties. The way ties are to be handled merits attention later in the paper; it is an important question that cannot be avoided. For example, differences in the way ties are handled account for major distinctions among three of the most commonly used measures of ordinal association: Somers' d_{yx}, Kendall's τ_b^2, and Goodman and Kruskal's gamma.

Issue 2: Predicting Single Observations vs. Pairs of Observations. A much more basic issue in dealing with ordinal association is whether the analysis should focus directly on single observations or on comparisons within pairs of observations. To clarify the distinction, we need to address an analytical problem involving two variables.

The two variables describing bureaucrats—namely, party affiliation and support for social services—will serve to illustrate the general analysis of association for ordinal variables. To ask if two such variables are associated or related is not a fully operational question. Consequently, we will focus instead on whether (and in what way) one variable is useful in *predicting* the other.

Consider the cross-classification shown as Table 1. Suppose the investigator used each bureaucrat's party affiliation (*Dem, Ind, Rep*) to predict the bureaucrat's support for increased social services (*left, left-center, center, right-center, right*). Let the statement x $\rightsquigarrow$ y mean, "if x then predict y" or "x tends to be a sufficient condition for y." Then the prediction $\mathcal{P}$, "*Dem* $\rightsquigarrow$ (*left* or *left-center*) & *Ind* $\rightsquigarrow$ *center* & *Rep* $\rightsquigarrow$ (*center* or *right-center* or *right*)," identifies the cells that are shaded in Table 1 as error events. Unshaded cells are successes for the prediction. Note that, for Democrats, two categories of the dependent variable constitute successes; for Republicans, three categories are successes.

Conventionally, predictions of this kind have not played much of a role in data analysis. The emphasis has been on predicting a single category of the dependent variable for each category of the independent variable. Such restrictions on the form of the predictions are not foreordained. Clearly, some scientific theories will vary in the precision with which they can predict outcomes and, alternatively, some categories of the independent variable may contain more information for prediction than others.

Predictions like $\mathcal{P}$ have three important advantages:

(1) Given any observation's state on the independent variable, we can make a definite prediction about its state on the dependent variable. If we are told that bureaucrat Nixman is a Republican, for example, we predict that he will be *center, right-center,* or *right* toward social services.

TABLE 1

Party Affiliation and Support for Social Services by Top-Level Bureaucrats in Social Service Agencies

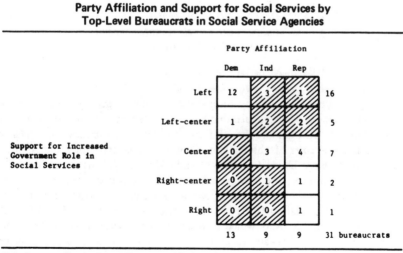

Data Source: Aberbach and Rockman (1976, p. 460).

(2) A related advantage is that we can make a definite statement as to whether the prediction for each bureaucrat is correct or incorrect. If Mr. Nixman turned out to be *left* on social services, the prediction was wrong.

(3) Ties pose no problem for analyzing this kind of prediction.

In practice, ordinal variables have seldom been analyzed with such predictions. The social science literature frequently contains statements of the form, "Social services support tends to increase with a more liberal party affiliation," or, "There is a 'U-shaped' relation between support for social services and party affiliation." Also frequent are statements of the form, "The more liberal the party affiliation (X), the greater will be support for social services (Y)." Later in this paper we will make such statements operational and discuss ways of evaluating them. First, though, we need to evaluate propositions like $\mathcal{P}$.

How can we assess the agreement of a given set of data with such predictions? An oversimplified way would be to count the number of errors. Consider the distribution of the 31 bureaucrats in Table 1 and the proposition $\mathcal{P}$ that identifies the cells shaded there as error events. Counting the total number of bureaucrats who are assigned to some error cell, we discover that out of the 31 bureaucrats, we made errors in nine cases (3+1+2+2+0+0+1+0+0). This raw number of errors is not really adequate to evaluate the prediction, but it is at least a start.

It is less obvious what can be done about assessing the "Y increases with X" or "the more the X, the more the Y" type of statement. One approach to evaluating this proposition would be to try to find a specific prediction of observations that is consistent with it. For example, the prediction $\mathcal{P}$ used above is one that appears consistent with "Y increases with X." On the other hand, an alternative prediction,

$$\mathcal{P}': \quad Dem \rightsquigarrow \textit{left} \text{ or } \textit{left-center}$$
$$Ind \rightsquigarrow \textit{center} \text{ or } \textit{right-center} \text{ or } \textit{right}$$
$$Rep \rightsquigarrow \textit{left} \text{ or } \textit{left-center}$$

identifies the "U-shaped" pattern of unshaded cells shown in Table 2. The prediction $\mathcal{P}'$ makes 11 errors—two more than $\mathcal{P}$.

This prediction approach to ordinal data has hardly been applied in any of the social sciences. The approach that has been widely applied involves analyzing "The more the X, the more the Y" form in terms of predictions about *relative comparisons* of *pairs* of observations. Consider bureaucrats Amy and Nixman. Amy can be *more* liberal (in terms of party affiliation). This would happen if she were a *Democrat*, and he was an *Independent* or *Republican*, or if she were an *Independent* and he was a *Republican*. Alternatively, Amy and Nixman would have the *same* liberalism (tied) if both were *Dem*, if both were *Ind* or if both were *Rep*. Otherwise, Amy would be *less* liberal than *Nixman*. These three categories—*more, same, less*—are the only ones we can have that use only ordinal information in making comparisons. For this reason, we define these categories as the *condensed ordinal form of* X^{*2} derived from the original variable X (support

TABLE 2
An Alternative Prediction About Support for Social Services

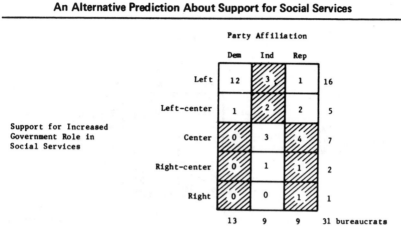

Party Affiliation

	Dem	Ind	Rep	
Left	12	3	1	16
Left-center	1	2	2	5
Center	0	3	4	7
Right-center	0	1	1	2
Right	0	0	1	1
	13	9	9	31 bureaucrats

Support for Increased Government Role in Social Services

Data Source: Aberbach and Rockman (1976, p. 460).

for party affiliation). The superscript on X^{*2} indicates that observation *pairs* are being compared on the variable X. We can also develop a condensed ordinal form for the social services variable.

With these new forms of the variables, we can now make predictions for pairs similar to the ones we originally made for observations. For example, consider the prediction, P^*:

> If the first of two bureaucrats has a *more* liberal party affiliation than the second, his support for social services will be the *same* or *more* than that of the second bureaucrat. If the two bureaucrats are the *same* on liberalism, then they tend to give the *same* support to social services. If the first of the two bureaucrats is *less* liberal than the second, his support for social services will be the *same* or *less* than that of the second bureaucrat.

As a shorthand, we write

$$P^*: \quad more \rightsquigarrow more \text{ or } same,$$
$$same \rightsquigarrow same, \&$$
$$less \rightsquigarrow same \text{ or } less$$

If we want to evaluate this prediction, we can make a table for the two condensed form variables similar to Table 1. If the 31 officials are Amy, Bob, Cal, . . . and Nixman, we note that they can be paired $31^2 = 961$ different ways as (Amy,Amy), (Amy,Bob), (Amy,Cal), . . . , (Amy,Nixman), (Bob,Amy), (Bob,Bob), (Bob,Cal), . . . , (Nixman,Nixman). Note that in 31 of these pairs [(Amy,Amy), (Bob,Bob), (Cal,Cal), . . . , (Nixman,Nixman)] the same bureaucrat appears twice. Table 3 locates each of the 961 pairs in the cross-classification

TABLE 3
A Prediction for Pairs

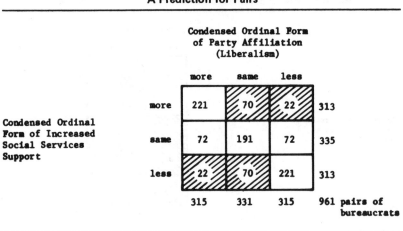

Condensed Ordinal Form
of Party Affiliation
(Liberalism)

		more	same	less	
Condensed Ordinal Form of Increased Social Services Support	more	221	70	22	313
	same	72	191	72	335
	less	22	70	221	313
		315	331	315	961 pairs of bureaucrats

of the *condensed form* variables. How Table 3 relates to Table 1 is deferred to section 3. For the moment, we note that, as in Table 1, we can look at the shaded cells in Table 3 that represent errors for $\wp^*$ and count the number of incorrect pairs. There are $22 + 70 + 70 + 22 = 184$ of the 961 pairs that are errors for $\wp^*$.

Most widely used measures of ordinal association, such as gamma and various d and tau measures, can be related to this cross-tabulation of condensed form variables. These measures can be interpreted as being based on predictions that are operational statements of "the more the X, the more the Y," or, alternatively, "Y increases with X." The condensed form thus plays a central role in this essay.

Some writers have gone so far as to argue that the condensed form analysis of paired comparisons should be at least the predominant (if not the only) mode of analysis for ordinal variables:

> The restriction to pairs in the case of ordinal statistics is compatible with the inherently comparative nature of ordinal data. And in a fundamental sense, the empirical foundation of science is comparison and contrast rather than the study of a single, isolated observation, *in vacuo* [Somers, 1974: 231].

While we agree that comparison is a vital part of the scientific process, it can occur as part of the evaluation of the prediction and need not necessarily enter in defining the variables that are the subject of prediction. More importantly, for many purposes it may be more relevant to make predictions about single observations than about pairs. Certainly, some, perhaps most, researchers will attach greater interest to predicting the degree of support each bureaucrat actually gives to social services increases than to predicting how his support will compare to that of another bureaucrat.

The proponents of the condensed form (Table 3) may still respond that predictions such as P and P' (Tables 1 and 2) are not really ordinal but nominal. After all, even with simple nominal categories one could state predictions that would lead to patterns of shaded error cells as in the first two tables. In contrast, since the relations *more* and *less* are meaningless to simple categorization (Caucasian is neither *more* nor *less* than Native American), the condensed ordinal form requires at least ordinal measurement. With pairs, the ordinality thus affects the prediction via the manner in which the condensed form categories are defined.

Predictions for single observations can, however, also reflect the ordinal characteristic of the variables. The researcher will use the ordinality to impose some constraints as to the configuration, pattern or "shape" of the unshaded success cells. The proposition of Table 1 predicts a "monotone increasing" shape; Table 2 a "U-shape." Except in very unusual circumstances, there should be a single bloc of shaded cells or of unshaded cells in a given column or row. A prediction like that shown in Table 4 leads to a configuration of cells that seems unlikely to arise from a theory relating two *ordinal* variables. Thus, when variables are ordinal, the ordinality will influence the prediction, even for single observations.

Issue 3: Ordinal vs. Quantitative Variables. A final issue concerning ordinal variables asks whether they are worth much attention. Rather than devoting effort to improving methodologies for analyzing ordinal variables, Wilson (1970) and Blalock (1960) among others have argued that social scientists

TABLE 4
An Implausible Prediction for Two Ordinal Variables

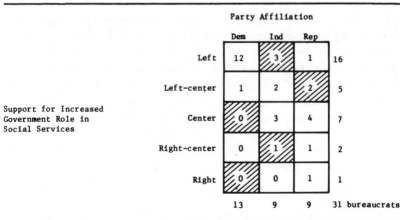

	Party Affiliation			
	Dem	Ind	Rep	
Left	12	3	1	16
Left-center	1	2	2	5
Center	0	3	4	7
Right-center	0	1	1	2
Right	0	0	1	1
	13	9	9	31 bureaucrats

Support for Increased Government Role in Social Services (row label for Left through Right)

Data Source: Aberbach and Rockman (1976, p. 460).

should seek to quantify concepts they now treat ordinally. After all, much of the advance in physical science might be attributed to quantification.

There are at least two related reasons which suggest that ordinal variables will long remain at the core of social science. First, ordinality appears to be important in many social phenomena. The ranking of people (in terms of their performance or seniority, for example) is often the primary criterion used to allocate rewards such as raises in pay and promotion to positions of higher responsibility, whether in professional baseball, Congress, business firms, or other institutions. Second, recent research in human cognition (Newell and Simon, 1972) suggests that it is useful to assume that people have limited information processing, hence quantifying, capacity. Similarly, in a different research tradition, mathematical economists and game theorists have actively sought to base social theory on ordinal rather than quantitative measures of preference. For example, it is plausible that, in response to a survey item, a voter can say that she preferred Reagan to Ford to Carter as president in 1976. Can she also provide a meaningful indication of *how much* she preferred Reagan to Ford relative to how much she preferred Ford to Carter? Viewed from the perspective of social choice theory or game theory, such a quantitative evaluation is equivalent to the voter's specifying the odds for a lottery between Reagan and Carter that would make her indifferent between the lottery and, on the other hand, a sure victory for Ford. While some psychophysicists would be prepared to argue that such quantitative judgments can be made, placing such a demand on a respondent in practice is both difficult and costly. Since typical measurements of political preferences are likely to remain ordinal, we need methods for analyzing ordinal variables.

Or do we? Some authors treat ordinal variables as quantitative by assigning numerical values to the variable states and then using Pearson r correlations in regression analysis methods designed for quantitative data (regression analysis is surveyed in Uslaner, forthcoming). For example, the *left, left-center, center, right-center,* and *right* ordinal categories could be assigned values 1, 2, 3, 4, and 5. Does this arbitrary numerical assignment eventually lead us to different substantive conclusions? Consider the data in Table 1. Pearson's r^2, the standard measure of association for quantitative data, equals .456 when these numerical values are used. In many respects, as we show later, Kendall's τ_b^2 is an ordinal variable analog of r^2. Its value for the table is .402, .05 less than r^2. Both measures can lie between 0 (no association) and 1 ("perfect" association). For other data sets, the difference between r^2 and τ_b^2 can easily be greater or less than .05. Whether such differences are substantively important depends on the purposes of a specific investigation but, clearly, the differences will sometimes matter.

Focusing on differences between r^2 and some ordinal measure such as τ_b^2 which evaluates "the more of this, the more of that" really misses the central point. Neither the "linear" pattern of association examined via r^2 nor "the more of this, the more of that" may be the correct expression of the investigator's research hypothesis. We show later that different measures of "association" can give widely different values when applied to the same data. It is appropriate, therefore, to proceed to a serious analysis of the measurement of association between ordinal variables. We prefer to recast this problem as one of evaluating the prediction success of a specific proposition. Section 2 discusses the evaluation of bivariate prediction success for single observations and develops the quadrant measure and Cohen's kappa as special measures for particular propositions. Section 3 discusses the evaluation of prediction success for propositions about pairs of observations, developing measures proposed by Goodman and Kruskal, Kendall, Kim, Somers, and Wilson as special cases. We also interpret Spearman's rho_S as a measure for the prediction of observation triples. In section 4, we illustrate how an ordinal variable may be analyzed in conjunction with a nominal variable or a quantitative variable. Section 5 discusses the multivariate analysis of ordinal variables, and section 6 briefly surveys questions of computation and statistical inference.

2. BIVARIATE PREDICTION FOR SINGLE OBSERVATIONS

Population versus Sample

Let us go back to our bureaucrats and attempt to evaluate the original prediction represented in Table 1:

$\mathcal{P}$:   *Dem* $\leadsto$ *left* or *left-center*
       Ind $\leadsto$ *center*
       Rep $\leadsto$ *center, right-center,* or *right*

To evaluate this prediction, we must first ask how the data were obtained or are to be interpreted. In this case the data are the results of a sample survey. Obviously, there are problems in generalizing from the survey results to a relevant population. For now, we nonetheless consider the 31 bureaucrats as a population. The fundamental question in the evaluation of predictions is most simply stated in terms of a population: what is the appropriate measure? The problems that arise when we try to estimate the true population value of a measure from sample data can be deferred and mentioned briefly later.

To evaluate the prediction, we calculate its proportionate reduction in error. The (hoped-for) reduction occurs when we make a prediction for each case with knowledge of its independent variable state in contrast to predicting without such information. That is, we wish to compare the observed error rate when a prediction $\mathcal{P}$ is applied to a given population with the error rate for a benchmark prediction that does not make use of the independent variable information.

Predicting With Knowledge of the Independent Variable State

It is easy to use the proposition, P, to make a prediction for each bureaucrat knowing his party affiliation. We are given each of the 31 officials, one at a time. For each bureaucrat, knowing whether he is *Dem, Ind,* or *Rep,* we make the appropriate prediction associated with P. If the prediction is wrong, we add one to our error total. Thus, for the 13 Democrats, we predict *left* or *left-center* and consequently make no errors (see Table 1). The proposition P predicts *center* for each of the nine Independents so the six non-*center* cases are errors. Finally, the prediction for Republicans identifies *left* and *left-center* as error events, contributing three errors for the nine Republican bureaucrats. Therefore, we observe nine (0+6+3) prediction errors, the number of bureaucrats who lie in the set of cells that are shaded in Table 1.

The number nine, or even the fraction 9/31, is not enough information to evaluate the prediction adequately. For example, what if all 31 bureaucrats were Democrats and we still made nine errors, as shown in Table 5? Clearly we are not gaining much from knowing the party affiliation state here. Or, put differently, we cannot say that the two variables are "associated" when one of the variables does not vary. Similarly, consider Table 6 which shows a hypothetical population and the error cells of a prediction. The prediction there also makes nine errors, but we would want to regard them as more serious than those in Table 1. After all, the prediction of Table 6 makes the wrong prediction for every bureaucrat (Independent) for whom it possibly *could* be wrong. The total of nine errors, then, will only be meaningful if it is compared to an appropriate benchmark.

TABLE 5
Hypothetical Population Without Variation in Party Affiliation

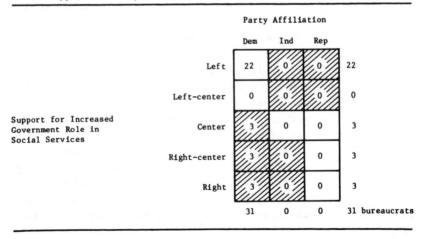

Support for Increased Government Role in Social Services		Dem	Ind	Rep	
	Left	22	0	0	22
	Left-center	0	0	0	0
	Center	3	0	0	3
	Right-center	3	0	0	3
	Right	3	0	0	3
		31	0	0	31 bureaucrats

TABLE 6
Hypothetical Population for Which Prediction Shown is Always Wrong

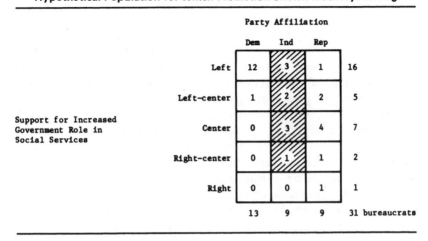

Party Affiliation

	Dem	Ind	Rep	
Left	12	3	1	16
Left–center	1	2	2	5
Center	0	3	4	7
Right–center	0	1	1	2
Right	0	0	1	1
	13	9	9	31 bureaucrats

Support for Increased Government Role in Social Services

Predicting Without Information About the Independent Variable State

As a benchmark, we replicate the prediction of $\wp$, but without knowledge of the actual independent variable state. The motivation of this procedure is beyond the scope of this paper. (For details, see Hildebrand, Laing, and Rosenthal, 1974a; 1977, ch. 3.) Suffice it to say that the benchmark prediction is both (a) *a priori* in the sense that no information about the predicted (dependent) variable is used, and (b) invariant with changes in category definition and ordering that have no effect on the prediction being evaluated. (As an example of definitional changes, consider combining the categories *left* and *left-center* into a single category *any left*. Also combine *right-center* and *right* into *any right*. The prediction *Dem* $\rightsquigarrow$ *any left, Ind* $\rightsquigarrow$ *center*, and *Rep* $\rightsquigarrow$ (*center* or *any right*) is logically equivalent to $\wp$.) Moreover (c) the benchmark procedure is comparable to that used when each observation's state of the independent variable is known since the same number of each type of prediction is made in the two information conditions. Thus, the same predictions are made in the benchmark procedure, but this time they are made without each observation's independent variable state. It turns out, as we shall see, that most of the existing measures of ordinal association can be given a unified interpretation via this benchmark.

The replication procedure, as applied to the data in Table 1, follows. Thirteen of the 31 bureaucrats are selected at random. For each of these we predict *left* or *left-center*, the same prediction we made earlier for Democrats. Error occurs if the case is *center, right center*, or *right*. Similarly, we predict *center* for nine cases drawn at random, thus replicating the predictions made earlier for Independents. Any of these nine bureaucrats who is not described as *center* on the support variable is an error. Finally, again drawing nine bureaucrats at random and without knowing their party, we predict *center, right-center,* or *right,* replicating the predictions made earlier for each of the Republicans. Any bureaucrat who is *left* or *left-center* represents an error for this prediction. Note that in the benchmark procedure, we need to know the marginal totals for the independent variable, but do not know each individual case's state on the variable. Moreover, we need no information about the population's distribution (marginal or otherwise) on the dependent variable in order to *make* the prediction.

We obviously always need dependent variable information to calculate the extent to which the predictions were wrong. To begin this calculation we note that in the whole population there are $7 + 2 + 1 = 10$ bureaucrats whose support for social welfare is *center, right-center,* or *right,* the error events for the benchmark replications of the Democratic predictions. Since we are drawing at random from the whole population, an error therefore will occur with probability 10/31, or, on average, in a little less than one out of three predictions. Since there are 13 such replication predictions, we expect, *on average,* to make $13(10/31) = 4.19$ errors.

For the replication of the predictions made earlier for Independents, only *center* is not an error event. In the whole population there are $31 - 7 = 24$ cases that are not *center.* The error probability for the *center* prediction is thus 24/31. Multiplying by the nine cases for which this prediction was made leads to $9(24/31) = 6.97$ expected errors. Finally, for the benchmark replication of the predictions made earlier for Republicans, the probability of error is 21/31 since there are 16 *left* and 5 *left-center* bureaucrats in the entire population of 31 bureaucrats. Therefore, this portion of the replication is expected to make $9(21/31) = 6.10$ errors. Summing over all the predictions, there are $\frac{1}{31}$ [13(10) + 9(24) + 9(21)] = 535/31 = 17.26 errors expected from this replication.

The ∇_P Measure

Define the measure of prediction success as

$$\nabla_P = \frac{\text{Expected Errors} - \text{Observed Errors}}{\text{Expected Errors}}$$

$$= 1 - (\text{Observed Errors/Expected Errors})$$

$$= 1 - 9/17.26 = .479$$

If there had been no observed error, the measure would have been equal to 1.0. If there had been as many observed errors as expected in this replication, the measure would have been zero. In fact, the prediction led to a little less than 50 percent error reduction.

If the prediction had been that illustrated in Table 6, the reader can calculate that

Observed errors = 3 + 2 + 3 + 1 = 9

Expected errors = 9 $[(16 + 5 + 7 + 2)/31]$ = 270/31 = 8.71

$\nabla = 1 - 9/8.71 = -.033$

(The subscript $\wp$ on ∇ emphasizes that the $\nabla_\wp$ measure always reflects a specific prediction. When the prediction being applied is evident, as in the preceding example, we may omit the subscript.) Not only does this value accord with our earlier assessment that the prediction should be less successful for Table 6 than for Table 1, but it also shows that the $\nabla_\wp$ measure of prediction success can be negative. This occurs when, as in this case, the prediction does worse than the benchmark replication.

To generalize this measure beyond the bureaucrats example requires some notation. The general table has R rows and C columns. In the example of Table 1, R = 5 and C = 3. The letter i indexes the row, i = 1,2, ..., R and j = 1,2,..., C the columns. In the example i = 3 designates the *center* row. Rather than speaking in terms of number of cases, it is more convenient to speak in terms of probabilities. In a finite population, the probability P_{ij} of an observation having both row state i and column state j is the number of cases in the corresponding cell in the population divided by the population size. In the example, $P_{22} = 2/31$, $P_{43} = 1/31$, and so on. Now consider the row and column totals ("marginals"). The marginal probability of row i is designated as $P_{i.}$, of column j as $P_{.j}$. Once again, we can divide numbers of cases by total population size, so for the rows of Table 1,

$$P_{1.} = 16/31, \quad P_{2.} = 5/31, \quad P_{3.} = 7/31, \quad P_{4.} = 2/31, \quad P_{5.} = 1/31$$

while for the columns,

$$P_{.1} = 13/31, \quad P_{.2} = P_{.3} = 9/13$$

Overall, the following identities must hold. First summing over columns gives the row total

$$\sum_{j=1}^{C} P_{ij} = P_{i.}$$

and summing over rows yields

$$\sum_{i=1}^{R} P_{ij} = P_{.j}$$

Finally,

$$\sum_{i=1}^{R}\sum_{j=1}^{C} P_{ij} = \sum_{i=1}^{R} P_{i.} = \sum_{j=1}^{C} P_{.j} = 1.0$$

Each cell (ij) in the table can be assigned an error measure, ω_{ij}. If the prediction for the table identifies the cell as a success, then $\omega_{ij} = 0$. Often, an investigator will want to treat all errors equally. That is, all observations that fall into error cells are assigned the same "degree" or "amount" of error. Without loss of generality, it is then appropriate to set $\omega_{ij} = 1$ for every cell (ij) that is an error cell. If the investigator wishes to assign different degrees of severity to various error events, he can assign any error weight strictly greater than zero to an error cell. For example, such differential weighting of errors will be shown to underly several measures of ordinal association, reflecting the idea that ties might be regarded as less serious errors than are outright reversals of order. Again without loss of generality, it often is convenient to set the largest such error weight equal to one. In the bureaucrats example of Table 1, we implicitly assigned all error events equal weight: so $\omega_{12} = \omega_{13} = \omega_{22} = \omega_{23} = \omega_{31} = \omega_{41} = \omega_{42} = \omega_{51} = \omega_{52} = 1$, and every other $\omega_{ij} = 0$.

Given the ω_{ij} notation to represent a bivariate prediction $\wp$ and the P_{ij} notation for the general specification of population probabilities, the procedure we have illustrated for calculating observed and expected error rates and then forming the proportionate-reduction-in-error measure leads to the general definition:

$$\nabla_{\wp} = 1 - (\text{Observed Errors/Expected Errors})$$

$$= 1 - \frac{\displaystyle\sum_{i=1}^{R}\sum_{j=1}^{C} \omega_{ij} P_{ij}}{\displaystyle\sum_{i=1}^{R}\sum_{j=1}^{C} \omega_{ij} P_{i.} P_{.j}}$$

For the prediction and data shown in Table 1,

Observed Error Rate = 0 + 3/31 + 1/31 + 0 + 2/31 + 2/31 + 0 + 0 +
0 + 0 + 1/31 + 0 + 0 + 0 + 0 = 9/31 = .290

Expected Error Rate = 0 + (16/31) (9/31) + (16/31) (9/31) + 0 +
(5/31) (9/31) + (5/31) (9/31) + (7/31) (13/31) +
0 + 0 + (2/31) (13/31) + (2/31) (9/31) +
0 + (1/31) (13/31) + (1/31) (9/31) + 0 = 535/961 = .557

$\nabla_{\wp} = 1 - .290/.557 = .479$

Similar but slightly abbreviated calculations for the data and proposition of Table 4 show

Observed Error Rate = 3/31 + 2/31 + 0/31 + 1/31 + 0/31 = 6/31 = .194

Expected Error Rate = (16/31) (9/31) + (5/31) (9/31) + (7/31) (13/31) + (2/31) (9/31) + (1/31) (13/31) = 311/961 = .324

$\nabla_{\mathcal{P}} = 1 - .194/.324 = .402$

Precision. From the computation of the ∇ measures for Table 1 and Table 4, one can note that the "expected" error rate for Table 4, 311/961 = .324, is less than that for Table 1, 535/961 = .557. In fact, there must be fewer expected errors in Table 4 because every error cell in Table 4 is also an error cell in Table 1 and Table 1 also has some additional error cells. An event that is an error for Table 4 is always an error for Table 1, but the converse is not true, implying that Table 1 represents a "tougher" or more precise prediction. In general, the "expected" error rate measures the *precision* of a prediction. We denote this rate by the symbol U.

Dominance. We say that one prediction *dominates* another when the prediction has a higher ∇ (prediction success) value and at least as great a U (prediction precision) value than the other or, alternatively, a higher U value and at least as great a ∇ value. For example, we have seen that the prediction represented in Table 1 has both a higher ∇ value and a higher U value than the prediction represented in Table 4. Consequently, the first prediction cominates the second.

Statistical Independence and ∇. Inspection of the expressions for ∇ show that ∇ = 0 whenever the "observed" errors equal the "expected," that is, when

$$\sum_i \sum_j \omega_{ij} P_{ij} = \sum_i \sum_j \omega_{ij} P_{i.} P_{.j}$$

To see when this condition is met, consider another "population," the U.S. Senate, which conveniently has exactly 100 members. Assume that we had developed two scales for the senators (like those for the bureaucrats), based this time on roll call votes rather than interview responses. What if the data were as below?

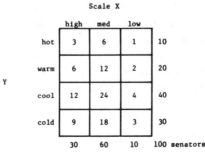

Scale X

Scale Y		high	med	low	
	hot	3	6	1	10
	warm	6	12	2	20
	cool	12	24	4	40
	cold	9	18	3	30
		30	60	10	100 senators

Note that the entries in any column in this table are proportional to those in any other column. A similar statement holds for the row entries. Consider first the 30 senators who are "high" on scale X and, therefore, lie in the first column of the table. The proportion of these "high" senators in each of the scale Y categores are, respectively,

$$3/30, 6/30, 12/30, \text{ and } 9/30$$

or, equivalently,

$$.1, .2, .4, \text{ and } .3$$

These same proportions hold for senators in the "medium" and "low" columns as well. From this it follows that these same proportions apply to the set of all 100 senators so that the row marginals also equal

$$.1, .2, .4, \text{ and } .3$$

In other words, for every column state x_j and row category y_i,

$$P(y_i | x_j) = P_{ij}/P_{.j} = P_{i.}$$

For example,

$$P(y_3 | x_2) = 24/60 = .40 = P_{3.}$$

Since this .40 figure is the probability of y_3 whatever the state x_j, knowing the independent variable state of an observation does *not* provide any information as to the likelihood that y_3 will occur or, in fact, that any other state y_i will occur. (As an exercise, show that a similar results holds if Y is the independent variable, X dependent.) Consequently, knowledge of the X state cannot benefit any prediction about Y. This implies that all ∇ values for such a distribution, whatever the specification of the error cells and weights, ought to be zero. From $P_{ij}/P_{.j} = P_{i.}$ for this special case, it follows that every $P_{ij} = P_{i.}P_{.j}$ and "observed" errors equal "expected" errors, hence $\nabla = 0$.

When $P_{ij} = P_{i.}P_{.j}$ holds for all i and j, the variables are said to be *statistically independent*. The "expected" error rate then equals the rate that would occur in a population that exhibited statistical independence and had marginal probabilities identical to those of the population under analysis. We ought to point out that ∇ can also equal zero when the variables are *not* statistically independent. All that is required is that the *sum* of probabilities (weighted by ω_{ij}) in the error cells equals the *sum* that would occur under statistical independence. This directly parallels the situation for quantitative variables where statistical independence is a sufficient *but not necessary* condition for a zero correlation.

The Quadrant Measure: A Special Application
for Ordinal Variables

A particular application of the general ∇ model is the quadrant measure discussed by Kruskal (1958). To illustrate, assume we were dealing with a hypothetical population of 10 bureaucrats that is cross-classified in Table 7(a). Note that half the bureaucrats are Republicans and the other half are either *Ind* or *Dem*. Similarly, *(left* and *left-center)* vs. *(center, center-right,* and *right)* give us a "50-50" split (in this case, 5-5) on social services. Heavy black lines divide the table into four quadrants. Consider the prediction identifying the shaded cells in Table 7(a) as error events. This proposition can be written equivalently as x *(Dem* or *Ind)* predicts y *(left* or *left-center)* and $\bar{x}$ *(Rep)* predicts $\bar{y}$ *(center* or *right-center* or *right)*. For short, we write $(x \rightsquigarrow y) \,\&\, (\bar{x} \rightsquigarrow \bar{y})$, or in even more compact notation, $x \leftrightsquigarrow y$, analogous to the formal logic expression "x if and only if y." In other words, this proposition predicts that the data should tend to be concentrated in the xy and $\bar{x}\bar{y}$ quadrants; the $x\bar{y}$ and $\bar{x}y$ quadrants are the error events. In Table 7(b), note that there are six observed errors. Whether we predict y or $\bar{y}$, without knowledge of party affiliation, we will err in one-half of the predictions, or five cases on average, because the 50-50 split makes y and $\bar{y}$ equally likely. In particular, we will expect to make five errors in applying the replication procedure. In this case, the

$$\text{quadrant measure} = 1 - (\text{Observed Errors})/(\text{Expected Errors})$$
$$= 1 - 6/5 = -.200$$

In general,

$$\text{quadrant measure} = 1 - \frac{P_{y\bar{x}} + P_{\bar{y}x}}{P_{y.}P_{.\bar{x}} + P_{\bar{y}.}P_{.x}}$$

$$= 1 - \frac{P_{y\bar{x}} + P_{\bar{y}x}}{(1/2)(1/2) + (1/2)(1/2)}$$

$$= 1 - 2(P_{y\bar{x}} + P_{\bar{y}x})$$

$$= 1 - 4P_{y\bar{x}}$$

where x is a combined category that contains the half of the observations that are in the "highest" categories on the independent variable and $\bar{x}$ combines the "lowest" categories. The states y and $\bar{y}$ are defined similarly for the dependent variable.[1]

As to its advantages, the quadrant measure does predict single observations and is easy to compute. Unlike some of the standard measures for pairs, however, it cannot be interpreted as being based upon a totally a priori prediction

TABLE 7
The Quadrant Prediction in a Hypothetical
Population of Ten Bureaucrats

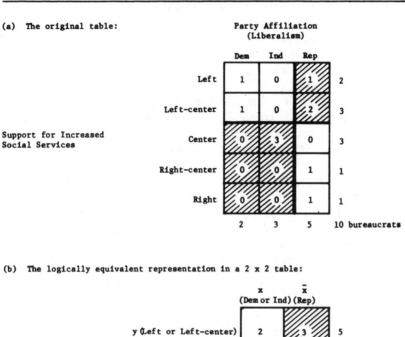

(a) The original table:

Party Affiliation
(Liberalism)

	Dem	Ind	Rep	
Left	1	0	1	2
Left–center	1	0	2	3
Center	0	3	0	3
Right–center	0	0	1	1
Right	0	0	1	1
	2	3	5	10 bureaucrats

Support for Increased
Social Services

(b) The logically equivalent representation in a 2 x 2 table:

	x (Dem or Ind)	x̄ (Rep)	
y (Left or Left–center)	2	3	5
ȳ (Right, Right–center, or Center)	3	2	5
	5	5	10 bureaucrats

Support for Increased
Social Services

since we must have information as to where (if anywhere) the 50-50 (median) split occurs on the dependent variable. A more important weakness of the measure is that the 50-50 split needed to apply the measure will occur only rarely in practice and in fact is guaranteed not to occur in a finite population with an odd number of total observations. (The quadrant measure, in fact, is most readily thought of as being applied to an infinite population where all observations are strongly ordered—no ties—on both variables.)

Modification for Uneven Splits: When an exact 50-50 split fails to exist, there will be one category that straddles a 50-50 division of the observations. If this happens for variable X, let us relabel this category as x_2'. Those categories higher than the straddling category can be relabelled x_1', those lower, x_3'. A similar definition is made for Y.

Now let the modified quadrant prediction be:

$$x_1' \rightsquigarrow (y_1' \text{ or } y_2')$$

$$x_2' \rightsquigarrow (y_1', y_2', \text{ or } y_3')$$

$$x_3' \rightsquigarrow (y_2' \text{ or } y_3')$$

If there is an exact 50-50 split on both variables, then the middle categories (x_2' and y_2') are empty and the prediction becomes that of the quadrant measure. It is quite possible that one of the redefined categories can be empty. For example, in Table 1, over half the population is *left* on social services, implying that *left* is y_2' and that y_1' is empty. While ∇ could be computed for the modified quadrant prediction even if y_1' is empty, for illustrative purposes it is more instructive to consider the modification for the population of bureaucrats in non-social services agencies. As shown in Table 8, x_1' is *Dem*, x_2' is *Ind*, and x_3' is *Rep* while y_1' is *left* or *left-center*, y_2' is *center*, and y_3' is *right* or *right-center*.

Applying the general definition of ∇ to the modified quadrant prediction, as indicated by the error cells shown in Table 8, we obtain

$$\text{"modified quadrant measure"} = 1 - \frac{P_{1'3'} + P_{3'1'}}{P_{1'}.P_{.3'} + P_{3'}.P_{.1'}}$$

For Table 8 this measure equals

$$1 - \frac{(6/75) + (4/75)}{(28/75)(24/75) + (25/75)(35/75)} = 1 - \frac{.133}{.275} = .515$$

The major weakness of the quadrant measure, even if modified to allow for uneven splits, is that it evaluates a single, fixed prediction. This prediction underlying the measure may have little to do with a particular research hypothesis stated by an investigator a priori (prior to data analysis). Similarly, in ex post data analysis, the quadrant measure may miss an important relation in the data. For example, although the quadrant measure was negative for Table 7, applying the original proposition P, developed for Table 1, to the Table 7 data shows that $\nabla_P = .464$ and $U = .560$. Thus, the original proposition achieves substantially better prediction success with an accompanying increase in precision. By shifting predictions, we have caused the number for Table 7 to jump from $-.200$ to $+.464$, showing how important it is for the statistical measure to be attuned to the investigator's specific research hypothesis.

A related weakness of the quadrant measure is that it can have the same value in quite different populations. By inspection, Table 9 can be seen not to support the "Y increases with X" type of statement since six cases occur

TABLE 8

Party Affiliation and Support for Social Services Among Top-Level Bureaucrats in Non-Social Service Agencies

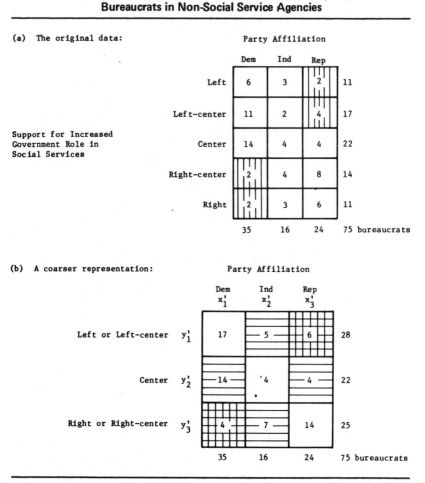

(a) The original data:

Party Affiliation

	Dem	Ind	Rep	
Left	6	3	2	11
Left-center	11	2	4	17
Center	14	4	4	22
Right-center	2	4	8	14
Right	2	3	6	11
	35	16	24	75 bureaucrats

Support for Increased Government Role in Social Services

(b) A coarser representation:

Party Affiliation

	Dem x'_1	Ind x'_2	Rep x'_3	
Left or Left-center y'_1	17	5	6	28
Center y'_2	14	4	4	22
Right or Right-center y'_3	4	7	14	25
	35	16	24	75 bureaucrats

Note: Vertically shaded cells are errors for **modified** quadrant measure. Horizontally shaded cells are errors for kappa.

Data Source: Aberbach and Rockman (1976, p. 460).

in the extreme cells at the lower left and upper right corners of the table. Likewise, applying the original proposition P to this table shows $\nabla_P = -.296$. In contrast, we saw that Table 7 shows P to be moderately successful with $\nabla_P = +.464$. Yet, for both tables, the quadrant measure is $-.200$.

Cohen's Kappa: Another Application

When both variables have the same number of categories (R = C), a prominent prediction is, for all i = 1, . . . , R, $\kappa: x_i \rightsquigarrow y_i$. That is, predict the data

TABLE 9
An Alternative Table for Application of the Quadrant Measure

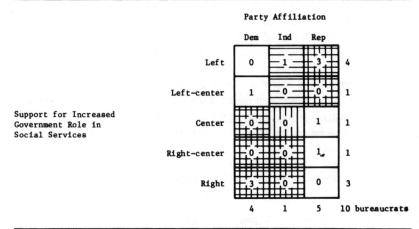

Note: Vertical shading shows error cells for quadrant measure. Horizontal shading shows error cells for the proposition P as in Table 1.

tend to fall on the main diagonal. For this prediction, we leave it to the reader as an exercise to show that the ∇ measure for unweighted errors simplifies to

$$\nabla_\kappa = \frac{\sum_i P_{ii} - \sum_i P_{i.}P_{.i}}{1 - \sum_i P_{i.}P_{.i}} = \text{kappa}$$

where kappa is a measure defined by Cohen (1960, 1968).

Like the quadrant measure, this prediction (κ) can be seen as an attempt to capture part of the "Y increases with X" statement. Note that if one variable has more categories than another, arbitrary combinations of various adjacent categories can always be used to make R = C. Which particular categories are combined will, of course, affect the value of kappa.

For the data in Table 8(b), we find

$$\sum_i P_{ii} = (17 + 4 + 14)/75 = 35/75 = .467$$

$$\sum_i P_{i.}P_{.i} = \left(\frac{28}{75}\right)\left(\frac{35}{75}\right) + \left(\frac{22}{75}\right)\left(\frac{16}{75}\right) + \left(\frac{25}{75}\right)\left(\frac{24}{75}\right) = 1932/5625 = .343$$

$$\text{kappa} = \frac{.467 - .343}{1 - .343} = .188$$

Note that the kappa prediction represented in Table 8 is logically equivalent to *Dem* $\leadsto$ (*left* or *left-center*), *Ind* $\leadsto$ *center*, and *Rep* $\leadsto$ (*Right-center* or *right*) for the original Table 8(a). One can check that these two equivalent propositions have identical ∇ values.

Suppose we transform Table 8(b) into a 2 x 2 table by combining y_2' and y_3' and combining *Ind* and *Rep*. Kappa for this table is based on the prediction *Dem* $\leadsto$ (*left* or *left-center*), *Ind* $\leadsto$ (*center, right-center* or *right*), and *Rep* $\leadsto$ (*center, right-center* or *right*). Kappa has a different value, namely .213, for the 2 x 2 table than it does for the original Table 8(b). This example illustrates a general point. When applying standard measures of association for ordinal variables, including those in the next section, changing from finer to coarser classifications or vice versa changes the underlying prediction represented in the measure (Goodman and Kruskal, 1954: 737-738). Consequently, the value of the measure also will be affected, often substantially.

Sensitivity Analysis for Predictions of Ordinal Variables: An Application to Reliability Assessment

Kappa was originally proposed by a psychologist, Jacob Cohen, as a measure of judgment reliability. Problems associated with the measurement of judgment reliability are prominent in various contexts of social science. The organization Freedom House (as reported in *Le Monde,* Jan. 4-5, 1976: 2) rated the 144 UN members as to whether they were *very free, free,* or *not free*. There were 16 *very free,* 23 *free,* and 105 *not free* countries. Another rater might give quite different ratings. Kappa gives a measure of the extent to which one rater's ranking predicts the other's (or vice versa, since $x_i \leadsto y_i$ for all i is logically equivalent to $y_j \leadsto x_j$ for all j). Cohen also proposed a weighted kappa (∇_κ with error weights) to allow for varying degrees of error severity. The weights can be especially useful with ordinal data.

Partial Order of Error Weights: How can we assign the weights to the UN ratings, where R=C=3? We know that an observation on the major diagonal is a success, so $\omega_{11} = \omega_{22} = \omega_{33} = 0$. Moreover, it would be reasonable to assume that when rater X says *very free* and rater Y says *not free,* the error is the same as when the reverse occurs. Put differently, observing *not free* when *very free* is predicted constitutes the same degree of error as observing *very free* when not *free* is predicted. (An analogous symmetry occurs in the use of squared error with quantitative variables.) Consequently, $\omega_{31} = \omega_{13}$. Also by symmetry, $\omega_{21} = \omega_{12}$ and $\omega_{32} = \omega_{23}$. (In the general case, $\omega_{ji} = \omega_{ij}$.) In the 3x3 example, therefore, we have only three unique non-zero weights: $\omega_{31}, \omega_{21},$ and ω_{32}.

What does the ordinal character of the variables tell us about their relative values? We can justify some relations among the error weights. Clearly, for any observations predicted to be *very free*, the outcome *not free* is at least as bad an error as is *free*, so $\omega_{31} \geqslant \omega_{21}$. Also, *not free* is no less serious an error when *very free* is predicted than when only *free* is predicted, so $\omega_{31} \geqslant \omega_{32}$. Thus, so far we have

$$\omega_{31} = \omega_{13} \geqslant \omega_{21} = \omega_{12} \geqslant 0$$

$$\omega_{31} = \omega_{13} \geqslant \omega_{32} = \omega_{23} \geqslant 0$$

$$\omega_{11} = \omega_{22} = \omega_{33} = 0$$

Without loss of generality, we can set the largest error weight equal to one, so $\omega_{31} = \omega_{13} = 1$. However, we may be unwilling to establish a relation between $\omega_{32} = \omega_{23}$ and $\omega_{21} = \omega_{12}$ because we cannot assess whether observing *free* when *very free* is predicted is more serious an error than when *not free* is predicted. Since we have established ordinal relations between some, but not all, of the error weights, we have only a partial order of the weights. This partial order is diagrammed in Figure 1.

Component Predictions: Now consider the three cross classifications in Table 10. Each of these tables contain two of the six error cells for the major diagonal (kappa) prediction shown in Table 11. Each of the three tables can be taken to represent components of the prediction

$$\kappa_i : x_i \rightsquigarrow y_i \text{ for all } i$$

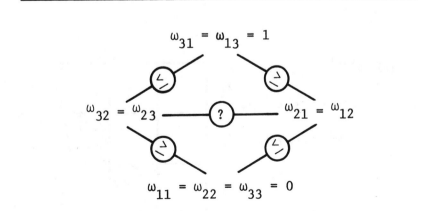

Figure 1: Partial Order of Error Weights for Kappa in a 3 x 3 Table

TABLE 10
The Three Components of κ for a 3 x 3 Table

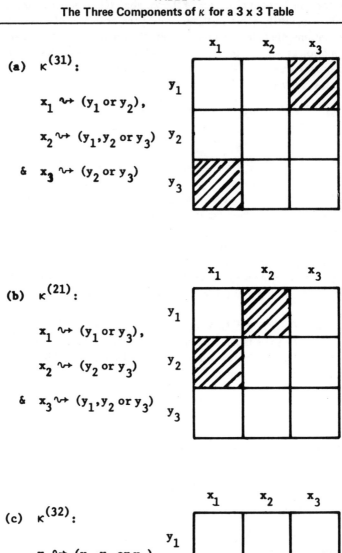

(a) $\kappa^{(31)}$:

    $x_1 \rightsquigarrow (y_1 \text{ or } y_2)$,

    $x_2 \rightsquigarrow (y_1, y_2 \text{ or } y_3)$

  & $x_3 \rightsquigarrow (y_2 \text{ or } y_3)$

(b) $\kappa^{(21)}$:

    $x_1 \rightsquigarrow (y_1 \text{ or } y_3)$,

    $x_2 \rightsquigarrow (y_2 \text{ or } y_3)$

  & $x_3 \rightsquigarrow (y_1, y_2 \text{ or } y_3)$

(c) $\kappa^{(32)}$:

    $x_1 \rightsquigarrow (y_1, y_2 \text{ or } y_3)$,

    $x_2 \rightsquigarrow (y_1 \text{ or } y_2)$

  & $x_3 \rightsquigarrow (y_1 \text{ or } y_2)$

TABLE 11
Cross-Tabulation of Two Hypothetical Ratings of 144 UN Members

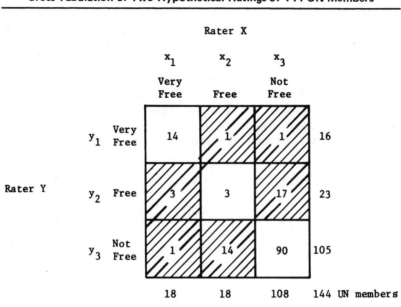

Shading shows error cells for K: $x_i \rightsquigarrow y_i$, $i = 1, 2, 3$.

The first component is named $\kappa^{(31)}$ since it corresponds to cells with error weight ω_{31}. It can be expressed as

$$\kappa^{(31)}:\ x_1 \rightsquigarrow (y_1 \text{ or } y_2)\ \&$$
$$x_2 \rightsquigarrow (y_1 \text{ or } y_2 \text{ or } y_3)\ \&$$
$$x_3 \rightsquigarrow (y_2 \text{ or } y_3)$$

Define $\kappa^{(21)}$ and $\kappa^{(32)}$ analogously.

∇ *as a Weighted Average of Component* ∇*'s:* It can be shown (again a possible exercise for the reader) that

$$\nabla_{\kappa,\omega} = \frac{1}{U^{(31)} + \omega_{21}U^{(21)} + \omega_{32}U^{(32)}} \left[U^{(31)}\nabla^{(31)} + \omega_{21}U^{(21)}\nabla^{(21)} \right.$$
$$\left. + \omega_{32}U^{(32)}\nabla^{(32)} \right]$$

$$= \frac{1}{.174 + .034\,\omega_{21} + .211\,\omega_{32}} \left[(.174)(.920) + \omega_{21}(.034)(.179) \right.$$
$$\left. + \omega_{32}(.211)(-.021) \right]$$

Specifically, $\nabla_{K,\omega}$ equals a weighted average of ∇'s for the three component predictions, the weights being the product of the error weights and the precision terms, U, for each component. We find the largest component is $\nabla^{(13)} = .920$ for the hypothetical data in Table 11. By our earlier analysis of the partial order of the weights, this component must be included with the largest possible weight (1.0). Since adding components with lower ∇'s into the average can only make the average worse, the maximum possible value of $\nabla_{K,\omega}$ occurs with $\omega_{21} = \omega_{32} = 0$. Thus, max $\nabla_{K,\omega} = .920$.

To find a lower bound for ∇, we would give the worst component ∇ as large a weight as possible. The worst component ∇ is $\nabla^{(32)} = -.021$. Consider therefore $\omega_{31} = \omega_{32} = 1$, $\omega_{21} = 0$. Then

$$\nabla_{K,\omega} = \frac{1}{.174 + 0 + .211} [(.174)(.920) + 0 + (.211)(-.021)] = .404$$

Should the remaining component (21) also be given weight in the average? The value of $\nabla^{(21)} = .179$ is less than .404. Therefore, the greater the weight placed on the (21) cells, the lower the overall ∇. Thus, also setting ω_{21} to one, its maximum value allowed by the partial order, we find:

$$\min \nabla_{K,\omega} = \frac{1}{.174 + .034 + .211} [(.174)(.920) + (.034)(.179)$$

$$+ (.211)(-.021)] = .386$$

In summary,

$$.920 \geqslant \nabla_{K,\omega} \geqslant .386$$

for all possible error weights consistent with the partial ordering. Although the two raters are not in perfect agreement, one using the ratings would be glad to find that the two raters have positive success in predicting one another, despite the presence of one negative component ∇. (That this is true for all possible error weights consistent with the ordering does not seem apparent from visual analysis of the table, indicating that even with small tables an important role can be played by statistical prediction analysis.) Nonetheless, the relatively low .386 value of the lower bound might indicate that caution should be exercised when using either rating scale, especially if one thinks that ω_{32} should be relatively large.

Working with kappa has illustrated a general property of ∇. Any ∇ can be expressed as a weighted average of components. This can often be used to advantage when one has ordinal information about the error weights. In addition to the "sensitivity analysis" procedure of establishing bounds on the value of ∇, as in the previous example, one can carry out a more fine-grained analysis by studying how the value of ∇ changes with changes in the numerical values of the error weights. For another illustration analyzing a triangular pattern of error cells with actual survey data, see Hildebrand, Laing, and Rosenthal (1978: section 4.1.2). The general development of ∇ as a weighted average is found in Hildebrand, Laing, and Rosenthal (1977: ch. 3).

In this section, we have developed both the general ∇ measure and the procedure of sensitivity analysis. The methods were applied to the analysis of two conventional measures of association for predictions about single observations. In the remainder of the paper, we extend the application of the methods, first to predictions for pairs of observations, then to joint prediction of quantitative and qualitative variables, and, finally, to multivariate analysis.

3. BIVARIATE PREDICTION FOR PAIRS OF OBSERVATIONS

Computing the Condensed Ordinal Form

To shift from the prediction of single observations to the prediction of pairs, let's return to the bureaucrats. As indicated earlier, any ordinal comparison of two observations on a variable can be condensed into three states: *more, same, less*. The cross-tabulation of the condensed forms of two variables creates 3×3 tables such as Table 3. The first task in the analysis of pair predictions is to compute the entries of Table 3 from the original data, Table 1. Again, we'll treat the party affiliation categories as being ordered along an underlying dimension, perhaps liberalism.

The first step is to compute the row and column totals. Let's start with party affiliation. There are nine *Ind* bureaucrats who are tied on this scale. They can be paired in $9^2 = 81$ different ways. Similarly, there will be 13^2 ties on *Dem* and 9^2 ties on *Rep*. Across all affiliation categories, there are $13^2 + 9^2 + 9^2 = 331$ ties, and these are assigned to the category *same* of the condensed affiliation variable.

The number of ties can be used to compute the number of *more* and *less* pairs. Note that these untied pairs cannot include self-pairs such as (Amy, Amy). Now if Amy has a more liberal party affiliation than Nixman, the pair (Amy, Nixman) will be classified as *more* but the pair (Nixman, Amy) will be classified as *less*. Because of this symmetric counting of pairs, the number of pairs in the *more* category must equal the number assigned to *less*. The total number of pairs is $31^2 = 961$. Since the number of untied pairs is $961 - 331 = 630$, *more* and *less* have the same number of pairs: $630/2 = 315$. This equals the column totals in Table 3.

To get the row (social services) totals, repeat the above procedure. There are $16^2 + 5^2 + 7^2 + 2^2 + 1^2 = 335$ tied pairs. By subtraction, there are $961 - 335 = 626$ untied pairs. By symmetry, there are $626/2 = 313$ pairs in both the *more* and *less* categories.

The center entry in Table 3, corresponding to a tie on both variables, can also be obtained easily. There are 12 bureaucrats that are both *left* and *Dem*. They are tied on both variables. They can be paired in 12^2 ways. There are three *left* and *Ind* bureaucrats for 3^2 pairs. Squaring and summing over all of Table 1 in this manner, compute the total as

$$12^2 + 3^2 + 1^2 + 1^2 + 2^2 + 2^2 + 0^2 + 3^2 + 4^2 +$$

$$0^2 + 1^2 + 1^2 + 0^2 + 0^2 + 1^2 = 191$$

pairs of bureaucrats who are tied on *both* variables, including the 31 self-pairs.

Four more entries in Table 3 can be calculated from symmetry considerations that parallel those invoked for the row and marginal totals. There are 331 tied pairs on affiliation and 191 pairs tied on *both* variables. So, there are $331 - 191 = 140$ that are tied on affiliation but not on social services. By symmetry, there are $140/2 = 70$ pairs that are *more* on social services but *same* on affiliation and 70 that are *less* on social services but *same* on affiliation. Similarly, $335 - 191 = 144$ pairs are tied on social services but untied on affiliation. These split equally, 72 being *more* on affiliation and 72 being *less*.

The only somewhat tricky part in the whole operation involves finding any one of the four corner cells in Table 3. Let's compute the number of *more-more* pairs. The remaining numbers then can be calculated simply.

The 12 *left-Dem* bureaucrats cannot be greater *on both variables* than any of the other bureaucrats in the first (*left*) row or first (*Dem*) column. But they do exhibit the *more-more* relation with all the other bureaucrats in the table. To find these, it is convenient to delete the first row and column, and to add the rest. Schematically, the (1,1) cell contributes

$$\text{12 bureaucrats times the } sum\ of \begin{bmatrix} 2 & 2 \\ 3 & 4 \\ 1 & 1 \\ 0 & 1 \end{bmatrix} = 12 \times 14 = 168 \text{ pairs}$$

There are three *left-Ind* bureaucrats. As was the case for *left-Dem*, the *left-Ind* bureaucrats exhibit the *more-more* relation with all individuals *below and to the right* in the table, contributing

$$\text{3 bureaucrats times the sum of } \begin{bmatrix} 2 \\ 4 \\ 1 \\ 1 \end{bmatrix} = 3 \times 8 = 24 \text{ pairs}$$

The *Rep* column can be ignored since there is no column further to the right. We next turn to the second row. The contributions in the *left-center* row are:

$$1 \; Dem \text{ times the sum of } \begin{bmatrix} 3 & 4 \\ 1 & 1 \\ 0 & 1 \end{bmatrix} = 1 \times 10 = 10 \text{ pairs}$$

$$2 \; Ind \text{ times the sum of } \begin{bmatrix} 4 \\ 1 \\ 1 \end{bmatrix} = 2 \times 6 = 12 \text{ pairs}$$

The third row contributions are:

$$0 \; Dem \text{ times the sum of } \begin{bmatrix} 1 & 1 \\ 0 & 1 \end{bmatrix} = 0 \times 3 = 0 \text{ pairs}$$

$$3 \; Ind \text{ times the sum of } \begin{bmatrix} 1 \\ 1 \end{bmatrix} = 3 \times 2 = 6 \text{ pairs}$$

The fourth row shows:

$$0 \; Dem \text{ times the sum of } \begin{bmatrix} 0 & 1 \end{bmatrix} = 0 \text{ pairs}$$

$$1 \; Ind \text{ times the sum of } \begin{bmatrix} 1 \end{bmatrix} = 1 \text{ pair}$$

The fifth (*right*) row can be ignored since there is no row below it.

In total, there are $168 + 24 + 10 + 12 + 6 + 1 = 221$ *more-more* pairs. Now if the pair (Amy,Nixman) is *more-more*, then (Nixman,Amy) must be a *less-less* pair, so there are 221 *less-less* pairs also. Therefore, $313 - 221 - 70 = 22$ pairs are *less* on affiliation but *more* on social services and also 22 pairs are *more* on affiliation but *less* on social services. These computations have allowed us to fill all the entries in Table 3.

Prediction in the Condensed Ordinal Form

We are now ready to evaluate some predictions for the condensed form. Six such predictions are shown in Table 12. For all of these predictions, the maximum weight of 1.0 is assigned to occurrences of the "serious" error of observing *less* when *more* is predicted (or vice-versa). Weights less than 1.0 are assigned to less "serious" errors such as observing *same* when *more* is predicted (or vice-versa).

266

TABLE 12
Four Condensed Form Propositions

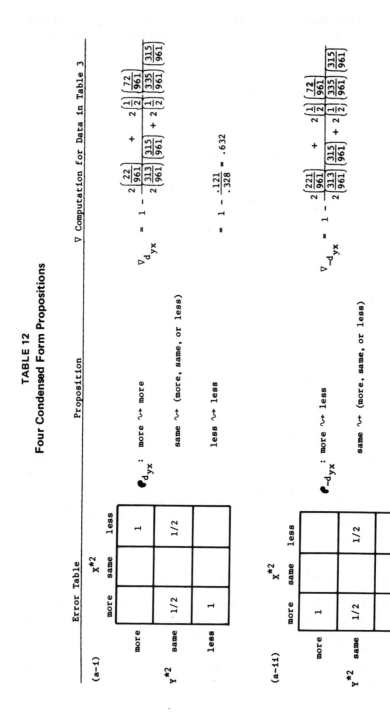

| Error Table | | | | Proposition | ∇ Computation for Data in Table 3 |

(a-i)

X^{*2}: more, same, less

Y^{*2}:
- more: (—, —, 1)
- same: (1/2, —, 1/2)
- less: (1, —, —)

$\nabla_{d_{yx}}$:
- more ⤳ more
- same ⤳ (more, same, or less)
- less ⤳ less

$$\nabla_{d_{yx}} = 1 - \frac{2\left(\frac{22}{961}\right) + 2\left(\frac{1}{2}\right)\left(\frac{72}{961}\right)}{2\left(\frac{313}{961}\right)\left(\frac{315}{961}\right) + 2\left(\frac{1}{2}\right)\left(\frac{335}{961}\right)\left(\frac{315}{961}\right)}$$

$$= 1 - \frac{.121}{.328} = .632$$

(a-ii)

X^{*2}: more, same, less

Y^{*2}:
- more: (1, —, —)
- same: (1/2, —, 1/2)
- less: (—, —, 1)

$\nabla_{-d_{yx}}$:
- more ⤳ less
- same ⤳ (more, same, or less)
- less ⤳ more

$$\nabla_{-d_{yx}} = 1 - \frac{2\left(\frac{221}{961}\right) + 2\left(\frac{1}{2}\right)\left(\frac{72}{961}\right)}{2\left(\frac{313}{961}\right)\left(\frac{315}{961}\right) + 2\left(\frac{1}{2}\right)\left(\frac{335}{961}\right)\left(\frac{315}{961}\right)}$$

$$= 1 - \frac{.535}{.328} = -.632$$

267

TABLE 12 (Continued)

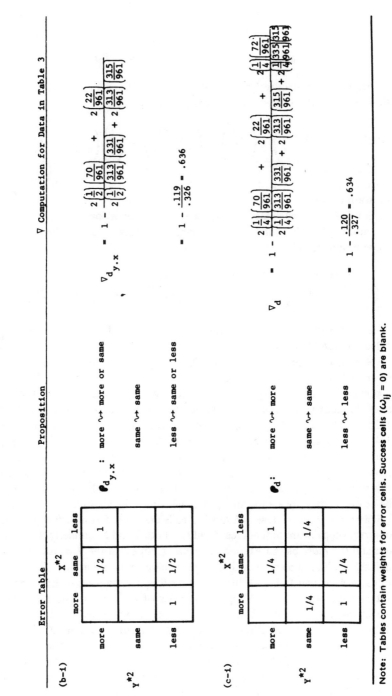

Error Table Proposition ∇ Computation for Data in Table 3

(b-1)

$\bullet d_{y.x}$: more $\rightsquigarrow$ more or same

same $\rightsquigarrow$ same

less $\rightsquigarrow$ same or less

$$\nabla_{d_{y.x}} = 1 - \frac{2\left(\frac{1}{2}\right)\left(\frac{70}{961}\right) + 2\left(\frac{22}{961}\right)}{2\left(\frac{1}{2}\right)\left(\frac{313}{961}\right)\left(\frac{331}{961}\right) + 2\left(\frac{313}{961}\right)\left(\frac{315}{961}\right)}$$

$$= 1 - \frac{.119}{.326} = .636$$

(c-1)

$\bullet d$: more $\rightsquigarrow$ more

same $\rightsquigarrow$ same

less $\rightsquigarrow$ less

$$\nabla_d = 1 - \frac{2\left(\frac{1}{4}\right)\left(\frac{70}{961}\right) + 2\left(\frac{22}{961}\right) + 2\left(\frac{1}{4}\right)\left(\frac{72}{961}\right)}{2\left(\frac{1}{4}\right)\left(\frac{313}{961}\right)\left(\frac{331}{961}\right) + 2\left(\frac{313}{961}\right)\left(\frac{315}{961}\right) + 2\frac{1}{4}\left(\frac{335}{961}\right)\left(\frac{315}{961}\right)}$$

$$= 1 - \frac{.120}{.327} = .634$$

Note: Tables contain weights for error cells. Success cells ($\omega_{ij} = 0$) are blank.

268

Table 12 also shows the calculation of ∇ for the data in Table 3. Recall that

$$\nabla_\rho = 1 - (\text{Observed Errors/Expected Errors})$$

Applying the error weights of Table 12(a-i) to the data in Table 3, we find that the (weighted) observed errors, as proportions, are

$$\left(\frac{22}{961}\right) + \left(\frac{22}{961}\right) + \left(\frac{1}{2}\right)\left(\frac{72}{961}\right) + \left(\frac{1}{2}\right)\left(\frac{72}{961}\right)$$

This term equals the numerator of the first right hand term in the $\nabla_{d_{yx}}$ calculation in (a-i).

Similarly, we calculate the expected error proportion for each error cell by multiplying the corresponding marginal proportions. We then multiply these proportions by the appropriate error weights and sum, to obtain

$$\left(\frac{313}{961}\right)\left(\frac{315}{961}\right) + \left(\frac{313}{961}\right)\left(\frac{315}{961}\right) + \left(\frac{1}{2}\right)\left(\frac{335}{961}\right)\left(\frac{315}{961}\right) + \left(\frac{1}{2}\right)\left(\frac{335}{961}\right)\left(\frac{315}{961}\right)$$

This term equals the denominator of the first right hand term in the $\nabla_{d_{yx}}$ calculation in the table.

Note that if one cell is an error cell, its opposite cell in the table is also an error cell and has the same weight. Examples include: In Table 12(a-i), the *less-more* cell has a weight of 1.0, matching the *more-less* cell; in Table 12 (b-i) the cells *more-same* and *less-same* are both error cells with weights of 1/2; in Table 12(c-i), the *same-more* and *same-less* cells are both weighted 1/4. This parallels our finding above that these cells, because of symmetry, must have an equal number of pairs. In general, condensed forms of any table always exhibit this *radial symmetry* about the center cell. Because of this symmetry, any two symmetric cells must either both be successes or both be errors. If they are errors, the error weights must be identical.

Pairs in the *more-more* and *less-less* cells are termed *concordant* since the observation pairs are ordered identically on both Y and X. Similarly, the *more-less* and *less-more* pairs are termed *discordant*. Note that the ∇ values displayed in Tables 12(a-i, a-ii) are equal in magnitude but opposite in sign. The predictions in each pair (a-i, a-ii) differ only by flipping the roles of the concordant and discordant pairs. Flipping the roles of concordant and discordant, we could also develop tables b-ii and c-ii as comparisons to b-i and c-i in Table 12. The (i) predictions are representations of "the more X, the more Y"; the (ii) predictions are representations of "the more X, the less Y." Since the magnitudes of both members of the (i-ii) pairs must be equal and since ∇ has a maximum value of 1.0, these special predictions must all have a minimum value of -1.0. The ∇ for the (i) predictions equals

(a) Somers' (1962) d_{yx},

(b) Kim's (1971) $d_{y.x}$, and

(c) Kim's (1971) symmetric d.

(In the next section, we develop these measures in greater detail.) All the measures shown in Table 12 were developed with X as the independent variable. For the first two "asymmetric" measures, Somers and Kim have proposed corresponding measures when X is the dependent variable, indicated by reversing the position of the subscripts. It can readily be shown that $d_{xy} = d_{y.x}$ and $d_{x.y} = d_{yx}$.

One way to use these measures is to compute them using prediction (i). Then, if the value is negative, ex post one can change the sign of the measure and adopt prediction (ii) as an interpretation of the data. One can also use the measure in an a priori sense, reporting a negative value as a strong indication of prediction failure.

In the case of Table 12, the magnitudes of the three measures show little variation. Results like these occur rather often, but wider variation can readily occur. In order to give some simplified computing formulas for these established measures, we first develop the general probability notation for the condensed form.

General Development of the Condensed Form

The entries for the condensed form are shown symbolically in Table 13. The symbol $P(\underset{\sim}{C})$ refers to the probability of concordance, $P(\underset{\sim}{D})$ to discordance, $P(T_X)$ to a tie on X, $P(T_{\overline{Y}X})$ to a tie on X but not on Y, $P(\overline{T}_X)$ to the probability of not being tied on X, etc. The entries in Table 13 can be calculated from the entries in an R x C table of population probabilities as:

$$P(T_Y) = \sum_{i=1}^{R} P_{i.}^2, \qquad P(\overline{T}_Y) = 1 - P(T_Y)$$

$$P(T_X) = \sum_{j=1}^{C} P_{.j}^2, \qquad P(\overline{T}_X) = 1 - P(T_X)$$

$$P(T_{YX}) = \sum_{i=1}^{R} \sum_{j=1}^{C} P_{ij}^2$$

$$P(T_{Y\overline{X}}) = P(T_Y) - P(T_{YX})$$

$$P(T_{\overline{Y}X}) = P(T_X) - P(T_{YX})$$

TABLE 13
The General Condensed Ordinal Form

$$\text{X}^{*2}$$

	more	same	less	
more	$\frac{1}{2}P(\underset{\sim}{C})$	$\frac{1}{2}P(T_{\underset{\sim}{Y}X})$	$\frac{1}{2}P(\underset{\sim}{D})$	$\frac{1}{2}P(\bar{T}_{\underset{\sim}{Y}})$
same	$\frac{1}{2}P(T_{\underset{\sim}{Y}\bar{X}})$	$P(T_{\underset{\sim}{Y}X})$	$\frac{1}{2}P(T_{\underset{\sim}{Y}\bar{X}})$	$P(T_{\underset{\sim}{Y}})$
less	$\frac{1}{2}P(\underset{\sim}{D})$	$\frac{1}{2}P(T_{\underset{\sim}{Y}X})$	$\frac{1}{2}P(\underset{\sim}{C})$	$\frac{1}{2}P(\bar{T}_{\underset{\sim}{Y}})$
	$\frac{1}{2}P(\bar{T}_{\underset{\sim}{X}})$	$P(T_{\underset{\sim}{X}})$	$\frac{1}{2}P(\bar{T}_{\underset{\sim}{X}})$	1.0

where the row label is Y^{*2}.

$$P(\underset{\sim}{C}) = 2 \sum_{i=1}^{R-1} \sum_{j=1}^{C-1} \sum_{g=i+1}^{R} \sum_{h=j+1}^{C} P_{ij}P_{gh}$$

$$P(\underset{\sim}{D}) = 1 - P(\underset{\sim}{C}) - P(T_{Y\bar{X}}) - P(T_{\bar{Y}X}) - P(T_{YX})$$

Note that g is just an alternate index for the rows, h for the columns.[2] As an exercise, convert Table 1 to probabilities and use the above formula to compute the condensed ordinal form. As a check, convert Table 3 to probabilities.

Using the above general expressions for the condensed form, the d type measures may be expressed as:

$$d_{yx} = d_{x.y} = \frac{P(\underset{\sim}{C}) - P(\underset{\sim}{D})}{P(\bar{T}_{X})} = \frac{P(\underset{\sim}{C}) - P(\underset{\sim}{D})}{P(\underset{\sim}{C}) + P(\underset{\sim}{D}) + P(T_{Y\bar{X}})}$$

$$d_{xy} = d_{y.x} = \frac{P(\underset{\sim}{C}) - P(\underset{\sim}{D})}{P(\bar{T}_{Y})} = \frac{P(\underset{\sim}{C}) - P(\underset{\sim}{D})}{P(\underset{\sim}{C}) + P(\underset{\sim}{D}) + P(T_{\bar{Y}X})}$$

$$d = \frac{P(\underset{\sim}{C}) - P(\underset{\sim}{D})}{\frac{1}{2}[P(\bar{T}_{Y}) + P(\bar{T}_{X})]} = \frac{P(\underset{\sim}{C}) - P(\underset{\sim}{D})}{\frac{1}{2}[2P(\underset{\sim}{C}) + 2P(\underset{\sim}{D}) + P(T_{Y\bar{X}}) + P(T_{\bar{Y}X})]}$$

From Table 3, for example,

$$d_{yx} = \frac{2(221/961 - 22/961)}{2(315/961)} = .632$$

as before.

Expressed in this form, the d measures differ only in the denominators. In effect they are identical except for how they handle ties. In the asymmetric measures (d_{yx} and $d_{y.x}$) Somers adjusts the difference between concordance and discordance probabilities on the basis of independent variable ties while Kim adjusts using the dependent variable. Kim's symmetric measure (d) simply averages the two adjusting factors; hence, as illustrated in Table 12, the value of d must lie half-way between the two asymmetric measures.

Once one has the condensed form, these measures are easy to compute. That appears to be their primary advantage over other ∇ measures for the condensed form. One ought to be willing, however, to sacrifice computational facility if alternative error weights are more attuned to research purposes.

Sensitivity Analysis of the Condensed Ordinal Form

When one's research hypothesis is simply "The more X, the more Y," there is in fact no compelling reason to choose one of the three d measures. It is clear that concordant pairs and pairs simultaneously tied on both variables do not represent errors for this prediction. In contrast, discordant pairs are the most serious form of error and ought to receive the maximum error weight, $\omega_D = 1$. Pairs tied on only one variable are less serious errors. The two weights ω_{TYX} and ω_{TYX} ought not to exceed ω_D, but their relative weights are not indicated by the hypothesis. Which numerical values will be given to ω_{TYX} and ω_{TYX} are left to the investigator's judgment.

In summary, for evaluating "The more X, the more Y" in the full condensed form, the partial order of error weights is identical to that found for the analysis of kappa in 3x3 tables of single observations, as illustrated in Figure 2.

Performing the sensitivity analysis for the data in Table 3, first compute the ∇ and U statistics for the component predictions:

$$\nabla_D = .786 \qquad U_D = .214$$

$$\nabla_{TYX} = .344 \qquad U_{TYX} = .229$$

$$\nabla_{TYX} = .351 \qquad U_{TYX} = .224$$

To find the maximum possible value of ∇ consistent with the partial order of weights, note that ∇_D, which must have the highest error weight, is the largest of the three ∇'s. Therefore, max $\nabla = .786$. In this case, as in the earlier

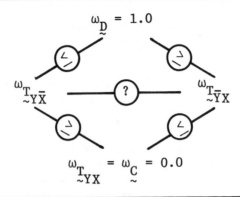

Figure 2: Partial Order of Error Weights for Condensed Ordinal Form

case concerning kappa, both of the other components must receive an error weight of 1.0 in computing

$$\min \nabla = \frac{1}{.214 + .229 + .224} \times [(.214)(.786)$$

$$+ (.229)(.344) + (.224)(.351)] = .488$$

Therefore

$$.786 \geqslant \nabla \geqslant .488$$

for all sets of error weights consistent with the research hypothesis. Reporting a range of values like the above appears to be preferable to any arbitrary selection of a single measure.

Restricting the Domain of the Prediction by Excluding All Ties

The Somers and Kim measures presented above recognize the typical prevalence of ties in ordinal data and allow for their occurrence within the prediction domain. Goodman and Kruskal (1954) adopt the extreme solution to the problem of ties: they exclude all tied pairs from the prediction domain. To discard all ties, simply form a new condensed form table with the middle (*same*) row and column deleted. The probability of not having a tie is $P(\overline{T}) = P(\underset{\sim}{C}) + P(\underset{\sim}{D})$. If the probabilities in the new domain are to sum to 1.0, all the relevant old probabilities have to be divided by $P(\overline{T})$. The result is shown in Table 14. The 50-50 marginals are another consequence of radial symmetry. Consider the prediction $\mathcal{H}$: *more* ←⋏→ *more*. Again, the radial symmetry im-

TABLE 14
The Condensed Form When the Domain Excludes Ties

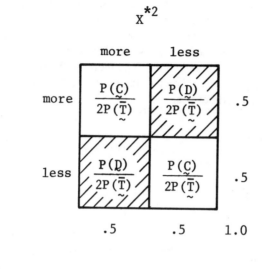

$$P(\bar{\underset{\sim}{T}}) = P(\underset{\sim}{C}) + P(\underset{\sim}{D})$$

Note: Shaded cells indicate errors for prediction underlying gamma, excluding all ties: more ←∿→ more.

plies that equal weights should be given to the errors (*more-less* and *less-more*). Applying the $\nabla_\wp$ model for this prediction,

$$\nabla_{\underset{\sim}{y}} = 1 - \frac{\frac{1}{2}P(\underset{\sim}{D})/P(\bar{\underset{\sim}{T}}) + \frac{1}{2}P(\underset{\sim}{D})/P(\bar{\underset{\sim}{T}})}{(1/2)(1/2) + (1/2)(1/2)}$$

$$= \frac{P(\underset{\sim}{C}) - P(\underset{\sim}{D})}{P(\bar{\underset{\sim}{T}})} = \frac{P(\underset{\sim}{C}) - P(\underset{\sim}{D})}{P(\underset{\sim}{C}) + P(\underset{\sim}{D})} = \text{gamma}$$

where gamma is a well-known measure of ordinal association developed by Goodman and Kruskal (1954). Thus gamma is a ∇ measure for the *more ←∿→ more* prediction after all tied pairs have been discarded. The $\nabla_\wp$ measure for the opposite prediction for this domain, *more ←∿→ less*, equals the negative of gamma. Recognizing the symmetry in the 2×2 cross classification of Table 14, these are the only two predictions of interest for this narrowly restricted domain. Moreover, the symmetry also implies that all error events should have the same weight in this case, so there is no need for sensitivity analysis.

For the data of Table 3, gamma = .819. This is one instance of a universally true fact that can be proved simply by comparing the expressions for gamma and the d measures: gamma must always have a larger numerical value than any of the d measures. By treating much of the data (ties) as irrelevant, gamma achieves large and perhaps misleading measures of error reduction. For this reason, even though it appeared earlier in the literature and, as a consequence, has been used more widely than any of the d measures, gamma seems inadequate for evaluating "The more X, the more Y." A particularly striking example is the following simple 2x2 table and its condensed ordinal forms with and without ties:

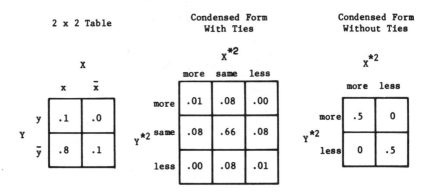

Clearly Y does not really increase strongly with X. When x occurs, 8/9 of the observations are still $\bar{y}$. Yet, for this table, gamma = 1.0. In contrast, all three d measures equal .111. For a 2x2 table, perhaps the most natural way to test "The more X, the more Y" and similar statements is to use the prediction $x \leftarrow\!\!\wedge\!\!\rightarrow y$ for single observations with equally weighted errors. Then

$$\nabla_{x \leftarrow\!\wedge\!\rightarrow y} = 1 - \frac{.8 + .0}{(.9)(.9) + (.1)(.1)} = .024$$

This value contrasts sharply with the "strong" positive association gamma "captures" after it excludes fully 98% of the observation pairs.

Restricting the Domain by Eliminating Ties on One Variable

We have criticized gamma for evaluating a prediction that is too imprecise because it applies only to a possibly small subset of the data for the entire condensed form. We can substantiate this criticism further by comparing gamma and the asymmetric d measures in a common domain. Both gamma and the asymmetric measures can also be developed as ∇ measures when the domain excludes ties on only one variable. That is, once we specify the appropriate error weights for this domain, then the corresponding ∇ measure is equivalent mathematically to the ordinal measure. Our discussion covers only exclusion of ties on the independent variable although the parallel treatment of the dependent variable is shown in Table 15.

When independent variable (X) ties are excluded, as shown in Table 15, concordant pairs are again successes for "The more X, the more Y" and discordant pairs errors with weight 1.0. We can regard ties on the dependent variable as less severe errors, so that

$$1 = \omega_D \geqslant \omega_{\underset{\sim}{T}_{Y\bar{X}}} \geqslant \omega_C = 0$$

Let us first examine the component $\nabla_{\underset{\sim}{T}_{Y\bar{X}}}$ for the prediction *more* $\rightsquigarrow$ (*more* or *less*) & *less* $\rightsquigarrow$ (*more* or *less*). Since, in the restricted domain excluding all X-ties, this component's error cells fill an entire row, it is a totally *undifferentiated* prediction which cannot possibly take advantage of information on the independent variable state. The usual computation of ∇ in fact shows that $\nabla_{\underset{\sim}{T}_{Y\bar{X}}}$ always equals zero if it is defined.

As to the second component identifying only discordant pairs as errors,

$$\nabla_D = 1 - \frac{P(D)/P(\bar{T}_X)}{\frac{1}{2}[P(C) + P(D)]/P(\bar{T}_X)} = \frac{P(C) - P(D)}{P(C) + P(D)} = \text{gamma}$$

If the ties component is assigned an error weight of $1/2$ and the components combined, given $\omega_{T_{Y\bar{X}}} = 1/2$ and $\omega_D = 1$, then

$$\nabla = \frac{1}{\omega_D U_D + \omega_{\underset{\sim}{T}_{Y\bar{X}}} U_{\underset{\sim}{T}_{Y\bar{X}}}} [\omega_D U_D \nabla_D + \omega_{\underset{\sim}{T}_{Y\bar{X}}} U_{\underset{\sim}{T}_{Y\bar{X}}} \nabla_{\underset{\sim}{T}_{Y\bar{X}}}]$$

$$= \frac{1}{\frac{\frac{1}{2}[P(C) + P(D)] + \frac{1}{2}P(T_{Y\bar{X}})}{P(\bar{T}_X)}} \left[\left[\frac{\frac{1}{2}[P(C) + P(D)]}{P(\bar{T}_X)} \right] \left[\frac{P(C) - P(D)}{P(C) + P(D)} \right] + 0 \right]$$

$$= \frac{P(C) - P(D)}{P(C) + P(D) + P(T_{Y\bar{X}})} = \frac{P(C) - P(D)}{P(\bar{T}_X)} = d_{yx}$$

Our development of d_{yx} in the above expression shows that the ties which gamma ignores do not affect the *sign* of overall ∇. The sign depends on $P(C)$ —

TABLE 15
Prediction Analysis When the Domain Excludes Ties on Only One Variable

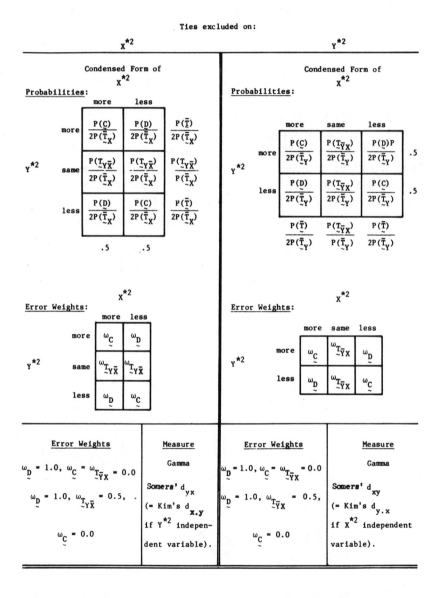

Ties excluded on:

X^{*2} — Y^{*2}

Error Weights (left, X^{*2}):

$\omega_D = 1.0, \ \omega_C = \omega_{T_{\tilde{Y}X}} = 0.0$

$\omega_D = 1.0, \ \omega_{T_{Y\tilde{X}}} = 0.5,$

$\omega_C = 0.0$

Measure:

Gamma

Somers' d_{yx}

(= Kim's $d_{x \cdot y}$ if Y^{*2} independent variable).

Error Weights (right, Y^{*2}):

$\omega_D = 1.0, \ \omega_C = \omega_{T_{\tilde{Y}X}} = 0.0$

$\omega_D = 1.0, \ \omega_{T_{\tilde{Y}X}} = 0.5,$

$\omega_C = 0.0$

Measure:

Gamma

Somers' d_{xy}

(= Kim's $d_{y \cdot x}$ if X^{*2} independent variable).

$P(\underline{D})$. Despite the fact that the ties component can never be successful, it does serve as an appropriate way of dampening the magnitude of gamma $(\nabla_{\underline{D}})$. For example, consider the following two tables for the restricted condensed form:

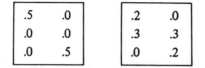

Clearly the left-hand table permits stronger prediction of relative order. Gamma, nonetheless, is 1.0 for both tables. Since there are no ties, d_{yx} also equals 1.0 in the first table. In contrast, discounting for the ties in the second table, we have $d_{yx} = 0.4$ there.

Again, if only ordinal specifications of the error weights can be justified, then we advocate sensitivity analysis rather than relying solely on either d_{yx} or gamma. Consider a sensitivity analysis of the condensed ordinal form omitting ties on the independent variable. The value of ∇ for "The *more* X, the *more* Y" in this domain is a weighted average of gamma $(\nabla_{\underline{D}})$ and $\nabla_{\underline{T} X \overline{Y}}$, and we have shown that the latter must be zero. Therefore, if gamma is positive, then it is the maximum possible value of ∇ for this proposition. Omitting ties on X from the data of Table 3, we have $\nabla_{\underline{D}} = .819$. Also, given $\nabla_{\underline{D}} > 0$, the minimum value of ∇ for the proposition occurs when $\omega_{\underline{T} Y \overline{X}} = 1$. Thus, omitting ties on X from the data of Table 3 yields $.434 \leqslant \nabla \leqslant .819$. If, instead, ties on the dependent variable are eliminated, then the corresponding bounds are $.520 \leqslant \nabla \leqslant .819$.

Eliminating a Cell Rather than a Row or Column from the Domain

Another approach to ties has been followed by Wilson (1974), who excludes pairs tied on *both* variables as irrelevant. Otherwise, as shown in Table 16, his prediction is the same as that for Kim's symmetric d, except the error weights for cells involving ties are 1/2 rather than 1/4. If we eliminate the center cell and renormalize the probabilities, we have the structure shown in Table 16.

Wilson's approach, as seen in the table, regards a single cell as irrelevant, rather than an entire row or column, as with gamma. Analyzing this type of prediction presents important conceptual and technical difficulties. We will skip these issues here, referring the reader to Hildebrand, Laing, and Rosenthal (1977, ch. 4). By applying the set-by-set procedure discussed there to Wilson's prediction for the error weights shown in Table 16, it can be shown that the resulting ∇ measure equals the measure proposed by Wilson and also by Deuchler (1914):

TABLE 16
Prediction With a Hole

Condensed Form With
(same, same)
Excluded from the Domain

X^{*2}

Error Matrix for
Wilson's e

X^{*2}

Y^{*2}	more	same	less	
more	$\dfrac{P(\underset{\sim}{C})}{2A}$	$\dfrac{P(T_{\sim\bar{Y}X})}{2A}$	$\dfrac{P(\underset{\sim}{D})}{2A}$	$\dfrac{P(\bar{T}_{\sim Y})}{2A}$
same	$\dfrac{P(T_{\sim Y\bar{X}})}{2A}$	irrele- vant cell	$\dfrac{P(T_{\sim Y\bar{X}})}{2A}$	$\dfrac{P(T_{\sim Y\bar{X}})}{A}$
less	$\dfrac{P(\underset{\sim}{D})}{2A}$	$\dfrac{P(T_{\sim\bar{Y}X})}{2A}$	$\dfrac{P(\underset{\sim}{C})}{2A}$	$\dfrac{P(\bar{T}_{\sim Y})}{2A}$
	$\dfrac{P(\bar{T}_{\sim X})}{2A}$	$\dfrac{P(T_{\sim\bar{Y}X})}{A}$	$\dfrac{P(\bar{T}_{\sim X})}{2A}$	1.0

Y^{*2}	more	same	less
more	0	1/2	1
same	1/2	irre- levant cell	1/2
less	1	1/2	0

Note: $A = 1 - P(T_{YX})$.

$$e = 1 - \frac{[P(\underset{\sim}{D}) + (1/2)\,P(T_{Y\bar{X}}) + (1/2)\,P(T_{\bar{Y}X})]\,/\,[1 - P(T_{YX})]}{1/2}$$

$$= \frac{P(\underset{\sim}{C}) - P(\underset{\sim}{D})}{1 - P(T_{YX})}$$

By looking at the denominator of the last expression for e, it can be seen that e is more conservative than either the d measure or, of course, gamma. For the data of Table 3, e = .517. The conservative behavior of e reflects the high error weight placed on pairs tied on one variable. The asymmetric d measures include only two of these cells as errors while Kim's symmetric measure weights the four such cells 1/4 rather than 1/2.

Comparing Predictions Across Domains

Within a given domain, we can evaluate predictions in terms of prediction success (∇) and precision (U). Recall that U simply equals the "expected" error rate, that is, the denominator of the ratio in the expression for ∇. If one prediction has higher values than another on both of these dimensions, then the first prediction is said to dominate the second. Very frequently, however, there is a trade-off between prediction success and precision. One may have to sacrifice precision to get a high ∇ value. The same remark can be applied to a given population even when predictions apply to different domains within that population. The only change is that we have to correct the precision measure to reflect the different population proportions included within the domain:

$$U^c = U \times \text{proportion of population in domain}$$

For example, when gamma is developed for the domain that excludes all ties, we found earlier that $U_{gamma} = (.5 \times .5) + (.5 \times .5) = .5$. Therefore $U^c_{gamma} = .5P(\overline{T})$.

We can apply U^c to compare some conventional measures of ordinal association. We have already seen that gamma is always greater than or equal to d_{yx} which in turn is always greater than or equal to e. There is a direct trade-off, however, in terms of precision since

$$U^c_{gamma} = .5P(\overline{T}) \leqslant U^c_{d_{yx}} = .5P(\overline{T}_X) \leqslant U^c_e = .5[1 - P(T_{YX})]$$

One can therefore either pick a measure for a relatively successful but imprecise prediction or vice versa. Since reporting prediction precision is almost always omitted, unfortunately, from the presentation of research results, researchers have had an incentive to use gamma.

Concordance and Discordance: Looking Backwards

As mentioned previously, the conventional condensed form measures can all be viewed as attempts to adjust the difference between the probability of concordant pairs and the probability of discordant pairs, $P(\underset{\sim}{C}) - P(\underset{\sim}{D})$. This quantity, Kruskal (1958) indicates, first began to appear in statistics around the turn of the century. It is commonly known as Kendall's (1962) tau. (Not to be confused with Kendall's τ_b, which we discuss in a later section.) The measure was originally thought of as being applied to populations without ties, excluding self-pairs from the prediction's domain. For the case of ties, Kruskal views gamma as the generalization of tau. Rather than changing the domain as for gamma, another approach is to maintain the full domain of the condensed form and seek a prediction whose ∇-value is $P(\underset{\sim}{C}) - P(\underset{\sim}{D})$. When $\omega_{\underset{\sim}{D}} = 1.0$, $\omega_{\underset{\sim}{T}\overline{Y}X} = \omega_{\underset{\sim}{T}Y\overline{X}} = \omega_{\underset{\sim}{T}YX} = 1/2$, $\omega_{\underset{\sim}{C}} = 0$, we find that

$$\nabla = tau = P(\underset{\sim}{C}) - P(\underset{\sim}{D}), \quad U_{tau} = .5$$

The underlying prediction does not seem appropriate to evaluate "The *more* X, the *more* Y" since it regards simultaneous ties as errors. In other contexts, it seems appropriate. For example, suppose, as in various questions asked by the Survey Research Center of the University of Michigan, two voters are asked to assign each of a dozen or so candidates to one of the 101 positions on a 0 to 100 "thermometer" scale as an indication of how "warm" they feel towards each candidate. If the a priori prediction were both (a) that neither voter assigns two or more candidates to the same scale position, and (b) that both voters rank the candidates identically (although perhaps using different scores), then tau is a reasonable measure. In any event, tau will always be the least "successful" but most precise of the $P(\underset{\sim}{C}) - P(\underset{\sim}{D})$ family. For the data in Table 3, tau = $2[(221/961) - (22/961)] = .414$.

One More Normalization: Kendall's τ_c

Another method of normalizing the basic term $P(\underset{\sim}{C}) - P(\underset{\sim}{D})$ is to multiply by the fraction $M/M-1$, where M is the minimum of R and C. This gives

$$\tau_c = \frac{M}{M-1} \; [P(\underset{\sim}{C}) - P(\underset{\sim}{D})]$$

The motivation for this correction is that $M-1/M$ is the maximum possible value (Kendall, 1962) for $P(\underset{\sim}{C}) - P(\underset{\sim}{D})$ in an $R \times C$ table. This normalization is a convenient way of bounding a "tau" statistic between -1 and $+1$, but the procedure appears ad hoc from the viewpoint of prediction analysis. We have not been able to interpret τ_c within the "del" framework applied to all the other measures considered in this paper.

Kendall's τ_b^2: Mixed Strategy Prediction for the Condensed Form and Analogies to Prediction for Quantitative Variables

Kendall's (1962) τ_b^2 is a measure intimately related to the $P(\underset{\sim}{C}) - P(\underset{\sim}{D})$ family, as is evident in the expression

$$\tau_b^2 = d_{yx}d_{xy} = \frac{[P(\underset{\sim}{C}) - P(\underset{\sim}{D})]^2}{P(\overline{T}_Y)P(\overline{T}_X)}$$

The Linear Model Analogy: The Somers-Hawkes (Somers, 1968, 1974; Hawkes, 1971) interpretation of this measure involves assigning quantitative scores to the categories of the condensed ordinal form. For both variables, the category *more* is scored as $+1$, *same* as 0, and *less* as -1. With knowledge of the independent variable, one makes the ex post linear prediction

$$Y^{*2} = d_{yx}X^{*2}$$

as shown in Figure 3. In other words, if (the condensed ordinal form of) X^{*2} is *more*, then $d_{yx}(+1) = d_{yx}$ is the predicted score; if *same*, then 0 is predicted; and if *less*, then $-d_{yx}$ is predicted. Thus, the measure d_{yx} can also be thought of as analogous to the slope of a linear regression equation. (On re-

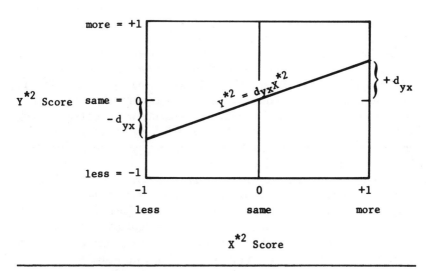

Figure 3: The Linear Model Analogy for the Condensed Form

gression, see the forthcoming paper by Uslaner in this series.) Without knowledge of the independent variable, one always predicts the average score value of the dependent variable, namely zero. Errors are assessed as the square of the difference between observed and predicted values. Thus, for example, if d_{yx} is predicted and *more* (+1) observed, the error is $(1 - d_{yx})^2$; if *same* is observed, $(0 - d_{yx})^2 = d_{yx}^2$; if *less*, $(-1 - d_{yx})^2 = (1 + d_{yx})^2$. Within this scoring, prediction, and error framework, one can now compute r^2, the coefficient of determination. (r^2 is the standard measure of prediction success for linear models of quantitative variables.) It can be shown (but not here) in this instance that $r^2 = \tau_b^2$. Because the +1, 0, −1 scoring system for the condensed form permits this analogy with the linear model, it has received significant attention as a method for analyzing ordinal variables. If the scoring system is accepted, then one can use the whole panopoly of techniques—such as multiple regression, simultaneous equations models, and causal models— that have been developed for quantitative variables.

Before yielding to such a temptation, the researcher should be aware of several limitations. The most fundamental concern relates to the basic analogy. In a linear model for quantitative variables, the assumption is that, if we could remove all the random effects on an observation, the observation's value would lie exactly on the regression line. In the condensed form context, this would mean that when X^{*2} equals *more*, removing the random effects would result in a Y^{*2} value of d_{yx}. But such a value is typically impossible since a pair is always scored +1, 0, or −1. Therefore, it is rather strained to claim a linear, additive relation can exist in the condensed form.

Other limitations relate to using a standard regression program for estimation with *sample* data. One assumption of ordinary least squares regression is that the prediction errors are independent. The radial symmetry property of the condensed form indicates that this assumption is not satisfied. Every time we predict "0" and observe "+1" for example, there must be another pair with a "−1" value. Similarly, another standard assumption is that the amount of variation about the regression line will be the same for all values of the independent variable. It can be shown that this does not hold in general. These limitations imply that standard regression programs will not make the most efficient use of the data. These efficiency limitations become less critical as the sample size grows larger, and can be overcome by a more complex technique known as generalized least squares.

Finally, many testing procedures for linear models assume that the errors have the familiar bell-shaped, unimodal (a bell has only one top), normal distribution. While the procedures are rather robust (one can safely use the tests) under distortions from normality, the distortions are likely to be severe in the case of the condensed form. One can construct condensed form populations where the errors have a bimodal distribution (squared errors of zero occur less frequently than squared errors of one). In addition, the errors are limited to three discrete values, whereas normality pertains to a continuous density.

Mixed Strategies: Mainly as a result of the substantive rather than the statistical limitations of the linear model analogy, we find it useful to relate τ_b^2 to the ∇ framework. To do this we need to extend the prediction framework to include probabilistic or *"mixed"* prediction strategies. (Hildebrand, Laing, and Rosenthal, 1977:ch. 4, contains a more general discussion of mixed strategies.)

To understand mixed strategies, reconsider the predictions underlying d_{yx}. They are *pure* strategy predictions: when the condensed ordinal form of X^{*2} equals *more, always* predict that Y^{*2} is *more,* and so on. Now consider what would happen if, on average, we used the predictions associated with Somers' d_{yx} half the time and those associated with Kim's $d_{y.x}$ half the time. We would have half the observed error rate for d_{yx} plus half the observed error rate for $d_{y.x}$:

$$(.5)[P(\underset{\sim}{D}) + .5P(T_{Y\bar{X}})] + (.5)[P(\underset{\sim}{D}) + .5P(T_{\bar{Y}X})]$$

$$= P(\underset{\sim}{D}) + .25P(T_{Y\bar{X}}) + .25P(T_{Y\bar{X}})$$

This turns out to be the observed error rate for Kim's symmetric d. Similarly, in using 50-50 randomizations of the predictions underlying d_{yx} and $d_{y.x}$ when they are applied without knowledge of the independent variable, we obtain an expected error rate that also equals that of Kim's symmetric d.

Working through this simple example of mixing predictions illustrates two general facts: (a) we can also evaluate the success of *mixed* strategies as $\nabla = 1 - $ "observed" error/"expected" error and (b) every mixed strategy corresponds to a pure strategy prediction with the same ∇ measure. In this case, the pure strategy ∇-equivalent is the prediction underlying symmetric d.

An alternative and equivalent way of mixing the two asymmetric d predictions is to mix them state-by-state:

If X^{*2} state is	Then with probability	Predict Y^{*2} state is	And Use Error Weights
more	.5	*more*	$\omega_{\underset{\sim}{D}} = 1.0, \omega_{T_{Y\bar{X}}} = .5, \omega_{\underset{\sim}{C}} = 0.0$
	.5	*more* or *same*	$\omega_{\underset{\sim}{D}} = 1.0, \omega_{T_{Y\bar{X}}} = \omega_{\underset{\sim}{C}} = 0.0$
same	.5	*more* or *same* or *less*	$\omega_{T_{Y\bar{X}}} = \omega_{T_{YX}} = 0.0$
	.5	*same*	$\omega_{T_{\bar{Y}X}} = .5, \omega_{T_{YX}} = 0.0$
less	.5	*less*	$\omega_{\underset{\sim}{D}} = 1.0, \omega_{T_{Y\bar{X}}} = .5, \omega_{\underset{\sim}{C}} = 0.0$
	.5	*less* or *same*	$\omega_{\underset{\sim}{D}} = 1.0, \omega_{T_{Y\bar{X}}} = \omega_{\underset{\sim}{C}} = 0.0$

State-by-state mixing is the most natural way of stating the predictions that have τ_b^2 as their ∇ measure. In this development we parallel Wilson's (1968) interpretation of τ_b^2. The basic strategy of the τ_b^2 prediction rule is, given an observation pair's condensed ordinal form X^{*2} state, to predict the various Y^{*2} states with the conditional probability in the population in condensed ordinal form: for example, given $X^{*2} = $ *more*, predict $Y^{*2} = $ *more* with the conditional probability observed for this state. From Table 13, the probability that $X^{*2} = $ *more* and $Y^{*2} = $ *more* is $(1/2)P(\underset{\sim}{C})$ while the marginal probability of $X^{*2} = $ *more* is $(1/2)P(\bar{T}_X)$. Therefore, the appropriate conditional probability is $[(1/2)P(\underset{\sim}{C})] / [(1/2)P(\bar{T}_X)] = P(\underset{\sim}{C})/P(\bar{T}_X)$. The other prediction probabilities are similarly computed by dividing Table 13 cell entries by the appropriate column marginals. In evaluating the predictions use the following error weights:

If prediction for pair is that Y^{*2} equals:	then use the following error weights when the pair's observed Y^{*2} state equals:		
	more	*same*	*less*
more	0	1/4	1
same	1/4	0	1/4
less	1	1/4	0

Note that, like the linear model analogy, error weights chosen here are proportional to squared distance in terms of the $+1, 0, -1$ coding. For example, if *more* is predicted, but *less* is observed, the error weight is always $1 = (1/4)[1-(-1)]^2$ whereas when *more* is predicted but *same* observed, the error weight is always $1/4 = 1/4(1-0)^2$. Also like the linear model analogy, the predictions are determined ex post, reflecting the probabilities observed in the population. Unlike the linear model analogy, however, we always predict a state of the dependent variable that corresponds to one of the possible observed states.

How can we assess error rates for this prediction? Note that the state (*more, more*) occurs with probability $P(\underline{C})/2$. On average, following the mixed strategy given above, this event is assigned an error weight of zero for a fraction $P(\underline{C})/P(\overline{T}_X)$ of the times this state is observed; for a fraction $P(T_{Y\overline{X}})/P(\overline{T}_X)$, the weight is $1/4$; and for a fraction $P(\underline{D})/P(\overline{T}_X)$, the weight is 1.0.

On average, then, the (*more, more*) state is expected to contribute

$$\frac{P(\underline{C})}{2} \left[\frac{(1/4)\,P(T_{Y\overline{X}}) + P(\underline{D})}{P(\overline{T}_X)} \right]$$

to the "observed" error rate. Similarly, by multiplying the appropriate marginal probabilities in Table 13, we find the contribution to the "expected" error rate is

$$\frac{P(\overline{T}_X)\,P(\overline{T}_Y)}{4} \left[\frac{(1/4)\,P(T_{Y\overline{X}}) + P(\underline{D})}{P(\overline{T}_X)} \right]$$

Following analogous procedures, we can also compute the error rate contributions of the other states, make the appropriate summations, and find the ∇ measure, once again, as $1 - $ "observed" error/"expected" error. Some simplifying algebra then shows that $\nabla = \tau_b^2$. Thus, τ_b^2 is a ∇-measure for the ex post proposition that predicts each state of Y^{*2} in condensed ordinal form with its conditional probability as observed in the population.

Pure Strategy Equivalents: The bracketed term in the error rate contribution for the event (*more, more*) may be interpreted as an error weight for a ∇-equivalent pure strategy prediction. The set of all such error weights is shown in Table 17(a). This underlying pure strategy prediction treats *every* event as an error, but assigns various error weights as determined by the population data.

Having developed a ∇ interpretation of τ_b^2 and knowing that τ_b^2 can also be interpreted as an r^2 statistic suggests another finding, namely, that r^2 for quantitative variables can also be given a ∇ interpretation. We need not enter into that interpretation here. The important point is that the general use of ∇

TABLE 17
Error Weights for the Pure Strategy Prediction Having $\nabla = \tau_b^2$

		X^{*2}		
		more	same	less
Y^{*2}	more	$\dfrac{P(D) + \frac{1}{2}P(T_{Y\bar{X}})}{P(T_{\sim X})}$	$\dfrac{\frac{1}{2}P(T_{\bar{Y}X}) + \frac{1}{2}P(T_{TX})}{P(T_{\sim X})}$	$\dfrac{P(C) + \frac{1}{2}P(T_{Y\bar{X}})}{P(T_{\sim X})}$
	same	$\dfrac{\frac{1}{2}P(\bar{T})}{P(T_{\sim X})}$	$\dfrac{\frac{1}{2}P(T_{\bar{Y}X})}{P(T_{\sim X})}$	$\dfrac{\frac{1}{2}P(\bar{T})}{P(T_{\sim X})}$
	less	$\dfrac{P(C) + \frac{1}{2}P(T_{Y\bar{X}})}{P(T_{\sim X})}$	$\dfrac{\frac{1}{2}P(T_{\bar{Y}X}) + \frac{1}{2}P(T_{YX})}{P(T_{\sim X})}$	$\dfrac{P(D) + \frac{1}{2}P(T_{Y\bar{X}})}{P(T_{\sim X})}$

measures with ordinal variables presents striking similarities with the standard analysis of quantitative variables.

On to Triples: Spearman's rho_S

Spearman's rho_S is another measure of ordinal association; its relation to the linear model is better known than that of τ_b^2. To illustrate, in both 1975 and 1976 the final standings of the four teams in the Central Division of the National Football League were perfectly ranked—no ties. In 1975, the ranking was (1) Pittsburgh, (2) Cincinnati, (3) Houston, (4) Cleveland. In 1976 (1) Pittsburgh, (2) Cincinnati, (3) Cleveland, (4) Houston. If we were to treat these ranks as quantitative values, then we could compute the ordinary (Pearson) correlation coefficient between the two sets of ranks. In the special case of ranks, this is known as Spearman's (sample) rank correlation coefficient, and the computational procedure becomes very simple:

(1) For each observation, square the difference in ranks on the two variables.

(2) Sum these squares. Call the result SSQ. For the football example,

$$(1-1)^2 + (2-2)^2 + (3-4)^2 + (4-3)^2 = 2 = \text{SSQ}$$

(3) Then, define the rank correlation

$$1 - \frac{6(\text{SSQ})}{N(N^2 - 1)}$$

where N is the sample (or population) size.

In the example, rank correlation $= 1 - 6(2)/4(4^2 - 1) = .800$. Continuing to treat the ranks as quantitative information and evaluating prediction error as squared error, the proportionate-reduction-in-error measure analogous to r^2 is the square of this number, or .640. Spearman's rho_S is the population analog of the rank correlation.

Spearman's measure was and perhaps still is used frequently in applied research because, we suspect, it can be readily computed and because it might be interpreted as an analog to quantitative correlation. The interpretive advantage is negated by the disadvantage of making the strong and generally unwarranted assumption that all adjacent categories are separated by equal intervals. The computational advantage has disappeared with the advent of computers and pocket calculators.

Spearman's measure, as suggested by Kruskal (1958), can nonetheless be motivated without recourse to an arbitrary assignment of quantitative values. In the Kruskal approach, rho_S itself, not the square, has a proportionate-reduction-in-error interpretation. Instead of dealing with pairs, one has to deal with triples of observations. As was the case with our initial interpretation of Kendall's tau, consider an infinite, strictly ordered population. Alternatively, permit ties but restrict the domain of the prediction to the subset of triples containing no ties. On a given variable, then, we have only six possible states: $I > II > III$ (which is a shorthand way of saying that the first observation has a greater value—higher rank—than the second, and the second is higher than the third), $I > III > II, II > I > III, II > III > I, III > I > II, III > II > I$. By symmetry, each of these six states has marginal probability $1/6$. A 6×6 table could be needed to represent the relevant cross-tabulation of triples compared on two variables.

Having established the domain of analysis, we turn to the prediction. For the first independent variable state, $I > II > III$, predict that the dependent variable state of the triple $\{I > II > III, I > III > II$ belongs to $II > I > III\}$. For the other five independent variable states, make the analogous predictions by simply making the appropriate interchanges (permutations) of the symbols, I, II, and III. Then it can be shown that $\nabla = rho_S$.

There are several equivalent restatements of this prediction:

(a) At least one of the three members of the pair must be concordant with the other two;

(b) Either the highest of the three observations on the independent variable must also be highest on the dependent, or the lowest must also be lowest;

(c) The highest and lowest independent variable observations must be concordant while the middle observation must be concordant with at least one of the other two observations.

[Following publication of the original version of this monograph, Hildebrand, Laing, and Rosenthal (1985) found an alternative ∇ interpretation of rho$_S$. The prediction rule is "predicted Y-rank equals actual X-rank." The error weights are the squared errors for this prediction. The denominator in the expression for ∇ reduces to the expected squared error for predicting Y-ranks randomly. Given these choices, when there are no ties, then ∇-rho$_S$ (not its square).]

4. JOINT PREDICTION OF QUANTITATIVE, NOMINAL, AND ORDINAL VARIABLES

We now consider the analysis of predictions using a cross classification of a nominal variable with an ordinal variable, or of a quantitative variable with a qualitative variable.

Quantitative Variables

Many research applications involving ordinal variables include variables using other measurement levels as well. With quantitative variables, one can always elect to treat the variables as ordinal. For example, one can readily compute a condensed ordinal form for a quantitative variable. Positive monotonic transformations (such as multiplying every value by a positive constant or taking the logarithm) of a quantitative variable are order-preserving and, therefore, will not affect its condensed form. On the other hand, any prior decisions about how values are to be grouped into categories will affect the condensed form marginals by affecting the probability of ties. Cell entries for condensed form cross-tabulations also will be affected by decisions about categorization. Hence, all ∇ measures for the condensed form, including the standard measures, will depend on how the Y and X categories are defined— something that is true of ordinal as well as quantitative variables. (As an exercise, combine any two adjacent categories in Table 1 and recompute the condensed form measures.) In effect, choices of categories affect the prediction one is evaluating. Before adopting finer or coarser classifications, therefore, researchers ought to consider the prediction they wish to evaluate.

Nominal Variables and the Extensive Form

Quantitative variables can be analyzed jointly with ordinal variables simply by recognizing that any quantitative variable is also ordinal. But what about simple categorization or nominal variables? To return to the hypothetical population of 100 senators we used earlier, suppose these senators were categorized on region as Northern, Western, and Southern. These three categories have no apparent order. We can, of course, make predictions for single observations as shown earlier in Tables 1-2, 4-9, and 11. For example, the *hypothetical* cross tabulation of a roll call voting scale and region shown in Table 18(a) could be described by the prediction $n \rightsquigarrow$ (*hot, warm,* or *cool*),

TABLE 18
Predicting an Ordinal Variable With a Nominal Variable

(a) Predicting single observations

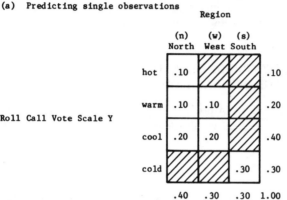

Region

	(n) North	(w) West	(s) South	
hot	.10			.10
warm	.10	.10		.20
cool	.20	.20		.40
cold			.30	.30
	.40	.30	.30	1.00 (N = 100 senators)

Roll Call Vote Scale Y

Shading indicates unweighted errors for the proposition:

n $\leadsto$ (hot, warm, or cool), w $\leadsto$ (warm or cool), and s $\leadsto$ cold.

(b) Predicting pairs

Region,[*2] Extensive Form

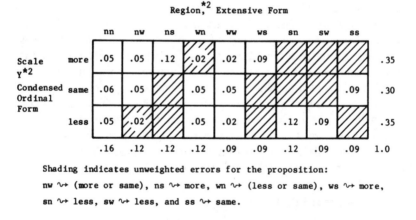

		nn	nw	ns	wn	ww	ws	sn	sw	ss	
Scale Y[*2]	more	.05	.05	.12	.02	.02	.09				.35
Condensed Ordinal Form	same	.06	.05		.05	.05				.09	.30
	less	.05	.02		.05	.02		.12	.09		.35
		.16	.12	.12	.12	.09	.09	.12	.09	.09	1.0

Shading indicates unweighted errors for the proposition:

nw $\leadsto$ (more or same), ns $\leadsto$ more, wn $\leadsto$ (less or same), ws $\leadsto$ more, sn $\leadsto$ less, sw $\leadsto$ less, and ss $\leadsto$ same.

Note: Cells containing no number define events having zero probability.

w $\leadsto$ (*warm* or *cool*), & s $\leadsto$ (*cold*). There are no errors, so $\nabla = 1.0$, while the precision is U = .450.

In order to deal with predictions for pairs, one useful approach is to create the condensed *nominal* form of the region variable by identifying the two states {*same, different*} and proceeding in ways analogous to the foregoing treatment of the condensed ordinal form. The condensed nominal form could be analyzed for the success of a particular prediction using ∇_ρ.

For some research contexts, however, the condensed form destroys essential information. We can preserve this information in the context of prediction of pairs by creating the *extensive* form of a variable. The extensive form of the variable consists of all pairs of variable categories. In the example, the extensive form of the region variable is defined as the $C^2 = 3^2 = 9$ pairs of categories *nn, nw, ns, wn, ww, ws, sn, sw,* and *ss.* The marginal probability of any pair is simply the product of the marginals for the two categories entering the pair. For example, $P(ns) = P(sn) = P(n)P(s) = .4(.3) = .12.$

Analysts then might proceed to look at the relation between this *extensive form* of the region variable and the *condensed ordinal form* of the roll call scale. The relevant probabilities are shown in Table 18(b). For example, the probability of (*same, nn*) is found simply by summing up the squares of the cell probabilities in the *n* column of Table 18(a):

$$P(same, nn) = (.1)^2 + (.1)^2 + (.2)^2 + (.0)^2 = .06$$

Paralleling analysis of the condensed ordinal form, we can now use symmetry to obtain the other probabilities in the *nn* column in Table 18(b):

$$P(more, nn) = P(less, nn) = (1/2)[P(nn) - P(same, nn)]$$

$$= (1/2)(.16 - .06) = .05$$

Similarly, the probability (*same, nw*) is found by multiplying, row-by-row, the probabilities in column *n* and column *w* of Table 18(a) and summing:

$$P(same, nw) = (.1)(.0) + (.1)(.1) + (.2)(.2) + (.0)(.0) = .05$$

The probability of (*more, nw*) can be computed by taking each entry in column *n* and multiplying it by the sum of all entries in column *w* that have lower roll call scores, and then summing the resulting products:

$$P(more, nw) = .1(.1 + .2 + .0) + .1(.2 + .0) + 2(.0) = .05$$

To obtain the final entry in the *nw* column,

$$P(less, nw) = P(nw) - P(more, nw) - P(same, nw) = .02$$

Note that symmetry can now be used to obtain the entries of the *wn* column from the *nw* column.

Consider the prediction that both northern and western senators will have higher roll call scores than southerners, and that northerners will have scores at least as high as westerners. Moreover, within regions, southerners are expected to have identical scores whereas no prediction is made for pairs of northerners or pairs of western senators. This prediction, shown in Table 18(b), has a ∇ value of .905 and U = .420.

Now consider the alternative prediction with weighted errors shown in Table 19(a). We can clearly get an equivalent prediction and equal ∇ value by

TABLE 19

**The Equivalent Extensive Form Representation
of a Condensed Form Proposition**

(a) The extensive form representation

Region,[*2] Extensive Form

		nn	nw	ns	wn	ww	ws	sn	sw	ss
Roll Call Scale,[*2] Condensed Form	more				1			1	1	
	same		1/2	1/2	1/2		1/2	1/2	1/2	
	less		1	1			1			

(b) A condensed form representation

Region[*2]

		(nw,ns,ws) "more"	(nn,ww,ss) same	(wn,sn,sw) "less"
Roll Call Scale,[*2] Condensed Form	more			1
	same	1/2		1/2
	less	1		

Note: Both tables show error weights underlying Somers' d_{yx}.

combining columns with identical error weights. As shown in Table 19(b), let *"more"* be the combination of *nw, ns,* and *ws, same* combine *nn, ww,* and *ss,* and *"less"* combine *wn, sn,* and *sw.* From inspection of Table 19(b), we see that the combination reflects a scaling of the three categories in the order n, w, s and that the prediction of Table 19(a) is equivalent to that underlying Somers' d_{yx}, except, of course, that d_{yx} is defined for two ordinal variables. (The scaling, suggested by inspection of Table 18(a), may be relevant only to that cross-tabulation. On some other issue, the three nominal categories could well have a different order. Note further that the prediction of Table 18(b) cannot be represented in this condensed form.)

Treating the region as a set of ordered categories shows that we can represent ordinal as well as nominal variables in extensive form. While for some purposes, an extensive form analysis of two ordinal variables might be preferable to a condensed form analysis, this paper has emphasized the condensed form because of its prominence in the literature. In any event, *every condensed form prediction has an equivalent representation in extensive form.*

When the hypothetical data of Table 18(a) are analyzed with the categories of Table 19(b), the values of various measures are

	∇	U^c
gamma	.857	.280
d_{yx}	.727	.330
$d_{y.x}$	.686	.350
d	.706	.340
e	.600	.400

These results show that the prediction represented in Table 18(b), for which we found $\nabla = .905$ and $U = .420$, dominates the predictions underlying the conventional measures.

Another equivalence theorem states that *every prediction for single observations can be represented as an equivalent prediction for pairs in extensive form* (Hildebrand, Laing and Rosenthal, 1977: appendix 5.1). We can use this theorem with the ∇_ρ and U^c measures to conclude that the prediction represented in Table 18(b) is, in turn, dominated by the proposition which identifies the error events shaded in Table 18(a) since this latter proposition has both a larger ∇ (1.0 vs. .905) and U^c (.450 vs. .420).

Thus, to conclude this section, we find that the extensive form for pairs provides a framework for the comparative analysis of predictions involving different levels of measurement and relating either pairs or single observations.

5. MULTIVARIATE ANALYSIS

The limits of this paper permit only a brief glance at multivariate analysis. Whereas the basic methods for multivariate analysis of quantitative variables using linear models have been around for half a century, multivariate methods for ordinal variables are only beginning to be worked out. For one thing, multivariate methods for ordinal data should provide "partial" measures that assess the relation between two variables when the effects of one or more other variables are controlled. Only a few partial measures of ordinal association have been provided earlier in the literature. These are often inappropriate for many research problems. The multivariate methods should be designed to evaluate specific predictions.

In this section we suggest an approach to the evaluation of multivariate predictions with ordinal data. The methods described in this section can be used in general to design ∇ measures of overall and partial prediction success for evaluating multivariate predictions. Fortunately, the basic principles of the multivariate ∇ methods in general can be illustrated with a three-variable problem. These principles apply whether single observations or pairs are the focus of interest. In working out the details of an example, we have chosen to look at pair prediction since pairs have occupied most of the literature on ordinal association. A general treatment of the ∇ methods for multivariate prediction analysis of qualitative variables is offered in Hildebrand, Laing, and Rosenthal (1977: ch. 7).

Let us return to the bureaucrat example, adding a third (hypothetical) variable. Let this be whether the bureaucrat believes corporate taxes should be *raised, unchanged,* or *lowered.* We are interested in using the previous variables—party affiliation and support for social services—to predict attitudes toward taxes. There are important causal problems: perhaps views on taxes also influence both party affiliation and support for social services. In this paper, however, we focus only on prediction, leaving interpretations based on beliefs about causation to the judgment of the investigator.

Setting Up the Trivariate Condensed Form

The easiest way to handle a multivariate problem is to transform it into an equivalent bivariate problem. To do this, consider the 5 x 3 = 15 ways of pairing each of the first independent variable (social services) states with a state of the other independent variable (affiliation). The categories of this composite independent variable are (*left,Dem*), (*left,Ind*), (*left,Rep*), (*left-center,Dem*), (*left-center,Ind*), . . . , (*right,Rep*). The joint distribution of 31 bureaucrats on these 15 categories with the three categories of the dependent variable is shown in the 3 x 15 arrangement of Table 20(a). While the joint distribution is hypothetical, note that the marginals of the composite independent variable are just the cell entries from Table 1.

Similarly, the *condensed ordinal forms* of the two independent variables can be combined into a composite variable with the nine states (*more,more*), (*more,same*), (*more,less*), (*same,more*), . . . , (*less,less*). The joint distribution of the 961 pairs of bureaucrats on these nine categories and the three condensed form categories of the dependent variable is shown in Table 20(b). The marginal numbers of cases on the composite independent variable are equal to the cell entries of Table 3.

The cell entries in Table 20(b) can be computed from those in Table 20(a) in a manner similar to those used to compute Tables 3 and 18(b). For example, the number of pairs that are the *same* on *all three* variables is found by

TABLE 20
Three-Way Tabulation of Corporate Tax Attitudes versus Party Affiliation and Social Services Support

(a) Single observations

Corporate Tax \ Social Services → Affiliation	Left Dem	Left Ind	Left Rep	Left-center Dem	Left-center Ind	Left-center Rep	Center Dem	Center Ind	Center Rep	Right-center Dem	Right-center Ind	Right-center Rep	Right Dem	Right Ind	Right Rep	
Raised	12	2														14
Unchanged		1	1	1	2	1		3	3							12
Lowered						1			1		1	1			1	5
	12	3	1	1	2	2	0	3	4	0	1	1	0	0	1	31 bureaucrats

(b) Condensed ordinal form for observation pairs

Corporate Tax *2 \ Social Services *2 → Affiliation *2	more / more	more / same	more / less	same / more	same / same	same / less	less / more	less / same	less / less	
more	204	43	7	32	6		3	3		298
same	17	24	12	40	179	40	12	24	17	365
less		3	3		6	32	7	43	204	298
	221	70	22	72	191	72	22	70	221	961 pairs

Note: Blank cells contain zero cases.

squaring each cell entry in Table 20(a) and summing. This sum equals 179. Subtracting from 191, the marginal total of *same-same* cases on the composite independent variable, and (by symmetry) dividing by two, yields six pairs in both the (*more, same, same*) and (*less, same, same*) cells.

To find the number of pairs that are in the upper left-hand cell (*more, more, more*) begin by noting that the 12 (*raised, left, Dem*) bureaucrats exhibit the (*more, more, more*) relation with all bureaucrats who are neither *raised* nor *left* nor *Dem*. Inspection of the table shows there are $2 + 1 + 1 + 3 + 3 + 1 + 1 + 1 + 1 = 14$ such bureaucrats. Therefore, (*raised, left, Dem*) contributes $12 \times 14 = 168$ relevant pairs. Similarly, the two (*raised, left, Ind*) observations exhibit the desired relation with all observations that are *Rep* but neither *raised* nor *left*. There are $1 + 1 + 3 + 1 + 1 + 1 = 8$ such observations, so (*raised, left, Ind*) contributes $2 \times 8 = 16$ relevant pairs. Continuing in this way to process all cells of Table 20(a), we find that the single (*unchanged, left, Ind*) bureaucrat is (*more, more, more*) with all bureaucrats who are *lowered* and *Rep* but not *left*. The $1 + 1 + 1 + 1 = 4$ such bureaucrats lead to a contribution of four pairs. The other non-zero contributions are $1 + 1 + 1 + 1 = 4$ for (*unchanged, left-center, Dem*), $2 \times (1 + 1 + 1) = 6$ for (*unchanged, left-center, Ind*), and $3 \times (1 + 1) = 6$ for (*unchanged, center, Ind*). Finally, summing all contributions shows $168 + 16 + 4 + 4 + 6 + 6 = 204$ (*more, more, more*) pairs. Analogous computations and the use of symmetry considerations allow all the entries in the Table 20(b) to be computed from those in Table 20(a).

Trivariate Representation of Bivariate Predictions: As a prelude to multivariate analysis, note first that any bivariate prediction for the condensed form can be represented in terms of Table 20(b). Consider the bivariate proposition $\mathcal{Q}$ which contains the d_{yx} predictions of each bureaucrat's attitude toward corporate tax on the basis of his party *affiliation*. Table 21(a) shows the correct set of error weights for d_{yx}. The error weights for *more* on affiliation, for example, appear in *every column* that is *more* on affiliation. Table 21(b) shows the error weights for the proposition $\mathcal{J}$, representing the d_{yx} predictions of corporate tax attitudes from support for social services. We could compute the d_{yx} measures directly from Table 20(b). It is easier, especially since we have the short-hand formula $[P(\underset{\sim}{C}) - P(\underset{\sim}{D})]/P(\overline{T}_X)$ for d_{yx}, to collapse Table 20(b) into Tables 22(a) and (b). Applying this formula and recalling that $U_{d_{yx}} = \frac{1}{2}P(\overline{T}_X)$ yields

$$\nabla_{\mathcal{Q}} = d_{yx} = [478/961 - 14/961]/[630/961] = .737, \quad U_{\mathcal{Q}} = .328$$

$$\nabla_{\mathcal{J}} = d_{yx} = [508/961 - 12/961]/[626/961] = .792, \quad U_{\mathcal{J}} = .326$$

TABLE 21
The Trivariate Representation of a Bivariate Prediction

(a) Party affiliation predicting corporate tax attitudes

Social Services *2	more			same			less		
Affiliation *2	more	same	less	more	same	less	more	same	less
Corporate Tax Attitude *2 — more			1			1			1
Corporate Tax Attitude *2 — same	1/2		1/2	1/2		1/2	1/2		1/2
Corporate Tax Attitude *2 — less	1			1			1		

(b) Support for social services as predictor of corporate tax attitudes

Social Services *2	more			same			less		
Affiliation *2	more	same	less	more	same	less	more	same	less
Corporate Tax Attitude *2 — more							1	1	1
Corporate Tax Attitude *2 — same	1/2	1/2	1/2				1/2	1/2	1/2
Corporate Tax Attitude *2 — less	1	1	1						

Note: Error weights are those for predictions underlying Somers' d_{yx}.

Neither of these propositions dominates the other. One way to take both dimensions (precision and prediction success) into account is to compare the two propositions in terms of their reduction (not proportionate) in error:

$$\text{expected error rate} - \text{observed error rate} = U_\rho \nabla_\rho$$

In this case $U_\mathcal{J} \nabla_\mathcal{J} = .258 > U_A \nabla_A = .241$. Assume a researcher had in fact used $\mathcal{J}$ as the bivariate model and was interested in how the affiliation variable might be introduced into the prediction.

Introducing a Third Variable: The following asymmetric treatment of the variables is just one of many ways in which the third variable, affiliation,

TABLE 22
Bivariate Tabulations of Condensed Forms

(a)   Corporate tax attitude versus party affiliation

Party Affiliation^{*2}

		more	same	less	
	more	239	52	7	298
Corporate Tax^{*2}	same	69	227	69	365
	less	7	52	239	298
		315	331	315	961 pairs

(b)   Corporate tax versus social services attitudes

Social Services^{*2}

		more	same	less	
	more	254	38	6	298
Corporate Tax^{*2}	same	53	259	53	365
	less	6	38	254	298
		313	335	313	961 pairs

might affect the bivariate prediction. First, consider pairs that are tied (*same*) on social services. For these pairs, use the affiliation variable as a tiebreaker by imposing the $\mathcal{Q}$ predictions. Second, consider pairs that are concordant on the independent variables—the extreme columns of Table 20(b). Here one willing to treat ties as serious errors could make a strong prediction of concordance on the dependent variable and assign an error weight of one rather than the 1/2 shown in the cells in the *same* row and both the (*more,more*) and (*less, less*) columns. Otherwise, the social services prediction is maintained. The complete trivariate prediction is illustrated in Table 23.

TABLE 23
Set of Trivariate Error Weights After Modifying the
Bivariate Proposition

Social Services *2		more			same			less		
Affiliation *2		more	same	less	more	same	less	more	same	less
Corporate Tax *2	more						1	1	1	1
	same	1	1/2	1/2	1/2		1/2	1/2	1/2	1
	less	1	1	1	1					

Multiple ▽

The proportion of the total population that constitutes weighted observed errors for this trivariate prediction equals

$$\frac{2[17 + (.5)24 + (.5)12 + (.5)40 + 0 + 3 + 3 + 0]}{961} = \frac{122}{961} = .127$$

(The data are found in Table 20(b) and the error weights in Table 23. Errors from the left-hand side of Table 20(b) are entered in the sum, which then can be multiplied by 2 because of symmetry.)

The proportion of the pairs constituting weighted "expected" error is:

$$\frac{2\{365[221 + (.5)70 + (.5)22 + .5(72)] + 298[221 + 70 + 22 + 72]\}}{961^2}$$

$$= \frac{450,650}{923,521} = .488$$

Combining these results, we find

$$\text{multiple } \nabla = 1 - \frac{\text{trivariate prediction error observed}}{\text{trivariate prediction error expected}}$$

$$= 1 - \frac{.127}{.488} = .740$$

$$U = .488$$

Consequently, the trivariate prediction achieves a substantial increase in precision (.49 vs. .33) when compared to either bivariate proposition while its prediction success (∇) value is comparable to the bivariate measures (.74 vs. .72 for a and .79 for f). Accordingly, the trivariate proposition attains a reduction in error of $U\nabla = .361$, higher than either bivariate proposition.

Partial ∇

We next develop a measure for evaluating the contribution of one independent variable to the multivariate proposition's success when the effects of the other independent variable(s) are taken into account. In the example, we will define a partial del to measure that part of the trivariate proposition's success that can be attributed solely to the affiliation variable when the social services variable is held constant.

Let us create three subpopulations, so that all pairs within a subpopulation have the same state on the condensed ordinal form of the social services variable: *more, same,* or *less.* Within each of these subpopulations the social services variable is constant. One way to assess the partial contribution of the affiliation variable is to determine how well the trivariate proposition predicts in each of those three subpopulations.

Subpopulation Partial ∇'s: Recall that within the subpopulation of pairs that are tied (*same*) on social services, the trivariate prediction applies the d_{yx} predictions for affiliation. As a measure of the partial prediction success contributed by affiliation in the *same* social services subpopulation, compute d_{yx} for *only the 335 pairs in this subpopulation.* From Table 20(b), we have:

$$\textit{same} \text{ subpopulation partial } \nabla = d_{yx} = (64/335 - 0/335)/(144/335)$$

$$= .444$$

Thus, using affiliation as a tiebreaker for social services was only moderately successful. For future use, note that the weighted errors for the d_{yx} predictions in the social services[*2] = *same* subpoluation are:

"observed" $= 2[(.5)40 + 0] = 40$

"expected" $= [2(72)/335][(.5)259 + 38] = 72$

Thus, *same* subpopulation

$$\text{Partial } \nabla = 1 - \frac{\text{observed errors for the trivariate proposition,}}{\text{given the affiliation state in } \textit{same} \text{ subpopulation}}{\text{expected errors for the trivariate proposition,}}$$

Partial $\nabla = 1 - \dfrac{\text{observed errors for the trivariate proposition, given the affiliation state in } \textit{same} \text{ subpopulation}}{\text{expected errors for the trivariate proposition, given the } \textit{same} \text{ subpopulation but not the affiliation state}}$

Similarly, we can see how the trivariate prediction does within the 313 pairs of the subpopulation in which social services = *more* by computing ∇ for the trivariate proposition within this subpopulation. The weighted errors (refer to Table 23 for the weights) are

$$\text{"observed"} = [17 + (.5)24 + (.5)12 + 0 + 3 + 3] = 41$$

$$\text{"expected"} = \frac{53}{313} \times [221 + (.5)70 + (.5)22] + \frac{6}{313} \times$$

$$[221 + 70 + 22] = 51.21$$

so that the *more* subpopulation partial $\nabla = 1 - 41/51.21 = .199$. By symmetry, this is also the partial ∇ for the social services = *less* subpopulation.

Note that this partial has a low, but positive value. Comparing the error weights shown in Tables 21(b) and 23, we see that, in the *more* subpopulation, the trivariate prediction modifies S only by adding an additional .5 error weight to the cell in the *same* row and (*more,more*) column. The partial is low despite the fact that in this cell the component (partial) ∇ value is

$$1 - \frac{17/313}{(221/313)(53/313)} = .546$$

However, for the added weight, the subpopulation precision component is only $(.5)221 \times 53/313^2 = .060$. In contrast, the bivariate, undifferentiated predictions of S in this subpopulation have a subpopulation ∇ of zero but a precision of $6/313 + (.5)53/313 = .104$. The complete subpopulation ∇ (subpopulation partial) can be expressed as a weighted average of these two components:

$$\text{\textit{more} subpopulation partial } \nabla = \frac{1}{.060 + .104} [.060(.546) +$$

$$.104(0)] = .199$$

Thus, even though the trivariate prediction adds to the error weight of a cell with a moderately large ∇ value, the partial contribution to prediction success remains very modest because, over the entire subpopulation, the trivariate prediction is largely undifferentiated.

The Overall Partial ∇: Reviewing the results for the three subpopulations on social services, we can see that the primary contribution of the affiliation variable to the trivariate proposition's success is within the *same* subpopulation. Having the results for these three subpopulations is useful. It would also be helpful to have a single, partial measure for the contribution of affiliation to the trivariate prediction that takes all three subpopulations into account while controlling for the social services variable. To achieve this, we again take the standard approach: add up the observed errors for each subpopulation, add up the expected errors, and compute a ∇ measure. We have

$$\text{"observed"} = 41 + 40 + 41 = 122$$

$$\text{"expected"} = 51.21 + 72 + 51.21 = 174.4$$

partial ∇, controlling support for social services

$$= 1 - \frac{122}{174.4} = .301$$

$$= 1 - \frac{\text{trivariate prediction errors knowing condensed}}{\text{form states of both affiliation and social services}}$$
$$\overline{\text{trivariate prediction errors knowing condensed form}}$$
$$\text{state of social services only}$$

(As an exercise, continue to use the error weights shown in Table 23 but compute the partial controlling for affiliation.)

As before, we can express the overall partial as a weighted average of the subpopulation partials where the weights are precision measures. Note that the U^c value for the partial in the social services = *same* subpopulation is

$$U^c = (\text{precision of } same \text{ subpopulation partial}) \times (\text{proportion of}$$
$$\text{pairs for which social services} = same)$$

$$= (72/335)(335/961) = 72/961$$

Each of the other two components have $U^c = 51.21/961$. Then the overall partial ∇ is a weighted average of the three subpopulation partials, each weighted by its contribution to the overall expected error rate for the trivariate proposition. Thus, the partial ∇, controlling for social services

$$= \frac{1}{(51.21 + 72 + 51.21)/961} [(51.21/961)(.199) + (72/961)(.444)$$

$$+ (51.21/961)(.199)]$$

$$= .301$$

We emphasize that the subpopulation partials that can be averaged to form an overall partial are distinct from subpopulation component trivariate ∇ values that could be averaged to find multiple ∇. The observed errors are the same for both subpopulation quantities. But the expected errors for the subpopulation partial are based on marginal totals for the subpopulation only, whereas the expected errors for the components of the multiple del are based on the marginals for the whole population. For example, the "expected" errors for the social services = *more* component of the multiple would be

$$\frac{365}{961} \ [221 + (.5)70 + (.5)22] \ + \frac{298}{961} \ [221 + 70 + 22] = 198.47$$

rather than the 51.21 we found for the subpopulation partial.

The "expected" error rate used in the partial is the result of applying the trivariate theory with knowledge of the social services state but not the affiliation state. The "observed" errors are those that result when one has knowledge of both independent variables. Consequently, the partial assesses the proportionate-reduction-in-error when one applies the trivariate theory with knowledge of both variables rather than with knowledge of only one variable (social services in the example). In contrast, the multiple ∇ measures the proportionate-reduction-in-error when one predicts with knowledge of both as against predicting with knowledge of neither.

In classical multivariate analysis using a linear model there is the following result:

$$\frac{\text{errors of } trivariate \text{ prediction knowing BOTH independent variables}}{\text{errors of } trivariate \text{ prediction knowing NEITHER independent variable}}$$

$$= \left[\frac{\text{errors of } trivariate \text{ prediction knowing BOTH independent variables}}{\text{errors of } trivariate \text{ prediction knowing just ONE (social services) independent variable}} \right]$$

$$\times \left[\frac{\text{errors of } bivariate \text{ prediction } S \text{ knowing the independent variable (social services)}}{\text{errors of } bivariate \text{ prediction } S \text{ without knowing the independent variable (social services)}} \right]$$

In terms of the del measures, the analogous "accounting" expression would be

$$(1 - \text{multiple } \nabla) = (1 - \text{partial } \nabla) (1 - \text{bivariate } \nabla)$$

But, using the results from the example,

$$(1 - .740) = .260 \neq .145 = (1 - .301)(1 - .792)$$

The classical result for linear models provides a direct and convenient basis for error accounting. The result requires not only the assumption of squared error but also the assumption that variables enter a model by being added on. For example, when the bivariate prediction is, say, $Y = 1.5X$, the trivariate prediction must be something like $Y = .8X + .9Z$, the Z term being added to the prediction equation. In such cases, the classical result leads to the well-known partial measure. On the other hand, although non-additive equations such as $Y = XZ$ frequently appear in research, no one computes a partial measure for the contribution of Z in such cases—although the prediction analysis approach could be used for this purpose.

When the "accounting" equation fails to hold, as in our example, one has to take prediction "shifts" into account. These shifts relate to the changing form of the prediction when one goes from a bivariate to a trivariate prediction as against the additional information value of the variables summarized in the partial (see Hildebrand, Laing, and Rosenthal, 1977: ch. 7). Much useful analysis can be done using just multiple and partial dels, although complete mastery of multivariate analysis requires understanding of the shifts.

Davis' Partial gamma: We now relate the foregoing discussion to a special case which has been prominent in the literature. Consider the subpopulation shown in Table 24, where ties on the dependent variable have been deleted. As shown in an earlier section, we can interpret the bivariate gamma between social services and corporate tax as being based on the prediction identifying the horizontally shaded cells as error events. This gamma can be readily computed from Table 22 (b) as

$$\text{gamma} = (508 - 12)/(508 + 12) = .954$$

Davis' (1967) partial gamma is simply the bivariate gamma measure on the relation between two variables as applied only to the subpopulation of pairs that are tied (*same*) on the control variable. Thus, in the example, Davis'

TABLE 24
Trivariate Gamma Analysis

	Social Services *2	more			same			less			
	Affiliation *2	more	same	less	more	same	less	more	same	less	
Corporate Tax *2 — more		204	43	7	32	6		3	3		298
Corporate Tax *2 — less			3	3		6	32	7	43	204	298
		204	46	10	32	12	32	10	46	204	596 pairs

Horizontally-shaded cells are error events underlying bivariate gamma for Social Services and Corporate Tax Attitudes.

Vertically-shaded cells are error events for Davis' partial gamma.

All shaded cells are error events for "trivariate gamma."

partial gamma equals the simple gamma in the social services = *same* sub-population:

$$\text{Davis' partial gamma} = (64 - 0)/(64 + 0) = 1.000$$

This is fine as a subpopulation partial, but consider the precision of the prediction

$$U^c = .5(64/961) = .033$$

The numerical value is not only small in this example; it will always tend to be small because of the exclusion of ties and because the scope of the prediction extends to only one of the three subpopulations on social services.[3] If a single number is to be used as *the* "partial gamma," we think it ought to be an overall partial. What appears to be the natural trivariate prediction within the gamma framework is to retain the bivariate gamma predictions within the *more* and *less* subpopulations and to use the Davis tiebreaker prediction in the *same* subpopulation. In this case, the *more* and *less* subpopulation partials always will be zero. Affiliation does not differentiate predictions in these subpopulations and cannot contribute to error reduction there.

The resulting composite prediction identifies all shaded cells in Table 24 as error events. For multiple ∇,

$$\text{"observed errors"} = 2(3 + 3 + 0) = 12$$

$$\text{"expected errors"} = 2\left(\frac{298}{596}\right)(260 + 3) = 292$$

$$\text{multiple } \nabla = 1 - 12/292 = .959, \ U^c = .304$$

For partial ∇, controlling for social services, we have,

$$\text{"observed errors"} = 2(3 + 3 + 0) = 12$$

$$\text{"expected errors"} = 2(6) + 2(32/76)(38) = 44$$

$$\text{partial } \nabla = 1 - 12/44 = .727, \ U^c = .046$$

The Davis predictions make no error in the social services = *same* subpopulation, but there are still some errors left in the other subpopulations, reducing partial ∇ to .727 for the entire domain of the trivariate prediction.

Somers (1964, 1968, 1970, 1974) has developed various partial measures in the τ_b^2 and d_{yx} framework. (Again, as was shown earlier for the bivariate case, there is an analogy to the linear model; our earlier criticisms of this analogy obviously extend to multivariate analysis.) Like the Davis partial, Somers' work can be explicated via ∇, but the technical developments run beyond the scope of this paper. In any event, we suggest that researchers develop directly the particular bivariate and trivariate condensed form error weights that are appropriate to their research problems. This custom-designing strategy is better than searching the literature in the hope of finding a traditional measure that is appropriate.

6. COMPUTING AND STATISTICAL INFERENCE

The examples considered in the last section have been used to illustrate the basic mechanics of multivariate prediction analysis of ordinal variables. This discussion, like the bivariate treatment, always referred to populations. In research, the data almost always are a sample from a larger population. In the most common case, namely simple random sampling, the natural way to get a single number that is an *estimate* of the true population value of any ∇ is simply to compute the sample analog. Just plug in the number of sample cases or pairs where we used, for example, the population number of bureaucrats or pairs of bureaucrats. Alternatively, use sample proportions in place of population probabilities. (Computation is relatively simple, especially when the prediction is for single observations.) Sum the weighted observed errors. Compute the products needed to get the weighted "expected" errors and sum those. Divide the "observed" by the "expected" error rate, and subtract from one. Each of the calculations in this paper was done in a few minutes with a pocket calculator.

Computer Programs

Many of the standard measures for ordinal variables can be calculated using "canned" computer programs. For example, the SPSS program can be used to cross-classify qualitative data and to compute values of such bivariate measures as gamma, Kendall's τ_b^2, and the Somers' measures. Two free-standing programs in FORTRAN IV are available from the authors for computing ∇_ρ and various associated test statistics for (1) bivariate and (2) multivariate prediction analysis of qualitative data. These programs require as input the cross-classified data of interest, and the specific prediction and set of error weights to be evaluated. In addition, a bivariate ∇_ρ program which can be added to the Control Data Corporation version of SPSS as a subroutine is now available.[4] Programs can be obtained from the authors at the University of Pennsylvania.

Statistical Inference

With a sample, though, an estimate of ∇ is not enough. One also wants to know something about the variability of that estimate. For example, one often wants to test the hypothesis that the true value of ∇ is greater than zero. Or one may want to compute a *confidence interval* that gives a range of values that can be expected to include the true value of ∇ in, say, about 95 of every 100 independent samples. An introduction to methods for statistical inference is covered in the paper by Henkel (1976) in this series. The specific methods of statistical inference for prediction analyses based on the various ∇_P measures are given in Hildebrand, Laing, and Rosenthal (1977: Ch. 6 and 7). Consequently, we will not get into inference in this introductory paper, except for two brief comments.

First, especially with a priori predictions, the conventional wisdom of having at least five cases in each cell of a cross-tabulation does not hold. With ∇ it is the set of *all* error cells as a *whole* that matters. As long as the marginals are not too badly skewed, one should not be deterred from the prediction analysis of large tables, even if the sample has only 25 to 100 cases. (The ∇_P programs described earlier automatically print out a warning when the sample is too small to rely on the test statistics for the prediction under consideration.)

Second, with appropriate specification of the error weights, the ∇ program will produce any of the conventional measures discussed in this paper and, therefore, will also produce test statistics and confidence intervals for these measures, something that frequently is not supplied by the conventional canned programs.

Conclusion

This paper has presented an overview of prediction analysis methods for ordinal variables. A great deal of the paper was devoted to developing and interpreting some standard measures of ordinal association. We did not cover everything. But we aimed at what is most widely used in social science.

Because most of these measures are based on the condensed form for ordinal comparisons of observation pairs, prediction for pairs received more attention here than prediction for single observations. The emphasis of this paper is intended to be useful in reading past analyses of social science data. Hopefully, readers of this paper who encounter gamma, tau, and d measures in the literature will understand what is being measured and thereby understand the strengths and limitations of the measures and their relevance to the substantive problems of the investigation.

Despite the emphasis of past literature on a series of special measures for observation pairs, we by no means advocate continuing this emphasis in future research. We believe instead that future research should focus more on the prediction of individual observations than on paired comparisons. Above all, we urge researchers to specify predictions and related error weights that are relevant to their research purposes rather than somewhat blindly selecting, say, gamma because it is "accepted" and known to a certain audience.

306

We have provided some guidance to researchers interested in simple verbal propositions of "the *more* X, the *more* Y" variety. A sensitivity analysis approach was offered as an alternative to selecting a fixed measure. The real challenge to researchers, however, is to move beyond the analysis of loosely specified verbal theory relating two or three variables to the analysis of more precisely specified scientific models. When the task of model building is accomplished, the researcher should then apply methods of data analysis that are designed to evaluate the model's specific predictions.

NOTES

1. The last line holds because the 50-50 splits imply $P_{y\bar{x}} = P_{\bar{y}x}$. (Prove as an exercise.)

2. Note that $P(T_{YX})$ contains (but is not restricted to) the probability of self-ties. In finite populations, this probability of a self-tie equals $1/N$. For some purposes, one may wish to exclude self-ties from analysis. In infinite populations the problem does not arise since the limiting value of $1/N$ is zero.

3. The situation gets even worse if, as Davis (1967) suggests, we attempt to control for several variables by looking only at cases that are tied on *all* the control variables.

4. For this we are grateful for the efforts of Deborah Lurie, Temple University, and Professor Richard Heiberger, University of Pennsylvania.

REFERENCES

ABERBACH, J. D. and B. A. ROCKMAN (1976) "Clashing beliefs within the executive branch: the Nixon bureaucracy." Amer. Pol. Sci. Rev. 70: 456-468.

BLALOCK, H. M., Jr. (1960) Social Statistics. New York: McGraw-Hill.

COHEN, J. (1968) "Weighted kappa: nominal scale agreement with provision for scaled disagreement or partial credit." Psych. Bull. 70: 213-220.

――― (1960) "A coefficient of agreement for nominal scales." Educational and Psychological Measurement 20: 37-46.

DAVIS, J. A. (1967) "A partial coefficient for Goodman and Kruskal's gamma." J. of Amer. Stat. Assn. 62: 184-193.

DEUCHLER, G. (1914) "Über die Methoden der Korrelationsrechnung in der Pädagogik und Psychologie." Zeitschrift für Pädagogische Psychologie und Experimentelle Pädagogik 15: 114-131, 145-159, 229-242. Cited by Goodman and Kruskal (1959).

GOODMAN, L. A. and W. H. KRUSKAL (1959) "Measures of association for cross-classifications, II: further discussions and references." J. of Amer. Stat. Assn. 54: 123-163.

――― (1954) "Measures of association for cross-classifications." J. of Amer. Stat. Assn. 49: 732-764.

HAWKES, R. K. (1971) "The multivariate analysis of ordinal measures." Amer. J. of Sociology 76: 908-926.

HENKEL, R. (1976) Tests of Significance. Sage University Papers on Quantitative Applications in the Social Sciences, 07-004. Beverly Hills and London: Sage Pub.

307

HILDEBRAND, D. K., J. D. LAING, and H. ROSENTHAL (1977) Prediction Analysis of Cross Classifications. New York: Wiley.
——— (1976) "Prediction analysis in political research." Amer. Pol. Sci. Rev. 70: 509-535.
——— (1975) "A prediction logic approach to causal models of qualitative variates," pp. 146-175 in D. R. Heise (ed.) Sociological Methodology (1975) San Francisco: Jossey-Bass.
——— (1974a) "Prediction logic: a method for empirical evaluation of formal theory." J. of Math. Sociology 3: 163-185.
——— (1974b) "Prediction logic and quasi-independence in empirical evaluation of formal theory." J. of Math. Sociology 3: 197-209.
KENDALL, M. G. (1962) Rank Correlation Methods (3rd ed.) London: Charles Griffin.
KIM, J. (1971) "Predictive measures of ordinal association." Amer. J. of Sociology 76: 891-907.
KRUSKAL, W. H. (1958) "Ordinal measures of association." J. of Amer. Stat. Assn. 53: 814-861.
NEWELL, A. and H. A. SIMON (1972) Human Problem Solving. Englewood Cliffs, N.J.: Prentice-Hall.
REYNOLDS, H. T. (1977) Analysis of Nominal Data. Sage University Papers on Quantitative Applications in the Social Sciences, 07-007. Beverly Hills and London: Sage Pub.
SOMERS, R. H. (1974) "Analysis of partial rank correlation measures based on the product-moment model: part one." Social Forces 53: 229-246.
——— (1970) "A partitioning of ordinal information in a three-way cross-classification." Multivariate Behavioral Research 5: 217-234.
——— (1968) "An approach to multivariate analysis of ordinal data." Amer. Sociological Rev. 33: 171-177.
——— (1964) "Simple measures of association for the triple dichotomy." J. of Royal Stat. Assn. 127: 409-415.
——— (1962) "A new asymmetric measure of association." Amer. Sociological Rev. 27: 799-811.
USLANER, E. (forthcoming) Regression Analysis. Sage University Papers on Quantitative Applications in the Social Sciences. Beverly Hills and London: Sage Pub.
WILSON, T. P. (1974) "Measures of association for bivariate ordinal hypotheses," pp. 327-342 in H. M. Blalock (ed.) Measurement in the Social Sciences. Chicago: Aldine-Atherton.
——— (1970) "Critique of ordinal variables." Social Forces 49: 432-444.
——— (1968) "A proportional-reduction in error interpretation for Kendall's tau-b." Social Forces 47: 340-342.

Additional Reference

HILDEBRAND, D. K., J. D. LAING, and H. ROSENTHAL (1985) "Prediction analysis of rank correlation." Political Methodology 11: 43-48.

MEASURES OF ASSOCIATION

PART V

ALBERT M. LIEBETRAU

1. INTRODUCTION

Much human endeavor is devoted to the discovery of important relationships, or *associations*. It is seldom enough to know only that some relationship exists, so research is usually undertaken to quantify the association. The ultimate goal may be to establish a cause-effect relationship, but quantification is often the first step toward achieving that goal.

This monograph focuses on measures of association between two attributes, or *variables*. Roughly speaking, two variables are associated if they are not independent. Two variables are said to be *independent* if changes in the value of one have no effect on the value of the other.

I begin by discussing some basic statistical ideas. Whatever the objective, an important first step is to identify an appropriate *population*. The population may be quite explicitly defined (the voting population of the United States, for example), or it may be more conceptual in nature (the target population of an advertising campaign to introduce a new soft drink). There are many situations in which members of a population can be quite difficult to identify (people with emotional characteristics that make them especially susceptible to hypertension).

Suppose that we can observe two variables for the members of some population. It is customary to denote the variables by capital letters, such as X and Y. An example is instructive: Consider all the high school seniors who have taken Scholastic Aptitude Tests (SATs) within the past year (the population), and let X and Y denote math and verbal scores, respectively. It is natural to ask how X and Y are related. As a second example, suppose we are interested in the relationship between education and income. For a population of individuals in the 40 to 60 age range, let X denote the number of years of formal education and let Y be current annual income.

It would be ideal if values of X and Y could be observed for each member of the population. This is seldom practical and often impossible; usually

309

one must settle for observations on some subset of the population. The subset selected is called a *sample*, and the method of selection is called a *sampling plan*. It is convenient to let $(X_1, Y_1), \ldots, (X_n, Y_n)$ denote the values of X and Y, called *observations*, for a sample of n members of the population.

A sample may be selected purely for convenience, but a more formal sampling plan is preferable. In this monograph, I will nearly always assume that sampling is random. A *random sample* is one in which each member of the population has the same chance of being selected in the sample as does any other member of the population.

Statisticians distinguish between *descriptive* and *inferential* methods. When all members of the population are sampled, then we know everything there is to know about X and Y, both individually and jointly, for that population. We need only to *describe* the results in some meaningful and concise way; hence, the term "descriptive statistics."

If the sample is a subset of the population, the sample values of (X, Y) are only one of many possible sets that might have been observed. Here one must use the sample values to *infer* properties of the entire population. Valid inferences depend on knowledge of the way in which observed values vary from sample to sample, that is, on the *sampling distribution* of the variables of interest. The sampling distribution, in turn, depends on both the sampling plan and the nature of the variables themselves. Strictly speaking, inferential methods apply only to data obtained by some systematic, well-defined sampling plan, such as random sampling. In particular, they are not applicable to data acquired by "convenience sampling."

Random variables are classified as continuous or discrete according to the set of possible values they can assume. Discrete variables are further classified as nominal, ordinal, or scalar. As might be expected, proper methods of statistical inference differ from class to class.

Variables that can at least theoretically assume all possible values in some interval are called *continuous* or *interval* variables. *Discrete* variables are those for which the set of all possible values is some discrete set of numbers. Since discrete variables often identify categories into which population members fall, they are also called *categorical* variables.

An example will prove helpful. If "family income" is recorded for a sample of families to the degree of accuracy required by the Internal Revenue Service, this variable can be regarded as continuous. For many purposes, it suffices to classify families into broad income categories. When income is expressed in thousands of dollars, one possible classification consists of the categories 0-5, 5-10, 10-25, 25-50, and 50+. On this scale, "family income" is a discrete, or categorical, variable.

The class of discrete variables is divided into three subclasses: scalar, ordinal, and nominal. *Nominal* variables are those whose values serve only to identify categories. Values of a nominal variable (i.e., category labels) have no meaningful quantitative relationship to each other. "Sex" is an example of a nominal variable. The two categories can be identified by "M" and "F," or by "1" and "2," or by one of infinitely many other possibilities. The assignment 1 = Male and 2 = Female is equally as valid as the reverse assignment. Since the pairing of category names is quite arbitrary, no meaning can be derived from the fact that one category label is greater than the other.

Often the categories, or levels, of a discrete variable are ordered. When category labels are chosen to identify this order, the resulting variable is called *ordinal*. Ordinal and nominal variables are distinguished by the fact that categories of an ordinal variable are meaningfully ordered, while those of a nominal variable are not.

If the five categories of "family income" defined above are labeled 1, 2, 3, 4, and 5, respectively, "family income" is ordinal. Incomes of families in category 1 are less than incomes of families in other categories, incomes of families in category 4 are greater than incomes of families in category 3 and less than those of families in category 5, and so on.

The following attitude scale is another example of an ordinal variable. Consider the statement: "The United States should increase efforts to develop nuclear energy," where the interviewee is allowed one of five possible responses: (1) strongly agree, (2) agree, (3) no opinion, (4) disagree, or (5) strongly disagree. These responses are clearly ordered.

Category labels of ordinal variables tell us the order of categories, but do not allow the categories to be compared *quantitatively*. An "A" student has scored higher than a "B" student, but we cannot say *how much* higher. Families in category 5 have greater incomes than do those in category 2, but we cannot say that families in category 5 have 2.5 times the income of families in category 2. Discrete variables whose values carry quantitative information (such variables are necessarily ordinal) are called *scalar*, or ratio, variables. "Family income" can be made into a scalar variable by the assignment of "average" or "typical" values to each income category. We could, for example, assign the values 2.5, 7.5, 17.5, 37.5, and 60, respectively, to the five income categories.

Of the three classes of discrete variables, nominal variables are least like continuous variables, and scalar variables are most like continuous variables. It can be difficult to correctly classify a variable, especially if it is created from another variable as in some of the above examples. Nevertheless, it is important that variables be correctly classified if we hope to choose the most informative possible measure of association.

Ordinal and scalar variables arise in two ways: (1) directly from discrete ordinal scales, and (2) indirectly from partitioning the range of some continuous variable into categories. The scale of attitudes concerning increased use of nuclear energy is inherently ordinal, and cannot be made into a scalar variable by reassigning category labels. When a continuous scale is categorized, information is lost—the smaller the number of categories, the greater the loss of information. For this reason, categorical data should be used with caution to make inferences about an underlying continuous variable.

2. SAMPLING DISTRIBUTIONS FOR DISCRETE DATA

Under suitable assumptions, the multinomial distribution is the correct model for random samples from discrete populations. Consequently, this distribution and a special case, the binomial distribution, are fundamental to any discussion of measures of association for discrete data.

The Binomial and Multinomial Distributions

Suppose the members of a population are partitioned into k categories $C_1, \ldots, C_k$ on the basis of some discrete random variable. Let $X_1, X_2, \ldots, X_k$ be the numbers of members in a random sample of size n that are observed to fall into categories $C_1, C_2, \ldots, C_k$, respectively. Provided the population is large enough relative to n, the multinomial distribution is the correct sampling model for $X_1, X_2, \ldots, X_k$.[1]

The sum of the X_is is necessarily equal to the sample size; that is,

$$\sum_{i=1}^{k} X_i = n \qquad .$$

Since one of the X_is can be determined from the others, it is sometimes convenient to work with a reduced set containing only k − 1 of the X_is.

The case in which k = 2 is not only simple, but also quite important. Suppose that a population is partitioned into two categories, C_1 and C_2. Let X_1 be the number of members in a sample of size n that fall into C_1 (for the reason cited above, $X_2 = n - X_1$ can be ignored). The variable X_1 is called a *binomial random variable,* or X_1 is said to have a *binomial distribution.* Further, if the proportion of the population in C_1 is denoted by p_1, then X_1 is said to have a binomial distribution with parameters n and p_1. The binomial distribution has been extensively tabulated, and a discussion of its properties can be found in any good elementary statistics text. Those that are important to this monograph are summarized below.

If X_1 is a binomial random variable with parameters n and p_1, X_1 has expected value (or mean) $E(X_1) = np_1$ and variance $V(X_1) = np_1(1 - p_1)$.

A version of the famous Central Limit Theorem asserts that for large n, the random variable

$$Z = \frac{X_1 - E(X_1)}{\sqrt{V(X_1)}} = \frac{X_1 - np_1}{\sqrt{np_1(1 - p_1)}}$$

has approximately the distribution of a standard normal random variable. This means that approximate percentage points of the binomial distribution can be computed from tables of the standard normal distribution, provided n is large enough. In practice, the farther p_1 is from 0.5, the larger the sample size must be for the approximation to be adequate. As a rule of thumb, it is probably safe to use the normal approximation if p_1 is between 0.2 and 0.8 and n_1 exceeds 30.[2]

When the proportion p_1 of population members falling into one of two categories is unknown, the population is sampled so that p_1 can be estimated. An obvious estimator is the proportion of members of the sample that fall into category C_1. In symbols, $\hat{p}_1 = X_1/n$, where "^" means "is an estimator of." In addition to being intuitively reasonable, p_1 also turns out to be a good estimator of p_1 on theoretical grounds.

Suppose now that the population is partitioned into more than two categories. If sampling is random and the population is large enough relative to sample size, the vector of random variables $(X_1, \ldots, X_k)$, or $(X_1, \ldots, X_{k-1})$, has a *multinomial distribution*. If the proportions of the population in categories $C_1, C_2, \ldots, C_k$ are denoted by $p_1, p_2, \ldots, p_k$, respectively, where $p_i \geq 0$ and

$$\sum_{i=1}^{k} p_i = 1$$

then $(X_1, \ldots, X_k)$ is said to have a multinomial distribution with parameters n and $p_1, p_2, \ldots, p_k$. The multinomial probability function specifies the probability of the event $(X_1 = n_1, X_2 = n_2, \ldots, X_k = n_k)$ for all k-tuples of nonnegative integers $(n_1, n_2, \ldots, n_k)$ for which

$$\sum_{i=1}^{k} n_i = n$$

Because it involves so many parameters, the multinomial distribution is seldom tabulated.

Marginally, or by itself, each X_i in the multinomial vector is a binomial random variable. In particular, this means that $E(X_i) = np_i$ and $V(X_i) = np_i(1 - p_i)$. Moreover, for large samples the random variables $Z_i = (X_i - np_i)/\sqrt{np_i(1 - p_i)}$ are approximately distributed as standard normal variables. Estimates of the unknown probabilities p_i can be obtained exactly as in the binomial case: A good estimate of p_i is $p_i = X_i/n$, the proportion of sample values that fall into category C_i. The binomial distribution can be regarded as a special case of the multinomial distribution, or conversely, the multinomial distribution can be regarded as a generalization of the binomial distribution. Both viewpoints will prove convenient from time to time.

Contingency Tables

Tables provide a convenient way to present discrete data, especially if the number of categories is less than the sample size. Table 2 in the next chapter is an example of a *two-way contingency table*. This table gives the joint classification of 3077 "witch hunts" with respect to two variables, the type of institution responsible for the witch hunt and the type of political party system of the country in which the hunt occurred. Classifications with respect to more than two variables produce multiway tables, with the number of dimensions being equal to the number of variables involved.

Note that the row totals in Table 2 are a classification according to type of institution and that column totals are a classification according to type of political system. Column totals are obtained by summing over levels of the row variable (type of institutions), and row totals are gotten by summing over levels of the column variable. Contingency tables obtained by summing over the levels of one or more variables of a higher-dimensional table are called *marginal* tables. In other words, a marginal table results from *collapsing* a higher-way table.

In this monograph, I will deal exclusively with two-way contingency tables and corresponding one-way marginal tables. Table 1 shows the terminology that will be employed for an $I \times J$ table. The row variable X has I levels and the column variable Y has J levels. The number of members of a sample of size n that fall into cell (i, j) of the table is denoted by n_{ij}. Thus, n_{ij} is the number of members in the sample classified at the ith level of X and the jth level of Y. The n_{ij}s can be thought of as the observed values of the multinomial variables N_{ij}.[3]

Marginal tables are obtained by summation. Row totals are obtained by summing over columns, and vice versa. Thus, n_{i+} is the number of members of the sample for which X = i and, similarly, n_{+j} is the number in the sample for which Y = j. It is convenient to write the total sample size $n_{++} = \Sigma_i n_{i+} = \Sigma_j n_{+j}$ without subscripts.

The p's shown in Table 1 have interpretations similiar to those of the corresponding n's, except that the p's denote population probabilities, rather than sample counts. The p_{ij}s are usually unknown in practice.

The probability that an arbitrarily chosen member of the population is classified into cell (i, j) is p_{ij}, so that $E(N_{ij}) = E_{ij} = np_{ij}$ is the number in the sample that can be expected to fall into that cell. Now, sets of values

TABLE 1
Notation for a Two-Way Contingency Table

		1	2	...	J	Totals
				Y		
X	1	n_{11}	n_{12}	...	n_{1J}	n_{1+}
		p_{11}	p_{12}		p_{1J}	p_{1+}
	2	n_{21}	n_{22}	...	n_{2J}	n_{2+}
		p_{21}	p_{22}		p_{2J}	p_{2+}
	...	...	...	...	...	...
	I	n_{I1}	n_{I2}	...	n_{IJ}	n_{I+}
		p_{I1}	p_{I2}		p_{IJ}	p_{I+}
	Totals	n_{+1}	n_{+2}	...	n_{+J}	$n_{++}=n$
		p_{+1}	p_{+2}		p_{+J}	$p_{++}=1$

$\{p_{ij}\}$ can be hypothesized for the population. Statistical methods exist that enable us to decide whether the corresponding *hypothesized* cell frequencies $\{np_{ij}\}$ are consistent with *observed* cell frequencies $\{n_{ij}\}$. One method is based on the chi-square goodness-of-fit statistic, which (in the present context) has the general form

$$X^2 = \sum_{i=1}^{I} \sum_{j=1}^{J} \frac{(n_{ij} - np_{ij})^2}{np_{ij}} \qquad [2.1]$$

In case X and Y are independent, $p_{ij} = p_{i+}p_{+j}$ for each i and j. Substitution of the estimates

$$\hat{p}_{ij} = \hat{p}_{i+}\hat{p}_{+j} = \frac{n_{i+}}{n} \frac{n_{+j}}{n}$$

into equation 2.1 yields

$$X^2 = \sum_{i=1}^{I} \sum_{j=1}^{J} \frac{(n_{ij} - n_{i+}n_{+j}/n)^2}{n_{i+}n_{+j}/n} \qquad [2.2]$$

If X and Y are independent, equation 2.2 has approximately the distribution of a chi-square variable with parameter (degrees of freedom) df = $(I - 1)(J - 1)$. The chi-square statistic can be used to establish association: If X^2 is larger than a suitable percentage point of the appropriate chi-square distribution, then X and Y are not independent.

The chi-square statistic plays an important role in the development of Chapter 3. For future reference, it should be noted that equation 2.2 is algebraically identical to

$$X^2 = \frac{n(n_{11}n_{22} - n_{21}n_{12})^2}{n_{1+}n_{+1}n_{2+}n_{+2}}$$ [2.3]

in the fourfold case $I = J = 2$.

3. MEASURES OF ASSOCIATION FOR NOMINAL DATA

Measures of association for nominal data should not depend on the particular order in which the categories are listed, and all the measures discussed in this chapter share that property. Among the oldest measures for nominal data are those based on the *chi-square statistic*, some of which are described in the next section.

Measures Based on the Chi-Square Statistic

One widely accepted interpretation of "no association" in a two-way contingency table is that row and column variables are independent. The classical test of the hypothesis of independence is based on the chi-square statistic X^2 of equation 2.2. For an $I \times J$ contingency table, let $q = \min\{I, J\}$. It is easy to show that X^2 achieves its maximum value of $n(q - 1)$ when each row (if $I \geqslant J$) or each column (if $I \leqslant J$) of the table contains a single non-zero entry.[4] Clearly, $X^2 \geqslant 0$, so that $0 \leqslant X^2 \leqslant n(q - 1)$.

PEARSON'S COEFFICIENT OF MEAN SQUARE CONTINGENCY

The population analogue of equation 2.2, defined by

$$\phi^2 = \sum_{i=1}^{I} \sum_{j=1}^{J} \frac{(p_{ij} - p_{i+}p_{+j})^2}{p_{i+}p_{+j}} = \sum_{i=1}^{I} \sum_{j=1}^{J} \frac{p_{ij}^2}{p_{i+}p_{+j}} - 1$$ [3.1]

is called the (Pearson) coefficient of mean square contingency. It follows by the reasoning of the previous paragraph that $0 \leqslant \phi^2 \leqslant q - 1$, with $\phi^2 = 0$ in the case of independence and $\phi^2 = q - 1$ in the case of perfect association. By replacing the p's in equation 3.1 with sample estimates, the estimator $\hat{\phi}^2 = X^2/n$ of ϕ^2 is obtained. Since its range depends on the dimensions of the table, $\hat{\phi}^2$ is not particularly suitable as a measure of association without modification.

PEARSON'S CONTINGENCY COEFFICIENT AND SAKODA'S MODIFICATION

To overcome this difficulty, Pearson (1948) proposed the measure

$$p = \left(\frac{\phi^2}{1 + \phi^2}\right)^{1/2}$$

which is bounded between 0 and 1. The measure p is called the (Pearson) contingency coefficient. The maximum likelihood estimator of p under the multinomial sampling model is

$$\hat{p} = \left(\frac{X^2/n}{1 + X^2/n}\right)^{1/2} = \left(\frac{X^2}{n + X^2}\right)^{1/2}$$

Since p assumes a maximum value of $\sqrt{[(q - 1)/q]}$ in the case of perfect association, the range of p still depends on the dimensions of the table. Various functions of ϕ^2 have been proposed to alleviate this difficulty. Sakoda (1977) suggests

$$p^* = p/p_{max} = \left(\frac{q\phi^2}{(q - 1)(1 + \phi^2)}\right)^{1/2} \qquad [3.2]$$

Although this measure has not found favor with previous authors, $p^* = 0$ in the case of independence, and $p^* = 1$ in the case of perfect association, both strict and implicit.

TSCHUPROW'S CONTINGENCY COEFFICIENT

Tschuprow (1919) considered

$$t = \left(\frac{\phi^2}{\sqrt{(I - 1)(J - 1)}}\right)^{1/2} \qquad [3.3]$$

which has a maximum value of $\sqrt[4]{[(q - 1)/\max\{I - 1, J - 1\}]}^{1/4}$ in the case of perfect association. Unless I and J are nearly equal, the range of t is severely restricted. If I = 3 and J = 10, for example, $t_{max} = \sqrt[4]{2/9} = 0.6866$.

CRAMER'S CONTINGENCY COEFFICIENT

Finally, Cramer (1946) proposed the coefficient

$$v = \left(\frac{\phi^2}{q - 1}\right)^{1/2} \qquad [3.4]$$

In the case of perfect association, $v = 1$ for all values of I and J, while $v = 0$ in the case of independence. Estimators of p*, t, and v are obtained by replacing ϕ^2 with $\hat{\phi}^2 = X^2/n$ in equations 3.2, 3.3, and 3.4, respectively. The resulting estimators are in fact maximum likelihood estimators under the multinomial sampling model. Each estimator has the same range as its population analogue.

The exact distributions of the estimators of p, p*, t, and v are difficult to obtain, but approximate large-sample distributions are known. In the case of independence ($\phi^2 = 0$), percentage points of the distributions of the various contingency coefficients are easily computed from those of equation 2.2. For example, the approximate significance level of the observed value t_0 of t can be obtained as follows: Since

$$\Pr(\hat{t} \geq t_0) = \Pr(\hat{t}^2 \geq t_0^2) = \Pr\left[\frac{X^2}{n\sqrt{(I-1)(J-1)}} \geq t_0^2\right]$$

$$= \Pr[X^2 \geq nt_0^2\sqrt{(I-1)(J-1)}]$$

it is necessary to evaluate only the last probability using tables of the chi-square distribution. Similar probabilistic statements can be made concerning p, p*, and v.

For correlated random variables ($\phi^2 \neq 0$), Bishop, Fienberg, and Holland (1975: 386) give the following formula for the asymptotic variance of $\hat{\phi}^2 = X^2/n$:

$$\sigma_\infty^2(\hat{\phi}^2) = \frac{1}{n}\left\{4\sum_{i=1}^{I}\sum_{j=1}^{J}\frac{p_{ij}^3}{p_{i+}p_{+j}} - 3\sum_{i=1}^{I}\frac{1}{p_{i+}}\left(\sum_{j=1}^{J}\frac{p_{ij}^2}{p_{i+}p_{+j}}\right)^2\right.$$

$$-3\sum_{j=1}^{J}\frac{1}{p_{+j}}\left(\sum_{i=1}^{I}\frac{p_{ij}^2}{p_{i+}p_{+j}}\right)^2 + 2\sum_{i=1}^{I}\sum_{j=1}^{J}\left[\frac{p_{ij}}{p_{i+}p_{+j}}\times\right.$$

$$\left.\left.\left(\sum_{i'=1}^{I}\frac{p_{i'j}}{p_{i'+}p_{+j}}\right)\left(\sum_{j'=1}^{J}\frac{p_{ij'}}{p_{i+}p_{+j'}}\right)\right]\right\} \qquad [3.5]$$

If the values of p_{ij} are unknown, an estimator $\hat{\sigma}_\infty^2(\hat{\sigma}^2)$ of equation 3.5 can be obtained by replacing p_{ij} with $\hat{p}_{ij} = n_{ij}/n$ throughout.

The asymptotic variances of p, p*, t, and v can be obtained from $\sigma_\infty^2(\hat{\phi}^2)$ by the δ method (see, for example, Bishop et al., 1975: chap. 14). They are (for $\phi^2 \neq 0$):

$$\sigma_\infty^2(\hat{p}) = \sigma_\infty^2(\hat{\phi}^2)/[4\phi^2(1+\phi^2)^3] \qquad [3.6]$$

$$\sigma^2_\infty(\hat{p}^*) = \frac{q}{q-1}\,\sigma^2_\infty(\hat{p}) = \frac{q\sigma^2_\infty(\hat{\phi}^2)}{4(q-1)\,\phi^2(1+\phi^2)^3} \qquad [3.7]$$

$$\sigma^2_\infty(\hat{t}) = \sigma^2_\infty(\hat{\phi}^2)/[4\phi^2\sqrt{(I-1)(J-1)}]$$

$$= \sigma^2_\infty(\hat{\phi}^2)/[4t^2(I-1)(J-1)] \qquad [3.8]$$

$$\sigma^2_\infty(\hat{v}) = \sigma^2_\infty(\hat{\phi}^2)/[4\phi^2(q-1)]$$

$$= \sigma^2_\infty(\hat{\phi}^2)/[4v^2(q-1)^2] \qquad [3.9]$$

Estimators of these variances (equations 3.6-3.9) are obtained by replacing population parameters with their sample analogues and using equation 3.5, with p_{ij} replaced by $\hat{p}_{ij} = n_{ij}/n$, to estimate $\sigma^2_\infty(\hat{\phi}^2)$.

The main difficulty in using measures of association based on the statistic X^2 is that of finding a meaningful interpretation. The measures do not have simple probabilistic interpretations, and, despite the fact that X^2 is generally considered to be a good statistic for testing the hypothesis of independence, there is no consensus among statisticians that it is also a good measure of association. In terms of squared difference between observed and expected frequencies (calculated under the assumption of independence), the measures are useful for comparing several tables, but those whose ranges depend on the dimensions of the table are not really comparable across tables of different sizes. The measures p* and v, at least, can be interpreted as the proportion of maximum variation due to association, or interaction, between the variables. Finally, Kendall and Stuart (1973: chap. 33) have shown that v^2 is the mean square canonical correlation between the row and column variables of the contingency table.

For 2×2 contingency tables, ϕ^2 is identical to the Pearson product-moment correlation coefficient ρ^2. Consequently, properties of either are properties of both in this context.

Major references for properties of measures based upon X^2 are the books by Kendall and Stuart (1973: chap. 33), Bishop et al. (1975: chap. 11), and Goodman and Kruskal (1980).[5] Brief discussions of these measures, including examples, are also given by Reynolds (1977a), Hays (1963), and Conover (1980).

Measures of Proportional Reduction in Predictive Error

The chi-square statistic and related measures are all motivated by attempts to measure a vaguely specified "lack of independence" between two categorical variables. Goodman and Kruskal (1980), however, discuss two measures that have meaningful interpretations in terms of proba-bilities of misclassification. Each is a measure of the relative usefulness of one variable in improving the ability to predict the classification of members of the population with respect to a second variable.

Let A be a (row) variable with I levels, let B denote a second (column) variable with J levels, let p_{ij} be the probability that a randomly selected member of the population falls into category i of variable A and category j of variable B, and let n_{ij} be the number of individuals in a sample of size n that fall into cell (i, j) of the classification table. The data (or the popu-lation probabilities, if they are known) can be used to predict the A category of a randomly selected individual. Moreover, the prediction can be accomplished either (1) without or (2) with knowledge of the individual's B category. The measures considered by Goodman and Kruskal are de-fined in terms of the reduction in the probability of misclassification re-sulting from knowledge of the individual's classification for the second variable. Different classification schemes result in different probabilities of error (measures), but the two schemes of Goodman and Kruskal seem most natural.

The Goodman-Kruskal measures of proportional reduction in pre-dictive error treat the variables asymmetrically. They are especially useful, therefore, in situations in which a causal relationship is sought.

THE GOODMAN-KRUSKAL λ

Suppose that the (marginal) distribution of the row variable A is known, and, with only that information, the task is to estimate the A category of an individual selected at random from the population. One reasonable classification rule specifies that the individual be assigned to the category, or row, with the greatest probability. Thus the individual is assigned to the category corresponding to row m of the table for which

$$p_{m+} = \max \left\{ p_{1+}, p_{2+}, \ldots, p_{I+} \right\}$$

This classification rule maximizes the probability of correct classification; the corresponding probability of misclassification is

$$1 - p_{m+} \hspace{5cm} [3.10]$$

Now, suppose that the individual is known to fall into category j of the column variable B. Application of the above classification rule to the probabilities *in column j* of the table dictates that the individual be assigned to the A category m for which

$$p_{mj} = \max \left\{ p_{1j}, p_{2j}, \ldots, p_{Ij} \right\}$$

so as to maximize the *conditional* probability p_{mj}/p_{+j} of correct classification, given his B classification. The corresponding probability of *conditional* misclassification is $1 - p_{mj}/p_{+j}$ and the *unconditional* probability of error is

$$\sum_{j=1}^{J} P(\text{Error}\,|\,B=j)\,P(B=j) = \sum_{j=1}^{J} (1 - p_{mj}/p_{+j})p_{+j}$$

$$= \sum_{j=1}^{J} (p_{+j} - p_{mj}) = 1 - \sum_{j=1}^{J} p_{mj} \qquad [3.11]$$

The relative reduction in the probability of prediction error is, from equations 3.10 and 3.11,

$$\lambda_{A|B} = \frac{(1 - p_{m+}) - (1 - \sum_j p_{mj})}{1 - p_{m+}} = \frac{\sum_j p_{mj} - p_{m+}}{1 - p_{m+}} \qquad [3.12]$$

In other words, $\lambda_{A|B}$ is the proportion of relative error in predicting an individual's A category that can be eliminated by knowledge of his or her B category.

The measure $\lambda_{A|B}$ can assume values between 0 and 1, inclusive, and is well defined unless all nonzero probabilities of the table are in a single row. If each column of the table contains at most one nonzero entry, the maximum probability in each column is the same as one of the column marginal probabilities. Consequently, knowledge of an individual's B category permits errorless prediction of his or her A category. The corresponding value of equation 3.12 is: $\lambda_{A|B} = 1$. At the other extreme, if all column maxima occur in the same row, $\lambda_{A|B} = 0$; this is the case if A and B are independent. The independence of A and B implies $\lambda_{A|B} = 0$, but the converse need not be true because all column maxima can also occur in a single row even though the variables are not independent. Bishop et al. (1975: 386-389) give an example in which one of two dependent variables is no help in predicting the other. The fact that measures of predictive association can be zero for correlated variables distinguishes them from measures based on the chi-square statistic. Like the chi-square measures, however, $\lambda_{A|B}$ does remain unchanged if any two rows or any two columns of the table are interchanged.

Measures based on X^2 are effective for determining departures from independence, but they treat variables symmetrically. If the goal is to use one variable to improve the predictability of another, asymmetric measures such as $\lambda_{A|B}$ are better. These remarks also apply to other asymmetric measures, such as the Goodman-Kruskal τ and Somers's d.

Situations certainly exist in which it is of interest to use knowledge of A to improve prediction of B. Interchanging the roles of A and B in the derivation of $\lambda_{A|B}$ yields

$$\lambda_{B|A} = \frac{\sum_i p_{im} - p_{+m}}{1 - p_{+m}}$$ [3.13]

as the relative decrease in the probability of error of predicting B gained from knowledge of A. In equation 3.13, p_{+m} is the maximum of the (marginal) probabilities of the B categories, and p_{im} is the maximum of these probabilities for the ith category of A; i.e., p_{im} is the maximum of the probabilities in the ith row of the contingency table.

Both $\lambda_{A|B}$ and $\lambda_{B|A}$ are designed for use in situations in which one of the variables can reasonably be assumed to depend upon the other. For situations in which no natural asymmetry exists, Goodman and Kruskal (1954) propose the measure

$$\lambda = \frac{\lambda_{A|B}(1 - p_{m+}) + \lambda_{B|A}(1 - p_{+m})}{(1 - p_{m+}) + (1 - p_{+m})}$$

$$= \frac{\sum_j p_{mj} + \sum_i p_{im} - p_{m+} - p_{+m}}{2 - p_{m+} - p_{+m}}$$ [3.14]

The measure λ arises from the following somewhat artificial prediction problem: Suppose that half the time the task is to estimate the B category and half the time the task is to estimate the A category of an individual selected at random from the population. Then λ is the reduction in the probability of prediction error resulting from knowledge of the individual's classification on the second variable relative to the probability of error if this information is not available.

The symmetric measure λ is well defined if at least two cells not both in the same row or the same column of the table contain nonzero probabilities. Since λ is a weighted averge of $\lambda_{A|B}$ and $\lambda_{B|A}$, its value must lie between those of the two asymmetric measures. If the table contains at most one nonzero probability in each row and column, $\lambda = 1$. If A and B are independent, $\lambda = 0$, although λ can be zero even if A and B are not independent.

Under the multinomial sampling model, the maximum likelihood estimators of $\lambda_{A|B}$, $\lambda_{B|A}$, and λ are, respectively,

$$\hat{\lambda}_{A|B} = \frac{\sum\limits_{j} n_{mj} - n_{m+}}{n - n_{m+}} \qquad [3.15]$$

$$\hat{\lambda}_{A|B} = \frac{\sum\limits_{i} n_{im} - n_{+m}}{n - n_{+m}} \qquad [3.16]$$

and

$$\hat{\lambda} = \frac{\sum\limits_{j} n_{mj} + \sum\limits_{i} n_{im} - n_{m+} - n_{+m}}{2n - n_{m+} - n_{+m}} \qquad [3.17]$$

In equations 3.15 through 3.17, the quantities n_{mj}, n_{m+}, and so on are sample analogues of p_{mj}, p_{m+}, and so on. If "probability" is replaced by "observed frequency," statements about the range, minimum, and maximum of equations 3.12, 3.13, and 3.4 apply verbatim to equations 3.15, 3.16, and 3.17, respectively. Whenever any one of the three measures is either 0 or 1, the corresponding estimator has the same value.

The exact sampling distributions of equations 3.15, 3.16, and 3.17 are unknown, but under the multinomial model, all three estimators are approximately normal for large samples. Provided n is sufficiently large, $n_{m+} \neq 1$, and $\lambda_{A|B}$ is not 0 or 1, Goodman and Kruskal (1963) show that $\hat{\lambda}_{A|B}$ has approximately a normal sampling distribution with mean $\lambda_{A|B}$ and variance

$$\sigma_{\infty}^2(\hat{\lambda}_{A|B}) = \frac{\left(1 - \sum\limits_{j} p_{mj}\right)\left(\sum\limits_{j} p_{mj} + p_{m+} - 2\sum\limits_{j}^{c} p_{mj}\right)}{(1 - p_{m+})^3} \qquad [3.18]$$

where $\sum\limits_{j}^{c} p_{mj}$ is the sum of all maximum column probabilities that fall in the same row as p_{m+}. The last factor in the numerator of equation 3.18 is the sum of the p_{mj}s that are not in the same row as p_{m+} and the probabilities in the same row as p_{m+} that are not p_{mj}s. The corresponding estimator of equation 3.18 is:

$$\hat{\sigma}_{\infty}^2(\hat{\lambda}_{A|B}) = \frac{\left(n - \sum\limits_{j} n_{mj}\right)\left(\sum\limits_{j} n_{mj} + n_{m+} - 2\sum\limits_{j}^{c} n_{mj}\right)}{(n - n_{m+})^3} \qquad [3.19]$$

where $\overset{c}{\underset{j}{\Sigma}}n_{mj}$ is the sum of all maximum column frequencies that occur in the same row as n_{m+}. If $n = n_{m+}$, then equation 3.19 is not defined. Moreover, if ties exist among candidates for n_{m+} or n_{mj}, equation 3.19 may not be uniquely defined, since its value depends on the choice of m. A conservative approach is to use the largest estimate obtained by evaluating equation 3.19 for the various choices of n_{m+} and n_{mj}. The estimator $\hat{\lambda}_{A|B}$ itself is uniquely defined even in the case of ties. Example 1 (later in this chapter) will help to clarify the meaning of the terms in equations 3.18 and 3.19.

The asymptotic distribution of $\hat{\lambda}_{A|B}$ may be used to perform significance tests and compute confidence intervals, provided suitable modifications are taken near 0 or 1. If $\hat{\lambda}_{A|B} = 0$ (or 1), Goodman and Kruskal suggest using the degenerate confidence interval 0 (or 1) for $\lambda_{A|B}$. Likewise, the hypothesis $\lambda_{A|B} = 0$ (or $\lambda_{A|B} = 1$) should be rejected unless $\hat{\lambda}_{A|B} = 0$ (or $\hat{\lambda}_{A|B} = 1$). Approximate confidence intervals with computed lower limits less than 0 or upper limits greater than 1 can be suitably truncated.

It follows by symmetry that $\hat{\lambda}_{B|A}$ is asymptotically a normal random variable with mean $\lambda_{B|A}$ and estimated variance

$$\hat{\sigma}^2_{\infty}(\hat{\lambda}_{B|A}) = \frac{\left(n - \underset{i}{\Sigma}n_{im}\right)\left(\underset{i}{\Sigma}n_{im} + n_{+m} - 2\overset{r}{\underset{i}{\Sigma}}n_{im}\right)}{\left(n - n_{+m}\right)^3}$$ [3.20]

where $\overset{r}{\underset{i}{\Sigma}}n_{im}$ is the sum of all maximum row frequencies that fall in the same column as n_{+m}. Comments made about $\hat{\lambda}_{A|B}$ apply also to $\hat{\lambda}_{B|A}$.

The sampling distribution of $\hat{\lambda}$ is also asymptotically normal. However, to write an expression for the estimated sampling variance of $\hat{\lambda}$, we need some additional notation. In each of the following, the symbol to the left of the colon denotes the quantity to the right:

n_{im} : maximum value in row i, i = 1, 2, ... , I

n_{mj} : maximum value in column j, j = 1, 2, ... , J

m_c : index of the column that contains the maximum column marginal, denoted n_{+m_c}

m_r : index of the row which contains the maximum row marginal, denoted n_{m_r+}

$\underset{i}{\Sigma}n_{im}$: sum of all row maxima

$\underset{j}{\Sigma}n_{mj}$: sum of all column maxima

$$\sum_{i}^{r} n_{im_c} : \text{ sum of row maxima that fall in column } m_c$$

$$\sum_{j}^{c} n_{m_r j} : \text{ sum of column maxima that fall in row } m_r$$

$$\sum_{i}^{*} n_{im} : \text{ sum of all column (row) maxima that are also row (column) maxima}$$

In addition, let

$$U_1 = \frac{1}{n} \left(n_{+m_c} + n_{m_r+} \right)$$

$$U_2 = \frac{1}{n} \left(\sum_i n_{im} + \sum_j n_{mj} \right)$$

$$U_3 = \frac{1}{n} \left(\sum_i^r n_{im_c} + \sum_j^c n_{m_r j} + n_{m_r m} + n_{mm_c} \right)$$

Provided λ is not equal to 0 or 1, Goodman and Kruskal (1963) show that for large n, $\hat{\lambda}$ is approximately a normal random variable with mean λ and estimated variance

$$\hat{\sigma}^2_\infty(\hat{\lambda}) = U/[n(2 - U_1)^4] \qquad [3.21]$$

where

$$U = (2 - U_1)(2 - U_2)(U_1 + U_2 + 4 - 2U_3)$$

$$- 2(2 - U_1)^2 \left(1 - n^{-1} \sum_i^* n_{im} \right) - 2(2 - U_2)^2 (1 - n_{m_r m_c}/n)$$

If all observations are concentrated in a single cell of the table, $U_1 = 2$ and equation 3.21 is undefined. Moreover, equation 3.21 is not uniquely defined if ties exist in the selection of row, column, or marginal maxima. Modifications in testing and estimation procedures recommended when $\hat{\lambda}_{A|B}$ is near 0 or 1 also apply to $\hat{\lambda}$. The estimate (equation 3.21) is not difficult to compute despite its formidable appearance. Calculations are illustrated in the following example.

Example 1. In an attempt to explain patterns in "witch-hunting" activities of various institutions by the extent to which societies express their corporate national interest (as measured by type of party system), Bergeson (1977) presents the data shown in Table 2. Can the number of political parties (B) be used to predict a country's institutional witch-hunting behavior (A), and vice versa?

Using the notation developed to write equation 3.21, we get

$$m_c = 1, \quad n_{mm_c} = 549, \quad n_{+m_c} = 2076$$

$$m_r = 1, \quad n_{m_r m} = 549, \quad n_{m_r +} = 815$$

$$\sum_i n_{im} = 2107, \quad \sum_j n_{mj} = 914$$

$$\sum_i n_{im_c}^r = 1983, \quad \sum_j n_{m_r j}^c = 761, \quad \text{and} \quad \sum_i n_{im}^* = 549.$$

Furthermore, $U_1 = (2076 + 815)/3077 = 0.93955$, $U_2 = (2107 + 914)/3077 = 0.98180$, and $U_3 = (1983 + 761 + 549 + 549)/3077 = 1.24862$.

For these data, equations 3.15, 3.16, and 3.17 have the values:

$$\hat{\lambda}_{A|B} = \frac{914 - 815}{3077 - 815} = \frac{99}{2262} = 0.0438$$

$$\hat{\lambda}_{B|A} = \frac{2107 - 2076}{3077 - 2076} = \frac{31}{1001} = 0.0310$$

$$\hat{\lambda} = \frac{99 + 31}{2262 + 1001} = \frac{130}{3263} = 0.0398$$

respectively. From equations 3.19, 3.20, and 3.21 we obtain the corresponding variance estimates: $\hat{\sigma}_\infty^2(\hat{\lambda}_{A|B}) = 0.3869 \times 10^{-4}$, $\hat{\sigma}_\infty^2(\hat{\lambda}_{B|A}) = 0.2099 \times 10^{-3}$, and $\hat{\sigma}_\infty^2(\hat{\lambda}) = 0.3478 \times 10^{-4}$.

Each estimator, when compared with its standard deviation, is significantly different from zero. The reduction in predictive error is small but statistically significant because of the large sample size. It is doubtful that the reduction is of practical significance, even granting that it is meaningful to make inferences about the "population" of witch hunts.

The chi-square statistic (equation 2.2) has the value $X^2 = 437.2$ for these data, so the two variables are clearly not independent. By way of comparison, the computed values of the measures based upon X^2 are $\hat{p} = 0.3527$, $\hat{p}^* = 0.4320$, $\hat{t} = 0.2025$, and $\hat{v} = 0.2665$. When compared with its standard deviation, each estimator turns out to be significantly different from zero. We reach the same conclusion in all cases: Association between the two variables is weak, but significant.

TABLE 2
Distribution of Witch-Hunting Activities by Institution
and Political Party System, 1950-1970

Institutional Areas (A)	Type of Political Party System (B)			Totals
	One-Party	Two-Party	Multiparty	
Government	549	212	54	815
Military	93	124	54	271
Education	233	78	33	344
Economy	119	42	13	174
Intellectuals	225	41	46	312
Religion	455	12	7	474
Foreigners	402	132	153	687
Totals	2076	641	360	3077

SOURCE: Bergeson (1977).

The most extensive discussion of the measures $\lambda_{A|B}$, $\lambda_{B|A}$, and λ, originally proposed by Guttman (1941), is contained in the papers of Goodman and Kruskal (1954, 1963), in which the measures are defined, their asymptotic distributions are derived, numerical examples are given, and various related measures are discussed. These measures are also discussed by Hays (1963), Reynolds (1977a), and Bishop et al. (1975). Each treatment includes numerical examples.

THE GOODMAN-KRUSKAL τ

The Goodman-Kruskal τ is derived like λ, except that a different classification rule is used. Suppose the (marginal) distribution of the row variable A is known, and, with only that information, the task is to estimate the A category of a randomly selected member of the population. In this case, classification must be accomplished so as to reproduce the marginal distribution of A. Thus the individual is assigned to category 1 with probability p_{1+}, to category 2 with probability p_{2+}, and so on. The individual is classified into class i with probability p_{i+}. That assignment is correct with probability p_{i+}; consequently, the individual is correctly classified *into class i* with probability p_{i+}^2. If this argument is applied to all I categories, it turns out that the individual is correctly classified with probability

$$p_{1+}^2 + p_{2+}^2 + \ldots + p_{I+}^2 = \sum_{i=1}^{I} p_{i+}^2$$

and misclassified with probability

$$1 - \sum_{i=1}^{I} p_{i+}^2 \qquad [3.22]$$

Now suppose we know that the individual falls into class j of a second (column) variable B. By applying the classification rule to the probabilities in column j, we must assign the individual (conditionally) to row i with probability p_{ij}/p_{+j}. (The probability p_{ij}/p_{+j} is the conditional probability that A = i, given B = j.) In this case, the *conditional* probability of misclassification turns out to be

$$1 - \sum_{i=1}^{I} (p_{ij}/p_{+j})^2$$

while the *unconditional* probability of misclassification is

$$\sum_{j=1}^{J} P(\text{Error} \mid B = j)\, P(B = j) = \sum_{j=1}^{J} \left[1 - \sum_{i=1}^{I} (p_{ij}/p_{+j})^2 \right] p_{+j}$$

$$= 1 - \sum_{j=1}^{J} \sum_{i=1}^{I} (p_{ij}^2/p_{+j}) \qquad [3.23]$$

The relative decrease in the probability of an incorrect prediction is, from equations 3.22 and 3.23:

$$\tau_{A|B} = \frac{\left(1 - \sum_{i=1}^{I} p_{i+}^2\right) - \left(1 - \sum_{j=1}^{J} \sum_{i=1}^{I} (p_{ij}^2/p_{+j})\right)}{1 - \sum_{i=1}^{I} p_{i+}^2}$$

$$= \frac{\sum_{j=1}^{J} \sum_{i=1}^{I} p_{ij}^2/p_{+j} - \sum_{i=1}^{I} p_{i+}^2}{1 - \sum_{i=1}^{I} p_{i+}^2} \qquad [3.24]$$

Unless all nonzero probabilities of the table are in a single row, $\tau_{A|B}$ is well defined. The measure ranges from 0 to 1, and can assume both extreme values. In a column j that contains exactly one nonzero entry, there is some row i for which $p_{ij} = p_{+j}$. If each column contains exactly one nonzero entry, equation 3.23 equals 0 and $\tau_{A|B} = 1$. Thus knowledge of an individual's B category permits prediction of his or her A category with certainty. If A and B are independent, on the other hand, then $p_{ij} = p_{i+} p_{+j}$ for each i, j, and $\tau_{A|B} = 0$. Here, too, it can happen that one variable is of no help in predicting another, even though the variables are not independent.

By interchanging the roles of A and B, we obtain the measure

$$\tau_{B|A} = \frac{\sum\limits_{i=1}^{I} \sum\limits_{j=1}^{J} p_{ij}^2/p_{i+} - \sum\limits_{j=1}^{J} p_{+j}^2}{1 - \sum\limits_{j=1}^{J} p_{+j}^2} \qquad [3.25]$$

which is the relative reduction in the error of predicting the B category of an individual resulting from knowledge of his or her A classification.

If no natural asymmetry exists between the variables under consideration, the measure

$$\tau = \frac{\tau_{A|B}\left(1 - \sum\limits_{i=1}^{I} p_{i+}^2\right) + \tau_{B|A}\left(1 - \sum\limits_{j=1}^{J} p_{+j}^2\right)}{\left(1 - \sum\limits_{i=1}^{I} p_{i+}^2\right) + \left(1 - \sum\limits_{j=1}^{J} p_{+j}^2\right)}$$

$$= \frac{\sum\limits_{i=1}^{I} \sum\limits_{j=1}^{J} p_{ij}^2/p_{i+} + \sum\limits_{i=1}^{I} \sum\limits_{j=1}^{J} p_{ij}^2/p_{+j} - \sum\limits_{i=1}^{I} p_{i+}^2 - \sum\limits_{j=1}^{J} p_{+j}^2}{2 - \sum\limits_{i=1}^{I} p_{i+}^2 - \sum\limits_{j=1}^{J} p_{+j}^2} \qquad [3.26]$$

has been proposed. Suppose that a member of the population is selected at random from the population and that half the time the task is to predict his or her A category and half the time to predict his or her A category and half the time to predict his or her B category. Then τ can be interpreted as the reduction in probability of prediction error resulting from knowledge of the individual's classification on the second variable relative to the probability of error in absence of that information.

The measure τ is well defined if at least two cells, not both in the same row or column of the table, contain nonzero probabilities. The value of τ lies between the values of $\tau_{A|B}$ and $\tau_{B|A}$; consequently $0 \leqslant \tau \leqslant 1$. If the table has exactly one nonzero probability in each row and column, then $\tau = 1$, while $\tau = 0$ when A and B are independent.

Under the multinomial sampling model, $\tau_{A|B}$, $\tau_{B|A}$, and τ have maximum likelihood estimators

$$\hat{\tau}_{A|B} = \frac{n \sum\limits_{i=1}^{I} \sum\limits_{j=1}^{J} (n_{ij}^2/n_{+j}) - \sum\limits_{i=1}^{I} n_{i+}^2}{n^2 - \sum\limits_{i=1}^{I} n_{i+}^2} \qquad [3.27]$$

$$\hat{\tau}_{B|A} = \frac{n \sum\limits_{j=1}^{J} \sum\limits_{i=1}^{I} (n_{ij}^2/n_{i+}) - \sum\limits_{j=1}^{J} n_{+j}^2}{n^2 - \sum\limits_{j=1}^{J} n_{+j}^2}$$ [3.28]

and

$$\hat{\tau} = \frac{n \left[\sum\limits_{i=1}^{I} \sum\limits_{j=1}^{J} (n_{ij}^2/n_{+j}) + \sum\limits_{j=1}^{J} \sum\limits_{i=1}^{I} (n_{ij}^2/n_{i+}) \right] - \sum\limits_{j=1}^{J} n_{+j}^2 - \sum\limits_{i=1}^{I} n_{i+}^2}{2n^2 - \sum\limits_{j=1}^{J} n_{+j}^2 - \sum\limits_{i=1}^{I} n_{i+}^2}$$ [3.29]

respectively. If "probability" is replaced by "observed frequency," statements about the minimum, maximum, and range of equations 3.24, 2.25, and 3.26 apply also to equations 3.27, 2.28, and 3.29, respectively. If any one of the measures is either 0 or 1, the corresponding estimator has the same value.

Using Gini's definition of total variation in a sample from a categorical variable, Light and Margolin (1971) use methods analogous to those for partitioning a sum of squares in analysis of variance to derive a measure R^2 for contingency tables. It turns out (Margolin and Light, 1974) that R^2 is equivalent to the Goodman-Kruskal τ.

If the columns of the table represent the levels of some control variable B, Gini (1912) defines the total sum of squares (TSS) in the response variable A as

$$\text{TSS} = \frac{n}{2} - \frac{1}{2n} \sum\limits_{i=1}^{I} n_{i+}^2$$ [3.30]

Further, equation 3.30 can be partitioned into a within-group sum of squares (WSS) and a between-group sum of squares (BSS):

$$\text{WSS} = \frac{n}{2} - \frac{1}{2} \sum\limits_{j=1}^{J} \sum\limits_{i=1}^{I} (n_{ij}^2/n_{+j})$$

$$\text{BSS} = \text{TSS} - \text{WSS} = \frac{1}{2} \sum\limits_{i=1}^{I} \sum\limits_{j=1}^{J} (n_{ij} - n_{i+} n_{+j}/n)^2 n_{+j}$$

Some algebra shows that the ratio of BSS and WSS is

$$\hat{R}^2_{A|B} = \frac{BSS}{TSS} = \frac{n \sum\limits_{i=1}^{I} \sum\limits_{j=1}^{J} (n_{ij} - n_{i+}n_{+j}/n)^2/n_{+j}}{n^2 - \sum\limits_{i=1}^{I} n_{i+}^2} = \hat{\tau}_{A|B} \qquad [3.31]$$

The form of τ_{AB} suggested by equation 3.31 is one that resembles the parameter ϕ^2. In fact, $\phi^2 = (I - 1)\tau$ if $p_{i+} = 1/I$ for each i. Likewise, $X^2 = n(I - 1)\hat{\tau}_{A|B}$ if $n_{i+} = n/I$ for each i.

The Margolin-Light derivation gives us another interpretation of the measure τ. Like the correlation coefficient, $\tau_{A|B}$ is the proportion of variability in A that is attributable to, or explained by, B. But unlike the correlation coefficient, $\tau_{A|B}$ is not symmetric in its treatment of the two variables.

The exact sampling distributions of equations 3.27, 3.28, and 3.29 are unknown, but all three estimators are approximately normal for large samples under the multinomial sampling model. The asymptotic mean of each estimator is the corresponding population parameter. Provided that $\tau_{A|B}$ is not 0 or 1 and that $p_{i+} < 1$ for all i, Goodman and Kruskal (1972) give the following estimator of the asymptotic variance of $\tau_{A|B}$:

$$\hat{\sigma}^2_{\infty}(\hat{\tau}_{A|B}) = \frac{1}{n^2\delta^4} \sum\limits_{i=1}^{I} \sum\limits_{j=1}^{J} n_{ij}(\hat{\phi}_{ij} - \hat{\bar{\phi}})^2 \qquad [3.32]$$

in which

$$\hat{\nu} = 1 - \sum\limits_{i=1}^{I} \sum\limits_{j=1}^{J} \left(\frac{n_{ij}}{n}\right)^2 \bigg/ \left(\frac{n}{n_{+j}}\right) = \frac{1}{n}\left(n - \sum\limits_{i=1}^{I} \sum\limits_{j=1}^{J} n_{ij}^2/n_{+j}\right) \qquad [3.33]$$

$$\hat{\delta} = 1 - \sum\limits_{i=1}^{I} \left(\frac{n_{i+}}{n}\right)^2 = \frac{1}{n^2}\left(n^2 - \sum\limits_{i=1}^{I} n_{i+}^2\right) \qquad [3.34]$$

$$\hat{\bar{\phi}} = \hat{\delta}(\hat{\nu} + 1) - 2\hat{\nu}$$

and

$$\hat{\phi}_{ij} = -2\hat{\nu}\left(\frac{n_{i+}}{n}\right) + 2\hat{\delta}\left(\frac{n_{ij}}{n}\right)\left(\frac{n}{n_{+j}}\right) - \hat{\delta} \sum\limits_{k=1}^{I}\left(\frac{n_{kj}}{n_{+j}}\right)^2$$

$$= -2\hat{\nu}\left(\frac{n_{i+}}{n}\right) + \hat{\delta}\left[\frac{2n_{ij}}{n_{+j}} - \sum\limits_{k=1}^{I}\left(\frac{n_{kj}}{n_{+j}}\right)^2\right] \qquad [3.35]$$

An estimator of the asymptotic variance of $\hat{\tau}_{B|A}$ can be obtained from equations 3.32, 3.33, 3.34, and 3.35 by interchanging the roles of i and j. The asymptotic variance of $\hat{\tau}$ is unpublished.

The asymptotic distribution of $\hat{\tau}_{A|B}$ can be used to perform significance tests and set up confidence intervals, provided that $\hat{\tau}_{A|B}$ is not equal to zero or one. The distributional properties given by Goodman and Kruskal cannot be used to test the hypothesis of independence since they do not hold for $\tau = 0$. However, $\hat{R}^2_{A|B} = \hat{\tau}_{A|B}$ when $\tau = 0$. Light and Margolin (1971) have shown that in this case the statistic

$$U^2_{A|B} = (n - 1)(I - 1)\hat{R}^2_{A|B} = (n - 1)(I - 1)\hat{\tau}_{A|B} \qquad [3.36]$$

is approximately distributed as a chi-square variable with $(I - 1)(J - 1)$ degrees of freedom. By symmetry,

$$U^2_{B|A} = (n - 1)(J - 1)\hat{R}^2_{B|A} = (n - 1)(J - 1)\hat{\tau}_{B|A} \qquad [3.37]$$

has the same asymptotic null distribution as $U^2_{A|B}$.

To continue the comparisons begun in the previous section, the values of $\hat{\tau}_{A|B}$, $\hat{\tau}_{B|A}$, and $\hat{\tau}$ are computed for the data of Example 1.

Example 1 (continued). Let

$$U_1 = \frac{1}{2076}(549^2 + 93^2 + \ldots + 455^2 + 402^2)$$

$$+ \frac{1}{641}(212^2 + 124^2 + \ldots + 12^2 + 132^2)$$

$$+ \frac{1}{360}(54^2 + 54^2 + \ldots + 7^2 + 153^2)$$

$$= 611.3839$$

$$U_2 = \frac{1}{815}(549^2 + 212^2 + 54^2) + \frac{1}{271}(93^2 + 124^2 + 54^2)$$

$$+ \ldots + \frac{1}{687}(402^2 + 132^2 + 153^2)$$

$$= 1705.3836$$

$$U_3 = 815^2 + 271^2 + \ldots + 474^2 + 687^2$$

$$= 1,680,267$$

$$U_4 = 2076^2 + 641^2 + 360^2$$

$$= 4,850,257$$

Then, from equations 3.27, 3.28, and 3.29

$$\hat{\tau}_{A|B} = \frac{nU_1 - U_3}{n^2 - U_3} = \frac{200,961.1829}{7,787,662} = 0.0258$$

$$\hat{\tau}_{B|A} = \frac{nU_2 - U_4}{n^2 - U_4} = \frac{397,208.4357}{4,617,672} = 0.0861$$

and

$$\hat{\tau} = \frac{200,961.1829 + 397,208.4357}{7,787,662 + 4,617,672} = 0.0482$$

The hypothesis $H_0^{(1)}$: $\tau_{A|B} = 0$ and $H_0^{(2)}$: $\tau_{B|A} = 0$ can be tested using equations 3.36 and 3.37. For these data, $U_{A|B}^2 = 3076 \times 6 \times (0.0258) = 476.2$ and $U_{B|A}^2 = 3076 \times 2 \times (0.0861) = 529.7$; both are significantly different from zero. The association between the two variables is statistically significant but of questionable practical significance because the improvement in predictability and the amount of explained variability are so slight.

The estimated asymptotic standard deviations of $\hat{\tau}_{A|B}$ and $\hat{\tau}_{B|A}$ can be computed from equation 3.32 and its symmetric counterpart: $\hat{\sigma}_\infty(\hat{\tau}_{A|B}) = (0.61386 \times 10^{-5})^{1/2} = 0.00248$ and $\hat{\sigma}_\infty(\hat{\tau}_{B|A}) = (0.48005 \times 10^{-4})^{1/2} = 0.00693$. These values can be used to construct confidence intervals for $\tau_{A|B}$ and $\tau_{B|A}$.

We cannot compute the variance of $\hat{\tau}$ directly, but the conservative method used here will often suffice. First, notice that

$$\sigma^2(aX_1 + bX_2) \leqslant [a\sigma(X_1) + b\sigma(X_2)]^2$$

for any two random variables (X_1, X_2) and any two constants (a, b). Now notice that

$$\hat{\tau} = a\hat{\tau}_{A|B} + (1 - a)\hat{\tau}_{B|A} \qquad [3.38]$$

where

$$a = \frac{n^2 - \sum\limits_{i=1}^{I} n_{i+}^2}{2n^2 - \sum\limits_{i=1}^{I} n_{i+}^2 - \sum\limits_{j=1}^{J} n_{+j}^2}$$

By setting $b = 1 - a$, $X_1 = \hat{\tau}_{A|B}$ and $X_2 = \hat{\tau}_{B|A}$ in equation 3.38, we see that

$$\hat{\sigma}_{\infty}^2(\hat{\tau}) \leqslant [0.62777 \, \hat{\sigma}_{\infty}(\hat{\tau}_{A|B}) + 0.37223 \, \hat{\sigma}_{\infty}(\hat{\tau}_{B|A})]^2$$

$$= (0.004134)^2 = 0.1709 \times 10^{-4}$$

Consequently, τ is also significantly different from zero.

The Goodman-Kruskal tau was first proposed by W. Allen Wallis. Goodman and Kruskal (1954, 1963, 1972) give asymptotic distributions under both the multinomial sampling model and the "product-multinomial" model (independent multinomial sampling at each level of one of the variables). Elementary discussions, with examples, are found in Blalock (1972), Reynolds (1977a, 1977b) and Bishop et al. (1975). Margolin and Light, in two joint papers (1974; Light and Margolin, 1971), demonstrate the equivalence of $\hat{R}_{A|B}^2$ and $\hat{\tau}_{A|B}$.

Measures of Agreement

As used so far, the term "association" is rather general. Two variables are said to be associated if they are not independent, or if one is useful in predicting the other. It is often of interest to measure *agreement*, which is a specific type of association. Suppose each of two judges (or raters) A and B independently classify items into one of I mutually exclusive categories, and we want a measure of agreement between the judges. In contingency table notation, n_{ij} is the number of objects assigned to category i by A and category j by B. The following simple example illustrates that a table may exhibit high association, but little or no agreement. Suppose ten items are classified by two judges as shown in the following table:

		B	
		1	2
A	1	0	5
	2	5	0

In terms of predictability, the ratings are perfectly associated, but the raters certainly are not in agreement!

How can agreement be measured? Surely, two judges agree on a given item if both assign it to the same category. The diagonal frequencies n_{11}, $n_{22}, \ldots, n_{II}$ are therefore of primary importance in measuring agreement. Three measures specifically constructed to measure agreement are discussed below.

COHEN'S κ AND WEIGHTED κ

Let p_{ij} denote the probability that an item is classified into category i by one judge and category j by another, where i and j range from 1 to I, inclusive. Then

$$\theta_1 = \sum_{i=1}^{I} p_{ii} \qquad [3.39]$$

represents the proportion of cases on which the judges agree. If the judges work independently, the proportion of times they agree purely by chance is

$$\theta_2 = \sum_{i=1}^{I} p_{i+} p_{+i} \qquad [3.40]$$

so $\theta_1 - \theta_2$ is a measure of agreement corrected for chance. To make this measure independent of the marginal totals, it is normalized by $1 - \theta_2$, the maximum possible value of $\theta_1 - \theta_2$ for the given sets of marginal totals $\{p_{i+}\}$ and $\{p_{+i}\}$. The resulting measure,

$$\kappa = \frac{\theta_1 - \theta_2}{1 - \theta_2} \qquad [3.41]$$

was proposed by Cohen (1960) as a measure of agreement, corrected for chance, between the classifications of a group of objects by two judges. Cohen's κ can also be interpreted as a measure of agreement between pairs of individuals, all of which are responding on the same scale to a given issue.

Values of κ can range from $-\theta_2/(1 - \theta_2)$ to 1 for a given set of marginal totals. If the judges are in complete agreement, $\theta_1 = 1$ and $\kappa = 1$, while $\kappa = -\theta_2/(1 - \theta_2)$ if the judges disagree completely. If the two classifications are independent so that $p_{i+} p_{+i} = p_{ii}$ for each i, $\theta_1 = \theta_2$ and $\kappa = 0$. It is possible to have $\kappa = 0$ even if the classifications are not independent. The measure in equation 3.41 is well defined if at least two cells of the table contain nonzero probabilities.

The maximum likelihood estimator of κ under the multinomial sampling model is

$$\hat{\kappa} = \frac{n \sum\limits_{i=1}^{I} n_{ii} - \sum\limits_{i=1}^{I} n_{i+} n_{+i}}{n^2 - \sum\limits_{i=1}^{I} n_{i+} n_{+i}}$$

When p_{ij} is replaced by $\hat{p}_{ij} = n_{ij}/n$, statements about the range of κ apply also to $\hat{\kappa}$.

For n sufficiently large, $\hat{\kappa}$ is approximately a normal variable with mean κ. The approximate large sample variance of $\hat{\kappa}$ is

$$\sigma_\infty^2(\hat{\kappa}) = \frac{1}{n} \left\{ \frac{\theta_1(1 - \theta_1)}{(1 - \theta_2)^2} + \frac{2(1 - \theta_1)(2\theta_1\theta_2 - \theta_3)}{(1 - \theta_2)^3} \right.$$
$$\left. + \frac{(1 - \theta_1)^2 (\theta_4 - 4\theta_2^2)}{(1 - \theta_2)^4} \right\} \qquad [3.42]$$

where θ_1 and θ_2 are defined by equations 3.39 and 3.40, respectively, and where

$$\theta_3 = \sum_{i=1}^{I} p_{ii}(p_{i+} + p_{+i}) \quad \text{and} \quad \theta_4 = \sum_{i=1}^{I} \sum_{j=1}^{J} p_{ij}(p_{j+} + p_{+i})^2$$

Under the hypothesis of independence, equation 3.42 reduces to

$$\sigma_\infty^2(\hat{\kappa}) = \frac{1}{n(1 - \theta_2)^2} \left[\theta_2 + \theta_2^2 - \sum_{i=1}^{I} p_{i+} p_{+i}(p_{i+} + p_{+i}) \right] \qquad [3.43]$$

Estimators of equations 3.42 and 3.43 are obtained as usual by substituting $\hat{p}_{ij} = n_{ij}/n$ for p_{ij}. The estimator obtained from equation 3.43 can be used to test the hypothesis $\kappa = 0$, while equation 3.42 can be used to establish confidence intervals for κ.

The calculations of $\hat{\kappa}$ and its variance are illustrated in the next example.

Example 2. Suppose 100 married couples are selected, and each spouse is asked to classify his or her marriage as happy (H), unhappy (U), or about average (A). The (fictitious) results are summarized in Table 3.

From equations 3.39 and 3.40 we get $\hat{\theta}_1 = 0.73$, $\hat{\theta}_2 = 0.335$, $\hat{\theta}_3 = 0.4935$, and $\hat{\theta}_4 = 0.4755$. Thus,

$$\hat{\kappa} = \frac{0.73 - 0.335}{1 - 0.335} = 0.5940$$

and its estimated large sample variance is, from equation 3.42,

$$\hat{\sigma}_{\infty}^2(\hat{\kappa}) = 0.004475 \qquad\qquad [3.44]$$

Approximate confidence intervals can be based on equation 3.44. However, this value should be replaced by $\hat{\sigma}_{\infty}^2(\hat{\kappa}) = 0.01983$ when testing the hypothesis $\kappa = 0$. From either a significance test or a confidence interval, we conclude that husbands and wives are in significantly greater agreement about their marriages than would be expected by chance.

Several extensions of κ have been proposed. One of the more important comes from introducing weights that permit the assignment of "degrees of agreement" to various responses. It could be argued in Example 2 that there is more agreement between a husband and wife who respond (H, A) than between a couple whose response is (H, U). If such comparisons can somehow be quantified in a meaningful way, this information can be incorporated into the calculation of κ by assigning a weight w_{ij} to each response category (i, j). In defining the weighted version of κ, Cohen (1968) requires (without loss of generality) that $0 \leqslant w_{ij} \leqslant 1$ and assumes that weights are interpretable as ratios; e.g., the weight 0.75 represents three times the agreement of the weight 0.25. With

$$\theta_1^* = \sum_{i=1}^{I} \sum_{j=1}^{J} w_{ij} p_{ij}$$

and

$$\theta_2^* = \sum_{i=1}^{I} \sum_{j=1}^{J} w_{ij} p_{i+} p_{+j}$$

the weighted version of kappa is defined by

$$\kappa_w = \frac{\theta_1^* - \theta_2^*}{1 - \theta_2^*}$$

Values of κ_w can range from $-\theta_2^*/(1 - \theta_2^*)$ to 1 for a given set of marginal totals. If the two ratings are in complete agreement, $\kappa_w = 1$, while $\kappa_w = 0$ if the two classifications are independent. The measure κ_w is well defined if at least two cells of the table contain nonzero probabilities.

The maximum likelihood estimator of κ_w under the multinomial sampling model is

$$\hat{\kappa}_w = \frac{n \sum\limits_{i=1}^{I} \sum\limits_{j=1}^{J} w_{ij} n_{ij} - \sum\limits_{i=1}^{I} \sum\limits_{j=1}^{J} w_{ij} n_{i+} n_{+j}}{n^2 - \sum\limits_{i=1}^{I} \sum\limits_{j=1}^{J} w_{ij} n_{i+} n_{+j}}$$

Statements about the range of κ_w apply to $\hat{\kappa}_w$ as well. For large samples, $\hat{\kappa}_w$ is approximately a normal variable with expected value κ_w and variance

$$\sigma_{\infty}^2(\hat{\kappa}_w) = \frac{1}{n(1 - \theta_2^*)^4} \left\{ \sum_{i=1}^{I} \sum_{j=1}^{J} p_{ij} [w_{ij}(1 - \theta_2^*) \right.$$
$$\left. - (\bar{w}_{i+} + \bar{w}_{+j})(1 - \theta_1^*)]^2 - (\theta_1^* \theta_2^* - 2\theta_2^* + \theta_1^*)^2 \right\} \quad [3.45]$$

where

$$\bar{w}_{i+} = \sum_{j=1}^{J} w_{ij} p_{+j}$$

and

$$\bar{w}_{+j} = \sum_{i=1}^{I} w_{ij} p_{i+}$$

If the two ratings are independent so that $\theta_1^* = \theta_2^*$ and $p_{ij} = p_{i+} p_{ij}$, equation 3.45 simplies to

$$\sigma_{\infty}^2(\hat{\kappa}_w) = \frac{1}{n(1 - \theta_2^*)^2} \left\{ \sum_{i=1}^{I} \sum_{j=1}^{J} p_{i+} p_{+j} [w_{ij} \right.$$
$$\left. - (\bar{w}_{i+} + \bar{w}_{+j})]^2 - \theta_2^{*2} \right\} \quad [3.46]$$

An estimate obtained from equation 3.46 can be used to test the hypothesis $\kappa_w = 0$, but equation 3.45 should be used in testing other hypotheses or for constructing confidence intervals.

Note that κ is a special case of κ_w. If

$$w_{ij} = \begin{cases} 1, i = j \\ 0, i \neq j \end{cases} \quad [3.47]$$

then $\kappa_w = \kappa$ and $\hat{\kappa}_w = \hat{\kappa}$. Furthermore, if equation 3.47 holds, $\bar{w}_{i+} = p_{+i}$ and $\bar{w}_{+j} = p_{j+}$, so equations 3.45 and 3.46 reduce to equations 3.42 and 3.43, respectively.

Example 2 (continued). We shall calculate $\hat{\kappa}_w$ for the data of Table 3 using the following weight matrix.

Wife

		H	A	U
	H	1.0	0.5	0.0
Husband	A	0.5	1.0	0.5
	U	0.0	0.5	1.0

Since $\hat{\theta}_1^* = 0.855$ and $\hat{\theta}_2^* = 0.570$,

$$\hat{\kappa}_w = \frac{0.855 - 0.570}{1 - 0.570} = 0.6628$$

Further, $\overline{w}_{1+}, \overline{w}_{2+}, \overline{w}_{3+}, \overline{w}_{+1}, \overline{w}_{+2}$, and $\overline{w}_{+3}$ have the values $0.575, 0.675, 0.425,$ $0.5, 0.7$, and 0.7 respectively, so equation 3.45 yields

$$\hat{\sigma}_\infty^2(\hat{\kappa}_w) = 0.003449 \qquad [3.48]$$

This value (equation 3.48) can be used for making inferences about κ_w, except that the value $\hat{\sigma}_\infty^2(\hat{\kappa}) = 0.005829$ obtained from equation 3.46 should be used for testing the hypothesis $\kappa_w = 0$.

The measures κ and κ_w were proposed by Cohen in 1960 and 1968, respectively. The main properties of both estimators are contained in the paper by Fleiss, Cohen, and Everitt (1969), as well as in the more recent books of Bishop et al. (1975) and Reynolds (1977a). All references cited contain numerical examples. Fleiss (1971) and Light (1971) have generalized κ to measure agreement between more than two groups or judges.

TABLE 3
Self-Assessment of Marital Happiness by 100 Couples

		Wife			
		H(1)	*A(2)*	*U(3)*	n_{i+}
	H(1)	28	2	0	30
Husband	A(2)	10	25	5	40
	U(3)	2	8	20	30
	n_{+j}	40	35	25	100

THE COLEMAN-LIGHT MEASURE OF CONDITIONAL AGREEMENT

The Coleman-Light measure of conditional agreement is similar to κ, except that here probabilities are calculated conditionally with respect to a particular rating of one of the judges. Now let A_i (or B_i) denote the event that an item is assigned to category i by rater A (or B), and suppose that we are interested in agreement only for those items classified into a particular category i (a row of the table) by rater A. The conditional probability that B places the item in category i, given that A has placed it in category i, is

$$\theta_1^* = P(B_i | A_i) = \frac{P(A_i B_i)}{P(A_i)} = \frac{p_{ii}}{p_{i+}}$$

Likewise, assuming independence,

$$\theta_2^* = p_{i+} p_{+i}/p_{i+} = p_{+i}$$

The conditional agreement between the two raters for those items assigned to the ith category by the first is now defined as

$$\kappa_i = \frac{\theta_1^* - \theta_2^*}{1 - \theta_2^*} = \frac{\dfrac{p_{ii}}{p_{i+}} - p_{+i}}{1 - p_{+i}} = \frac{p_{ii} - p_{i+} p_{+i}}{p_{i+} - p_{i+} p_{+i}}$$

Values of κ_i can range from $-\theta_2^*/(1 - \theta_2^*)$ to 1 for given sets of marginals $\{p_{i+}\}$ and $\{p_{+i}\}$. In the case of perfect (conditional) agreement, $\kappa_i = 1$, while $\kappa_i = 0$ if the classifications are independent. By writing $\kappa_i = \nu_i/\delta_i$, it is easy to see that

$$\kappa = \sum_{i=1}^{I} \nu_i / \sum_{i=1}^{I} \delta_i$$

showing that κ is a weighted sum of the κ_is.

The maximum likelihood estimator of κ_i under the multinomial sampling model is

$$\hat{\kappa}_i = \frac{n n_{ii} - n_{i+} n_{+i}}{n n_{i+} - n_{i+} n_{+i}}$$

For large samples, $\hat{\kappa}_i$ is approximately a normal variable with mean κ_i and variance

$$\sigma_\infty^2(\hat{\kappa}_i) = \frac{1}{n} \frac{p_{i+} - p_{ii}}{p_{i+}^3 (1 - p_{+i})^3} [(p_{i+} - p_{ii})(p_{i+}p_{+i} - p_{ii})$$

$$+ p_{ii}(1 - p_{i+} - p_{+i} + p_{ii})] \qquad [3.49]$$

Under the hypothesis of independence, equation 3.49 becomes

$$\sigma_\infty^2(\hat{\kappa}_i) = \frac{1}{n} \frac{p_{+i}(1 - p_{i+})}{p_{i+}(1 - p_{+i})} \qquad [3.50]$$

Both equation 3.49 and equation 3.50 can be estimated by substituting observed proportions for cell probabilities. The latter should be used for testing $\kappa_i = 0$, but equation 3.49 should be used for all other inferences.

Example 2 (continued). Calculating the measure of agreement between husband and wife for each possible response of the husband from the data in Table 3, we get

$$\hat{\kappa}_1 = \frac{100 \times 28 - 30 \times 40}{100 \times 30 - 30 \times 40} = \frac{1600}{1800} = 0.8889$$

$$\hat{\kappa}_2 = \frac{100 \times 25 - 40 \times 35}{100 \times 40 - 40 \times 35} = \frac{1100}{2600} = 0.4231$$

$$\hat{\kappa}_3 = \frac{100 \times 20 - 30 \times 25}{100 \times 30 - 30 \times 25} = \frac{1250}{2250} = 0.5556$$

From equation 3.49 we obtain $\hat{\sigma}_\infty^2(\hat{\kappa}_1) = 0.0054595$. Likewise, $\hat{\sigma}_\infty^2(\hat{\kappa}_2) = 0.0092598$ and $\hat{\sigma}_\infty^2(\hat{\kappa}_3) = 0.010316$. For testing H_0: $\kappa_1 = 0$, the variance estimates obtained from equation 3.50 are $\hat{\sigma}_\infty^2(\hat{\kappa}_1) = 0.01556$, $\hat{\sigma}_\infty^2(\hat{\kappa}_2) = 0.008077$, and $\hat{\sigma}_\infty^2(\hat{\kappa}_3) = 0.007778$, respectively. All three measures are significantly different from zero, but it appears there is somewhat more agreement between couples in which the husband considers his marriage happy than in the other two cases. Finally, note that

$$\frac{1600 + 1100 + 1250}{1800 + 2600 + 2250} = \frac{3950}{6650} = 0.5940$$

which equals the earlier estimate of κ.

The measure κ_1 was first proposed by Coleman (1966) and has been studied in detail by Light (1969, 1971). All the results presented here, with another example, are found in Bishop et al. (1975).

Special Measures for 2 × 2 Contingency Tables

Fourfold tables provide a relatively simple context in which to study measures of association. Three constraints are required to ensure that cell probabilities add correctly, so a single probability placed in any cell of the table fixes the probabilities in the other three cells. In other words, there is only "one degree of freedom for association" in a fourfold table. Consequently, nearly all measures reduce to functions of either the cross-product (odds) ratio or the mean square contingency. Further, distinctions between symmetric and asymmetic measures disappear, as do distinctions between measures for ordinal and nominal data.

MEASURES BASED ON THE CROSS-PRODUCT RATIO

The cross-product ratio, or odds ratio, plays an important role in the construction of log-linear models. The cross-product ratio is defined by

$$\alpha = \frac{p_{11} p_{22}}{p_{12} p_{21}} = \frac{p_{11}/p_{12}}{p_{21}/p_{22}} = \frac{p_{11}/p_{21}}{p_{12}/p_{22}} . \qquad [3.51]$$

The origin of the term "cross-product ratio" is evident from the first expression for α in equation 3.51, while the latter two expressions are the source of the term "odds ratio." Actually the "log odds ratio"

$$\alpha^* = \log \alpha$$

is often used instead of α because it has several nice mathematical properties. Because $\log \alpha^{-1} = -\log \alpha$, equal but opposite associations yield values of α^* with the same magnitude but opposite sign. The log odds ratio α^* is a symmetric measure that varies from $-\infty$ to ∞ and has the value $\log 1 = 0$ in the case of independence. The log odds ratio, like α, is unchanged if the rows of columns of the table are rescaled. The insensitivity of the odds ratio to marginal distribution means that comparisons can be made among tables obtained by sampling different populations (i.e., tables with different marginal distributions).

For present purposes, however, it is α which is of greatest interest. The maximum likelihood estimator of equation 3.51 under both the multinomial and product binomial[6] sampling models is

$$\hat{\alpha} = (n_{11} n_{22})/(n_{12} n_{21})$$

The estimator $\hat{\alpha}$ is approximately normally distributed for large samples under both the multinomial and product binomial models. Its asymptotic mean is α, and its approximate large sample variance is

$$\sigma_\infty^2(\hat{\alpha}) = \frac{\alpha^2}{n} \left(\frac{1}{p_{11}} + \frac{1}{p_{12}} + \frac{1}{p_{21}} + \frac{1}{p_{22}} \right) \qquad [3.52]$$

Provided all cell counts are positive, an estimate of equation 3.52 obtained by replacing p_{ij} with $\hat{p}_{ij} = n_{ij}/n$: Thus

$$\hat{\sigma}_\infty^2(\hat{\alpha}) = \hat{\alpha}^2 \left(\frac{1}{n_{11}} + \frac{1}{n_{12}} + \frac{1}{n_{21}} + \frac{1}{n_{22}} \right) \qquad [3.53]$$

If any observed frequency is zero, then formula 3.53 must be modified. One very simple modification is to add 0.5 to each cell count when any observed frequency is zero.

Two measures proposed by Yule are both functions of the cross-product ratio. Yule's (1900) "measure of association" is defined as

$$Q = \frac{p_{11}p_{22} - p_{12}p_{21}}{p_{11}p_{22} + p_{12}p_{21}} = \frac{\alpha - 1}{\alpha + 1} \qquad [3.54]$$

and his "measure of colligation" (1912) is defined as

$$Y = \frac{\sqrt{p_{11}p_{22}} - \sqrt{p_{12}p_{21}}}{\sqrt{p_{11}p_{22}} + \sqrt{p_{12}p_{21}}} = \frac{\sqrt{\alpha} - 1}{\sqrt{\alpha} + 1} \qquad [3.55]$$

Note that $Q = 2Y/(1 + Y^2)$. By replacing α with $\hat{\alpha}$ in equations 3.54 and 3.55 we obtain the estimators

$$\hat{Q} = \frac{\hat{\alpha} - 1}{\hat{\alpha} + 1} \qquad [3.56]$$

and

$$\hat{Y} = \frac{\sqrt{\hat{\alpha}} - 1}{\sqrt{\hat{\alpha}} + 1} \qquad [3.57]$$

respectively. Both Q and Y are maximum likelihood estimators under both the multinomial and product binomial models.

Both Y and Q are symmetric measures, both are unchanged by scale changes applied to rows or columns of the table, and both can assume all values between -1 and 1, inclusive. Both measures equal 1 when $\alpha = \infty$ (i.e., $p_{12}p_{21} = 0$), equal -1 if $\alpha = 0$ ($p_{11}p_{22} = 0$), and are 0 if $\alpha = 1$ (the case of independence). For other values of α, $|Y| < |Q|$, but the measures are consistent in the sense that $Q_1 > Q_2$ for a pair of tables whenever $Y_1 > Y_2$.

The estimators $\hat{Q}$ and $\hat{Y}$ possess all the properties of Q and Y, respectively. Moreover, for large samples $\hat{Q}$ and $\hat{Y}$ are distributed approximately as normal variables with means Q and Y, respectively, and large-sample variables.

$$\sigma^2_\infty(\hat{Q}) = \frac{(1 - Q^2)^2}{4n} \left(\frac{1}{p_{11}} + \frac{1}{p_{12}} + \frac{1}{p_{21}} + \frac{1}{p_{22}} \right)$$

and

$$\sigma^2_\infty(\hat{Y}) = \frac{(1 - Y^2)^2}{16n} \left(\frac{1}{p_{11}} + \frac{1}{p_{12}} + \frac{1}{p_{21}} + \frac{1}{p_{22}} \right)$$

The corresponding estimators are

$$\hat{\sigma}^2_\infty(\hat{Q}) = \frac{(1 - \hat{Q}^2)^2}{4} \left(\frac{1}{n_{11}} + \frac{1}{n_{12}} + \frac{1}{n_{21}} + \frac{1}{n_{22}} \right) \qquad [3.58]$$

and

$$\hat{\sigma}^2_\infty(\hat{Y}) = \frac{(1 - \hat{Y}^2)^2}{16} \left(\frac{1}{n_{11}} + \frac{1}{n_{12}} + \frac{1}{n_{21}} + \frac{1}{n_{22}} \right) \qquad [3.59]$$

As with the variance of α, equations 3.58 and 3.59 cannot be used without modification if any cell frequency is zero.

What about meaningful interpretations of Yule's measures? Consider Q first. Denote the classifications with respect to the (dichotomous) variables A and B of two individuals selected at random from the population by (a_1, b_1) and (a_2, b_2). Three possibilities exist: the pairs are *concordant* if $(a_2 - a_1)(b_2 - b_1) > 0$, *discordant* if $(a_2 - a_1)(b_2 - b_1) > 0$, or *tied* if $a_1 = a_2$ or $b_1 = b_2$ (see the section on Kendall's τ in Chapter 4). These events have probabilities $2p_{11}p_{22}$, $2p_{12}p_{21}$, and $1 - 2(p_{11}p_{22} + p_{12}p_{21})$, respectively. Since $2(p_{11}p_{22} + p_{12}p_{21})$ is the probability that the pairs are not tied and

$$Q = \frac{p_{11}p_{22}}{p_{11}p_{22} + p_{12}p_{21}} - \frac{p_{12}p_{21}}{p_{11}p_{22} + p_{12}p_{21}}$$

Q is the difference between the conditional probability that the A and B scores are concordant (have like order) and the conditional probability that

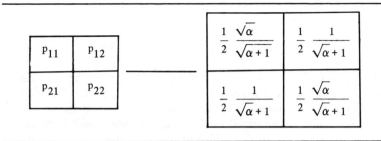

Figure 1: Construction of a Standardized Table

the scores are discordant (have unlike order), the condition in both cases being that scores are not tied.

For 2×2 tables, Yule's Q is identical to the Goodman-Kruskal γ (see the section on Measures Related to Kendall's τ_b in Chapter 5). The interpretation of Q given here is identical to that given for γ in Chapter 5.

The simplest interpretation of Yule's Y is given in terms of standardized tables. A standardized table results from adjusting the probabilities of a 2×2 table so that both row and column marginal totals become $(1/2, 1/2)$, while the cross-product ratio remains unchanged. The construction of a standardized table is shown in Figure 1. Let

$$p_{11}^* = p_{22}^* = \frac{1}{2} \frac{\sqrt{\alpha}}{\sqrt{\alpha}+1}$$

and

$$p_{12}^* = p_{21}^* = \frac{1}{2} \frac{1}{\sqrt{\alpha}+1}$$

Yule argues that standardization has removed all information about marginals, so a "reasonable measure of association" is the difference between the probabilities in the diagonal and off-diagonal cells. This difference is simply

$$(p_{11}^* + p_{22}^*) - (p_{12}^* + p_{21}^*) = \frac{\sqrt{\alpha}-1}{\sqrt{\alpha}+1} = Y$$

Finally, Y is a measure of proportional reduction in predictive error for standardized 2×2 tables, since then all versions of both the Goodman-Kruskal τ and the Goodman-Kruskal λ are equal to $|Y|$.

The measures Q and Y were originally studied by Yule (1900, 1912). Thorough discussions of measures of association based upon the odds ratio are given by Bishop et al. (1975) and Reynolds (1977a). Both contain numerical examples.

MEASURES BASED ON THE CORRELATION COEFFICIENT

The Pearson product-moment correlation coefficient has been so widely used for so long with continuous data that it is only natural to find modifications suitable for discrete data. For a 2×2 table in which the two levels of both row and column variables A and B are coded 0 and 1, Pearson's product-moment correlation coefficient (see equation 4.1 in Chapter 4) can be written as

$$\rho = \frac{p_{22} - p_{2+}p_{+2}}{(p_{1+}p_{2+}p_{+1}p_{+2})^{1/2}} = \frac{p_{11}p_{22} - p_{12}p_{21}}{(p_{1+}p_{2+}p_{+1}p_{+2})^{1/2}} \qquad [3.60]$$

We can see from equations 3.60 and 3.1 that $\rho^2 = \phi^2$; hence, measures based on the correlation coefficient are functions of Pearson's coefficient of mean square contingency and vice versa.

Since $\rho^2 = \phi^2$, measures based on one of them have the properties inherited from both. In particular, ρ is symmetric and remains unchanged if the rows or columns are scored by any positive linear transformation. If rows or columns, but not both, are interchanged, ρ changes sign; ρ is unchanged if both rows and columns are interchanged. Sinc ρ is a correlation coefficient, we know that $-1 \leqslant \rho \leqslant 1$. If A and B are independent, then $\rho = 0$. Moreover, $\rho = 1$ if $p_{12} = p_{21} = 0$, and conversely. Likewise, $\rho = -1$ if $p_{11} = p_{22} = 0$, and conversely.

The sign of ρ clearly depends on the labels assigned to the categories of A and B. This behavior is undesirable in a measure for nominal data because category labels are purely arbitrary. The use of ρ with fourfold (nominal) tables is an exception because it is easy to determine which categories are positively correlated regardless of the sign of ρ or how the categories are labeled.

Unlike the odds ratio, ρ is not independent of the marginal values of the table. For a standardized table, where the effect of marginal total has been removed, $\rho = Y$. For nonstandardized tables, $\rho = Y$ only if $\rho = 0$, 1, or -1; otherwise, $|\rho| < |Y|$. For tables with a given cross-product ratio, the difference between ρ and Y tends to increase as the disparity between marginal totals increases.

For interpretive purposes, ρ is best viewed as a correlation coefficient (see the section on Pearson's Product-Moment Correlation in Chapter 4). As such, ρ^2 is the proportion of variability in one of the variables explained by knowledge of the other, and is a measure of the degree of colinearity between the two variables A and B.

The maximum likelihood estimator of ρ under the multinomial sampling model is

$$R = \frac{n_{11}n_{22} - n_{12}n_{21}}{(n_{1+}n_{2+}n_{+1}n_{+2})^{1/2}}$$

For large samples, R is approximately distributed as a normal variable with mean ρ and variance

$$\sigma_\infty^2(R) = \frac{1}{n} \left\{ (1 - \rho^2) + \left(1 + \frac{1}{2}\rho^2\right) \frac{(p_{1+} - p_{2+})(p_{+1} - p_{+2})}{(p_{1+}p_{2+}p_{+1}p_{+2})^{1/2}} \right.$$
$$\left. - \frac{3}{4}\rho^2 \left[\frac{(p_{1+} - p_{2+})^2}{p_{1+}p_{2+}} + \frac{(p_{+1} - p_{+2})^2}{p_{+1}p_{+2}} \right] \right\} \qquad [3.61]$$

Equation 3.61 reduces to $\sigma_\infty^2(R) = 1/n$ under the hypothesis of independence, and to $\sigma_\infty^2(R) = (1 - \rho^2)/n$ for a standardized table. To estimate $\sigma_\infty^2(R)$, we substitute $\hat{p}_{ij} = n_{ij}/n$ for p_{ij} and the observed value of R for ρ in the appropriate formula.

Several equalities among various measures have already been mentioned. For any 2×2 table, Yule's Q is equal to the Goodman-Kruskal γ. Further, $\rho = Y$ for any standardized table, and all versions of the Goodman-Kruskal τ and Goodman-Kruskal λ equal $|Y|$. Also, ρ^2, ϕ^2, τ_b^2, $\tau_{A|B}$, $\tau_{B|A}$, and τ^2 are all equal for any 2×2 table.[7] Thus, of all the measures considered, only Q and ρ are distinct for fourfold tables.

The choice between Q and ρ is dictated by two considerations: (1) whether we want a measure sensitive to marginal totals, and (2) whether we want one that has the value ± 1 when only one cell of the table is zero.[8] Yule's Q is insensitive to marginal totals, while ρ is not. On the other hand, $Q = \pm 1$ when only one cell of the table is zero, but unequal marginal totals can constrain the upper limit for $|\rho|$ to be less than one.

Bishop et al. (1975) and Reynolds (1977a) discuss measures based on the correlation coefficient. Both contain numerical examples.

4. MEASURES OF CORRELATION FOR CONTINUOUS (INTERVAL) DATA

Pearson's product-moment correlation coefficient and Spearman's rank correlation coefficient are among the oldest measures of association. The product-moment correlation coefficient is still one of the most widely used. Nearly all the measures for ordinal data can be traced to Kendall's

348

coefficient of concordance. All three measures are discussed in this chapter.

We will suppose throughout this chapter that $(X_1, Y_1), \ldots, (X_n, Y_n)$ is a random sample of size n from a continuous bivariate population (X, Y). We will also suppose that X and Y have means μ_X and μ_Y and variances σ_X^2 and σ_Y^2, respectively.

Theoretically, we need not worry about ties, because the probability is zero that two observations are tied on either X or Y, or both. Ties do occur in practice, however, and estimators that take them into account are quite naturally used for ordinal data.

Pearson's Product-Moment Correlation Coefficient

Since it was fashioned into a statistical tool by Galton, Edgeworth, and K. Pearson in the late nineteenth century, no measure of association has enjoyed such widespread use (and misuse) as the product-moment correlation coefficient. The product-moment correlation coefficient bears Pearson's name because of his famous 1896 paper dealing with its properties.

Let (X, Y) be a continuous bivariate population. Then the product-moment correlation coefficient is defined by

$$\rho = \frac{\text{Cov}(X, Y)}{\sigma_X \sigma_Y} = \frac{\sigma(X, Y)}{\sigma_X \sigma_Y} \qquad [4.1]$$

where σ_X and σ_Y are the standard deviations of X and Y, and $\sigma(X, Y)$ is the covariance between the two variables.[9]

Properties of equation 4.1 are closely related to the problem of linear prediction. The *linear prediction problem* is that of finding the best linear function of X to predict Y in the sense of minimizing the mean squared predictive error. That is, among all linear functions $h(X) = \alpha + \beta X$, we want the one which minimizes $E(Y - h(X))^2$. The best linear predictor of Y in terms of X is known to be

$$h^*(X) = \mu_Y + \frac{\sigma(X, Y)}{\sigma_X^2} (X - \mu_X) = \mu_Y + \frac{\rho \sigma_Y}{\sigma_X} (X - \mu_X)$$

$$= \alpha_1^* + \beta_1^* X \qquad [4.2]$$

where $\beta_1^* = \rho \sigma_Y / \sigma_X$ and $\alpha_1^* = \mu_Y - \beta_1 \mu_X$. The corresponding mean squared predictive error is

$$\text{MSPE}^* = \sigma_Y^2 (1 - \rho^2) \qquad [4.3]$$

Note also that

$$V(h^*(X)) = V(\alpha_1^* + \beta_1^* X) = \sigma_Y^2 \rho^2 \qquad [4.4]$$

The function h* is called the *linear regressionof Y on X.*

Formulas 4.3 and 4.4 provide us with interpretations of ρ^2. From equation 4.3, we see that $1 - \rho^2$ is the proportion of variability in Y which is "free from X" or "unexplained by X." In other words, ρ^2 is the portion of the variance of Y that can be attributed to its linear regression on X, or that can be "explained" by its regression on X. If $\rho^2 = 1$, then all of σ_Y^2 is explained. In this case, all observations fall on the line

$$Y = \mu_Y + \rho \, \frac{\sigma_Y}{\sigma_X} \, (X - \mu_X)$$

If $\rho^2 = 0$, then MSPE* $= \rho_Y^2$, so no variability in Y is explained by its regression on X. It is important to remember that ρ is a measure of *linear* correlation. Formula 4.4 says that ρ^2 is the "variance of the 'best' estimate of Y based on X, relative to the variance of Y" (Kruskal, 1958: 817).

The roles of X and Y can be interchanged in the above discussion. If so, we obtain

$$g^*(Y) = \mu_X + \frac{\rho \sigma_X}{\sigma_Y} \, (Y - \mu_Y) = \alpha_2^* + \beta_2^* + \beta_2^* Y \qquad [4.5]$$

as the *linear regression of X on Y.* In equation 4.5, we see that $\beta_2^* = \rho \sigma_X / \sigma_Y$. It follows from equations 4.2 and 4.5 that

$$\beta_1^* \beta_2^* = \frac{\rho \sigma_Y}{\sigma_X} \, \frac{\rho \sigma_X}{\sigma_Y} = \rho^2$$

The estimates obtained by minimizing

$$Q = \sum_{i=1}^{n} (Y_i - \alpha - \beta X_i)^2$$

with respect to α and β for a random sample $(X_1, Y_1), \ldots, (X_n, Y_n)$ are called the *least squares* as estimates of α_1^* and β_1^*. These estimates are universally known to be

$$\hat{\beta}_1^* = \sum_{i=1}^{n} (X_i - \bar{X}) (Y_i - \bar{Y}) / \sum_{i=1}^{n} (X_i - \bar{X})^2 \qquad [4.6]$$

and $\quad \hat{\alpha}_1^* = \bar{Y} - \hat{\beta}_1^* \bar{X}.$

One might ask if a significant linear relationship exists between X and Y. The question can be answered affirmatively if the hypothesis H_o: $\beta_1^* = 0$ is rejected. We must make some assumptions about the distribution of $\hat{\beta}_1^*$ in order to proceed.

The usual assumptions are that Y has a normal distribution for each X and that the Xs are *known constants*, presumably under the control of the investigator. Under these assumptions, the statistic

$$T^* = \hat{\beta}_1^* / \hat{\sigma} (\hat{\beta}_1^*) \qquad [4.7]$$

obtained by dividing equation 4.6 by its estimated standard deviation, has a t distribution with n – 2 degrees of freedom under H_o.

Now suppose (X, Y) is some bivariate population, and let Y|x be a random variable whose distribution is that of Y for a given value x of X; that is, the distribution of Y|X is the conditional distribution of Y, given X. When X and Y are jointly normal, Y|X is a normal random variable with mean

$$\mu_{Y|X} = \mu_Y + \frac{\rho \sigma_Y}{\sigma_X} (X - \mu_X) \qquad [4.8]$$

and variance $\sigma_{Y/X}^2 = \sigma_Y^2 (1 - \rho^2)$.

Among all predictors of Y in terms of X, it is known that the conditional mean of Y, given X, is the one with minimum mean squared predictive error. Since equations 4.2 and 4.8 are identical, the best linear predictor and the best overall predictor coincide in the normal case. It is for this reason that the normal distribution is so closely associated with least squares regression theory.

We have seen that the distribution of (X, Y) is concentrated on a line if $\rho^2 = 1$. Further, ρ ranges from –1 to 1, and if X and Y are independent, then $\rho = 0$. These properties hold regardless of whether or not (X, Y) has a bivariate normal distribution. However, $\rho = 0$ does not imply that X and Y are independent *unless* X and Y have a bivariate normal distribution.

Now, let $(X_1, Y_1), \ldots, (X_n, Y_n)$ be a sample from the bivariate population (X, Y). It is natural to estimate ρ with its sample analogue:

$$R = \frac{\sum\limits_{i=1}^{n} (Y_i - \bar{Y})(X_i - \bar{X})}{\left[\sum\limits_{i=1}^{n} (X_i - \bar{X})^2 \sum\limits_{i=1}^{n} (Y_i - \bar{Y})^2\right]^{1/2}} \qquad [4.9]$$

For bivariate normal populations, equation 4.9 is the maximum likelihood estimator of ρ; it is the method-of-moments estimator of ρ for other distributions. Like ρ, R ranges from −1 to 1, inclusive.

What is the distribution of R? We consider this question only for samples from a bivariate normal population. As usual, there are two cases, depending on whether or not $\rho = 0$. If $\rho = 0$, the distribution of R is fairly easy to write down (see Morrison, 1976). It is more convient to work with the transformed variable

$$T = R \left(\frac{n-2}{1-R^2}\right)^{1/2} \qquad [4.10]$$

than directly with R. When $\rho = 0$, equation 4.10 has Student's t distribution with n − 2 degrees of freedom. The hypothesis H_o: $\rho = 0$ can be tested against a suitable alternative by referring the computed value of T to tables of the t distribution with n − 2 degrees of freedom.[10]

When $\rho \neq 0$, the distribution of R is known (see Anderson, 1958), but it is too complicated to present here. Indeed, an approximation based on Fisher's "z transformation" is much more widely used. Fisher (1921) showed that the variable

$$Z = \frac{1}{2} \ln \frac{1+R}{1-R} \qquad [4.11]$$

is distributed approximately as a normal variable with mean

$$\mu_Z \overset{\circ}{=} \frac{1}{2} \ln \frac{1+\rho}{1-\rho}$$

and variance

$$\sigma^2(Z) \overset{\circ}{=} 1/(n-3)$$

Using equation 4.11, it is possible (1) to test hypotheses of the form H_o: $\rho = \rho_o$ (where $\rho_o \neq 0$) against suitable alternatives, (2) to establish confidence intervals for ρ, and (3) to compare values of R obtained from two independent multivariate normal samples. The interested reader is referred to Morrison (1976) for details and examples.

From equation 4.1, it would appear that ρ treats the variables X and Y symmetrically. However, the discussion of conditional distributions implies that one variable must be considered "independent" and the other "dependent." It turns out that for inferential purposes the view we adopt is immaterial. When $\rho = 0$, Fisher (1915) showed that the distribution of R is the same whether or not X is normal, provided only that Y is normal. Thus the fact that the statistics in equations 4.7 and 4.10 have the same distribution is no coincidence! (In other cases, the distribution of R *does* depend on X, however.)

We have seen that the correlation coefficient ρ has a number of desirable properties: (1) It ranges from −1 to 1, inclusive, (2) it is zero when X and Y are independent, and (3) it has a straightforward interpretation in terms of "proportion of variability explained" or "degree of linearity." In the normal case, (4) the estimator R has the same distribution when the underlying variables are treated symmetrically as when they are not, and (5) the distribution of R is known and easy to approximate. Finally, ρ characterizes the correlational structure between X and Y in the normal case because the regression of Y on X, or vice versa, is linear. In a sense, ρ is the prototype for other measures discussed in this monograph. All have been defined so as to preserve one or more properties of ρ in other contexts.

A discussion of correlation and regression theory can be found in any good elementary statistics textbook. A classical treatment is found in Snedecor and Cochran (1967). The distributional results involving R are given by Morrison (1976). The interpretation of ρ is given by Kruskal (1958).

Kendall's τ

Two pairs of observation (X_i, Y_i) and (X_j, Y_j) are said to be *concordant* if either $X_i < X_j$ and $Y_i < Y_j$ or $X_i > X_j$ and $Y_i > Y_j$; that is, the pairs are concordant if the larger of the two X values is paired with the larger Y value. Equivalently, the pairs are concordant if

$$(X_j - X_i)(Y_j - Y_i) > 0$$

The pairs are said to be *discordant* if the larger X value is paired with the smaller Y value, that is, if

$$(X_j - X_i)(Y_j - Y_i) < 0$$

Pairs for which

$$(X_j - X_i)(Y_j - Y_i) = 0$$

or pairs for which either $X_i = X_j$ or $Y_i = Y_j$ are said to be *tied*.

Let π_c, π_d, and π_t be the probabilities, respectively, that the two randomly selected pairs are concordant, discordant, or tied. In symbols, we have

$$\pi_c = P[X_j - X_i)(Y_j - Y_i) > 0] \tag{4.12}$$

$$\pi_d = P[(X_j - X_i)(Y_j - Y_i) < 0] \tag{4.13}$$

and

$$\pi_t = P[(X_j - X_i)(Y_j - Y_i) = 0] \tag{4.14}$$

Two pairs of observations are necessarily concordant, discordant, or tied. Consequently, the probabilities (equations 4.12 through 4.14) must sum to one:

$$\pi_c + \pi_d + \pi_t = 1 \tag{4.15}$$

Kendall's coefficient of concordance is defined by

$$\tau = \pi_c - \pi_d \tag{4.16}$$

where π_c and π_d are given by equations 4.12 and 4.13, respectively. The coefficient τ is easy to interpret: If two observations (X_i, Y_i) and (X_j, Y_j) are selected at random from the population (X, Y), τ is the probability that they are concordant minus the probability that they are discordant.

If the population (X, Y) is continuous, $\pi_c + \pi_d = 1$ because $\pi = 0$ by assumption. Consequently, τ can range from -1 to 1. If X and Y are monotonically related,[11] $\tau = 1$ or $\tau = -1$, depending on whether the relationship is positive or negative. In particular, if the order of the population values when ranked according to X is the same as when they are ranked according to Y, $\tau = 1$. On the other hand, $\tau = -1$ if one ordering is the reverse of the other. When X and Y are independent, two observations are as likely to be discordant as concordant, so $\tau = 0$. The converse of the last statement need not be true: It is possible for τ to equal zero even though X and Y are not independent.

A natural estimator of τ is

$$\hat{\tau}_a = (C - D)/\binom{n}{2} = \frac{2(C - D)}{n(n - 1)}$$ [4.17]

where C is the number of concordant pairs, D is the number of discordant pairs, and $\binom{n}{2} = n(n - 1)/2$ is the total number of pairs of observations in a sample of size n. If the observations (X_i, Y_i) are arranged so that the Xs are in increasing order, the D turns out to be the minimum number of transpositions necessary to arrange the Ys in increasing order. For this reason, $\hat{\tau}_a$ is sometimes called a "coefficient of disarray."

Theoretically, $E(\hat{\tau}_a) = \tau$ for continuous populations, so $\hat{\tau}_a$ is an unbiased estimator of τ. Nevertheless, $\hat{\tau}_a$ is not a very good estimator of τ when ties are present in the data. The numerator of equation 4.17 is computed using only pairs that are not tied, while the denominator $\binom{n}{2}$ is the total number of pairs in the sample, both tied and otherwise. For this reason, $\hat{\tau}_a$ has a tendency to underestimate τ in the presence of ties.

Ideally, we would like an estimator in which the denominator, like the numerator, decreases as the proportion of ties in the sample increases. To get such an estimator, we must take a closer look at the ties. Consider a set of m observations that all have the same X value. There are $\binom{m}{2}$ pairs in this set, none of which is counted in computing C - D. The total number of pairs not counted in computing C - D because of tied X values is

$$U = \sum_i \binom{m_i}{2}$$ [4.18]

where m_i is the number of observations in the ith set of tied X values, and the sum extends over all sets of tied X values. Likewise, the total number of pairs not counted in computing C - D because of tied Y values is

$$V = \sum_j \binom{n_j}{2}$$ [4.19]

where n_j is the number of observations in the jth set of tied Y values, and the sum extends over all sets of tied Y values.

Starting with $\hat{\tau}_a$, it can be argued that we should decrease the denominator by U to compensate for tied Xs and by V to compensate for tied Ys. That is, the denominator of the estimator we seek should be a function of

$$\binom{n}{2} - U = \binom{n}{2} - \sum_i \binom{m_i}{2} \qquad [4.20]$$

and

$$\binom{n}{2} - V = \binom{n}{2} - \sum_j \binom{n_j}{2} \qquad [4.21]$$

The second estimator proposed by Kendall is obtained by replacing the denominator of equation 4.17 with the geometric mean of equations 4.20 and 4.21. The resulting estimator is

$$\hat{\tau}_b = \frac{C - D}{\left\{\left[\binom{n}{2} - U\right]\left[\binom{n}{2} - V\right]\right\}^{1/2}}$$

$$= 2(C - D)/\left\{[n(n-1) - 2U][n(n-1) - 2V]\right\}^{1/2} \qquad [4.22]$$

where U and V are defined by equations 4.18 and 4.19, respectively.

The distinction between $\hat{\tau}_a$ and $\hat{\tau}_b$ is best illustrated by a simple example.

Example 3. Consider the following eight observations.

Observation	1	2	3	4	5	6	7	8
X	1	2	2	3	3	3	4	5
Y	1	3	2	1	5	3	4	5

It is easily verified that C = 18, D = 3. Moreover, $m_1 = 2$ (corresponding to the two values X = 2) and $m_2 = 3$ (corresponding to the three values X = 3); likewise $n_1 = n_2 = n_3 = 2$. Thus, $U = \binom{2}{2} + \binom{3}{2} = 4$ and $V = \binom{2}{2} \times 3 = 3$, so we have

$$\hat{\tau}_a = \frac{2(18 - 3)}{8 \times 7} = \frac{30}{56} = 0.536$$

and

$$\hat{\tau}_b = \frac{2(18 - 3)}{[(56 - 8)(56 - 6)]^{1/2}} = 0.612$$

Note that equations 4.17 and 4.22 both give the same value when there are no ties in the data.

In the absence of ties, both $\hat{\tau}_a$ and $\hat{\tau}_b$ range from a minimum value of -1 when all possible pairs are discordant to a maximum of $+1$ when all pairs are concordant. The ranges of both are restricted when ties are present, with the restriction for $\hat{\tau}_a$ being more severe. In all cases, $|\hat{\tau}_a| \leqslant |\hat{\tau}_b|$. There are cases, however, where the maximum achievable value of τ_b is strictly less than one even though all untied pairs are concordant.[12]

Now suppose that each X_i is replaced by its rank among the X values and suppose Y_i is similarly transformed, so the data consist of n pairs of ranks. The calculation of either $\hat{\tau}_a$ or $\hat{\tau}_b$ is unaffected by this transformation. If the data are ranks, $\hat{\tau}_a$ admits yet another interpretation. Consider a set of m tied ranks, and suppose that ties are broken by arbitrarily selecting one of the m! permutations of the set of tied values. (For example, if ranks 4 to 7 are tied, arbitrarily replace these values by one of the 4! = 24 permutations of $\{4, 5, 6, 7\}$.) If equation 4.17 or 4.22 is now calculated for each possible ordering and all values are averaged, the result is identical to that given by equation 4.17. Thus, $\hat{\tau}_a$ is the average of all values of τ_a or τ_b obtained by the assignment of integral ranks to sets of tied ranks in all possible ways.

If the data are rankings, Kendall (1970: 36-37) discusses the question of whether $\hat{\tau}_a$ or $\hat{\tau}_b$ is the more appropriate measure. Essentially, the choice depends on which is a better measure of *agreement* in the situation at hand. If the Xs and Ys represent ratings by two judges, then ties represent agreement and $\hat{\tau}_b$ should be used. If the Xs represent ratings by an individual, and the Ys represent a *known objective ordering*, then ties do not indicate agreement, and $\hat{\tau}_a$ is recommended.

What about the moments of $\hat{\tau}_a$ and $\hat{\tau}_b$? It has already been noted that

$$E(\hat{\tau}_a) = E(\hat{\tau}_b) = \tau$$

for any continuous bivariate population, so both estimators are unbiased. Moreover, for any continuous variates, it is known (see Gibbons, 1971: 211-213, for example) that

$$\sigma^2(\hat{\tau}_a) = \frac{1}{n(n - 1)} [8\pi_c(1 - \pi_c) + 16(n - 2)(\pi_{cc} - \pi_c^2)] \qquad [4.23]$$

where π_{cc} is the probability that any one of three randomly selected observations is concordant with the other two. Note that $n^{1/2}\hat{\sigma}(\hat{\tau}_a) \to 16(\pi_{cc} - \pi_c^2)$ as $n \to \infty$.

In practice, it is necessary either to hypothesize or to estimate π_c and π_{cc}. If X and Y are independent, $\pi_c = 1/2$, and $\pi_{cc} = 5/18$, in which case equation 4.23 becomes

$$\sigma^2(\hat{\tau}_a) = (4n + 10)/[9n(n - 1)] \qquad [4.24]$$

In other cases, π_c and π_{cc} can be estimated from a sample by determining the number of concordant pairs and the number of triples in which one observation is concordant with the other two, respectively. When these estimates are substituted into equation 4.23, we get

$$\hat{\sigma}^2(\hat{\tau}_a) = \frac{16}{n^2(n-1)^2} \left[\sum_{i=1}^{n} C_i^2 - \frac{2(2n-3)}{n(n-1)} C^2 - C \right] \qquad [4.25]$$

where C_i is the total number of values in the sample concordant with (X_i, Y_i) and

$$\sum_{i=1}^{n} C_i = 2C$$

(because each pair is counted twice). An unbiased estimator is obtained by replacing the denominator in equation 4.25 with $n(n - 1)(n - 2)(n - 3)$. Unless n is rather large, equation 4.25 should be used with care, since it is possible to construct examples in which $\hat{\sigma}^2(\hat{\tau}_a)$ is negative for small values of n (Gibbons, 1971: 222).

The given variance formulas require modifications if the data contain ties. Only the case in which X and Y are independent is considered. If ties are present, a formula for the variance of C − D is

$$\sigma^2(C - D) = \frac{1}{18} \left[n(n - 1)(2n + 5) - A_2 - B_2 \right]$$

$$+ \frac{A_1 B_1}{9n(n - 1)(n - 2)} + \frac{2UV}{n(n - 1)} \qquad [4.26]$$

where

$$A_1 = \sum_i m_i(m_i - 1)(m_i - 2), \quad B_1 = \sum_j n_j(n_j - 1)(n_j - 2)$$

$$A_2 = \sum_i m_i(m_i - 1)(2m + 5), \; B_2 = \sum_j n_j(n_j - 1)(2n_j + 5)$$

$$U = \sum_i \binom{m_i}{2} \quad \text{and} \quad V = \sum_j \binom{n_j}{2}$$

All summations extend over all sets of ties of size m_i in the X values or over all sets of ties of size n_j in the Y values, whichever is appropriate. From equations 4.17, 4.22, and 4.26 we get the variance formulas

$$\hat{\sigma}_t^2(\hat{\tau}_a) = \sigma^2(C - D)/\binom{n}{2}^2 \tag{4.27}$$

and

$$\hat{\sigma}_t^2(\hat{\tau}_b) = \sigma^2(C - D)/\left\{ \left[\binom{n}{2} - U \right] \left[\binom{n}{2} - V \right] \right\} \tag{4.28}$$

respectively, for the estimators $\hat{\tau}_a$ and $\hat{\tau}_b$. If the sample contains ties in only one variable (say X), then equation 4.26 simplifies to

$$\sigma^2(C - D) = \frac{1}{18} \left[n(n - 1)(2n + 5) - A_2 \right] \tag{4.29}$$

Example 3 (continued). It can be verified that $A_1 = 2 \times 1 \times 0 + 3 \times 2 \times 1 = 6$; $B_1 = 3(2 \times 1 \times 0) = 0$; $A_2 = 2 \times 1 \times 9 + 3 \times 2 \times 11 = 84$; and $B_2 = 3(2 \times 1 \times 9) = 54$. Upon substitution of these values into equation 4.26, we get

$$\sigma^2(C - D) = \frac{1}{18} \left(8 \times 7 \times 21 - 84 - 54 \right) + 0 + \frac{2 \times 4 \times 3}{8 \times 7} = 58.095$$

which, when substituted into equations 4.27 and 4.28, gives $\hat{\sigma}_t^2(\hat{\tau}_a) = 58.095/\binom{8}{2}^2 = 0.07410$ and $\hat{\sigma}_t^2(\hat{\tau}_b) = 58.095/(24 \times 25) = 0.09683$ as estimates of the variances of $\hat{\tau}_a$ and $\hat{\tau}_b$, respectively. The value $\hat{\sigma}_t^2(\hat{\tau}_a) = 0.07410$ may be compared with the value $\hat{\sigma}^2(\hat{\tau}_a) = 0.08333$ obtained from equation 4.24.

We must know the appropriate percentage points of the distribution of either $\hat{\tau}_a$ or $\hat{\tau}_b$ in order to make inferences about τ. Several tables of the exact distribution of $\hat{\tau}_a$ (or $\binom{n}{2} \times \hat{\tau}_a$) have been published for the case in which X and Y are independent. One of the most extensive is given by Conover (1980), where $\binom{n}{2} \hat{\tau}_a$ is tabulated for n = 4(1)40. Others are given by Kendall (1970), Siegel (1956), and Owen (1962). The exact distribution of $\hat{\tau}_b$ is not tabulated because it depends on the observed configuration of ties in the data.

The normal distribution can be used to approximate the distributions of $\hat{\tau}_a$ and $\hat{\tau}_b$ for large samples since both estimates are asymptotically normal. The approximations are quite good even for moderate n because the distributions of $\hat{\tau}_a$ and $\hat{\tau}_b$ are symmetric if $\tau = 0$, and they rapidly become so with increasing n otherwise. When $\tau = 0$, Kendall suggests that the normal approximation is adequate for $n > 10$. Provided τ is not too close to one, we can use the normal approximation confidently with sample sizes in excess of 15 or 20. When computing variance estimates, it is important to note that formula 4.25 holds in general, but that formulas 4.26 through 4.29 hold only when X and Y are independent. Formulas 4.24 and 4.26 through 4.29 are suitable only for testing the null hypothesis H_o: $\tau = 0$. For testing other hypotheses about τ and for constructing confidence intervals, formula 4.25 should be used. In the event that one of the variables denotes "time," a test of H_o: $\tau = 0$ versus H_1: $\tau > 0$ or of H_o: $\tau = 0$ versus H_1 $\tau < 0$ may be interpreted as a test for trend.

Good references for further reading include Conover (1980), Hays (1963), Kendall (1970), Gibbons (1971: 209-224), and Noether (1967: 70-82). Kendall's book is definitive. It contains many examples and all of the results presented here. The treatments of Gibbons and Noether are more mathematically sophisticated than the others.

Spearman's Rank Correlation Coefficient

Starting with the product-moment correlation coefficient R, it is easy to derive Spearman's rank correlation coefficient. Suppose the sample values (X_i, Y_i) are replaced by ranks. If the ranks are used in formula 4.9 in place of the original data, the result is one version of the rank correlation coefficient. It is natural to regard the resulting value as an estimate of the population correlation coefficient. Unfortunately, it is not a good estimator of ρ and, in fact, turns out to be fairly difficult to interpret in terms of a meaningful population parameter. The rank correlation coefficient was first studied by Spearman (1904).

Let R_i denote the rank of X_i among the Xs and let S_i be defined similarly for Y. Then, by replacing X_i and Y_i in equation 4.9 by R_i and S_i, respectively, we get

$$\hat{\rho}_b = \frac{\sum\limits_{i=1}^{n} (R_i - \bar{R})(S_i - \bar{S})}{\left[\sum\limits_{i=1}^{n} (R_i - \bar{R})^2 \sum\limits_{i=1}^{n} (S_i - \bar{S})^2 \right]^{1/2}} \qquad [4.30a]$$

Several versions of equation 4.30a exist. Although all versions give the same value for a sample with no ties, they give different values when ties are present. Details are given here to aid the reader who is confused by the many formulas for a single measure, not all of which give the same result in all cases.

Suppose for the moment that there no ties in the data. Since

$$\sum_{i=1}^{n} R_i = \sum_{i=1}^{n} i = \frac{1}{2} n(n+1) = \sum_{i=1}^{n} S_i$$

and

$$\sum_{i=1}^{n} R_i^2 = \sum_{i=1}^{n} i^2 = \frac{1}{6} n(n+1)(2n+1) = \sum_{i=1}^{n} S_i^2$$

some algebra reveals that

$$\sum_{i=1}^{n} (R_i - \bar{R})^2 = \frac{1}{12} n(n^2 - 1) = \sum_{i=1}^{n} (S_i - \bar{S})^2 \qquad [4.31]$$

Substitution of equation 4.31 into 4.30a yields

$$\hat{\rho}_a = \frac{12 \sum_{i=1}^{n} (R_i - \bar{R})(S_i - \bar{S})}{n^3 - n}$$

$$= \frac{12 \sum_{i=1}^{n} R_i S_i}{n(n^2 - 1)} - \frac{3(n+1)}{n-1} \qquad [4.32a]$$

It is convenient to assume that the Xs are listed in increasing order, in which case $R_i = i$, and formula 4.32a can be simplified by replacing

$$\sum_{i=1}^{n} R_i S_i \quad \text{with} \quad \sum_{i=1}^{n} i S_i$$

Finally, let

$$D_i = R_i - S_i = (R_i - \bar{R}) - (S_i - \bar{S})$$

Then

$$\sum_{i=1}^{n} D_i^2 = \sum_{i=1}^{n} (R_i - \bar{R})^2 + \sum_{i=1}^{n} (S_i - \bar{S})^2 - 2 \sum_{i=1}^{n} (R_i - \bar{R})(S_i - \bar{S})$$

$$= \frac{1}{6} n(n^2 - 1) - 2 \sum_{i=1}^{n} (R_i - \bar{R})(S_i - \bar{S})$$

so yet another form of equation 4.30a is

$$\hat{\rho}_s = 1 - \frac{6 \sum_{i=1}^{n} D_i^2}{n(n^2 - 1)} \qquad [4.33]$$

There are two widely used modifications of $\hat{\rho}_s$ that take account of ties. Although different in appearance, these versions turn out to be algebraically equivalent to equations 4.30a and 4.32a. Let m_j denote the number of observations in the jth set of tied X ranks, and let n_j be defined similarly for the Y ranks. Suppose that each rank within a group of ties is replaced by the average of the ranks corresponding to the group (for example, if observations corresponding to the ranks 4, 5, 6, 7 are tied on X, then each observation in the group is assigned an X rank of 5.5). The effect of the group of m_j tied X ranks on the value ΣD_i^2 is to decrease it by $m_i(m_i^2 - 1)/12$ relative to its value *had there been no ties*. The total reduction in ΣD_i^2 from all the groups of tied ranks in both variables is U + V, where

$$U = \frac{1}{12} \sum_j m_j(m_j^2 - 1) \quad \text{and} \quad V = \frac{1}{12} \sum_j n_j(n_j^2 - 1)$$

If U + V is added to ΣD_i^2 in equation 4.33, the result is

$$\hat{\rho}_a = 1 - \frac{6 \left(\sum_{i=1}^{n} D_i^2 + U + V \right)}{n(n^2 - 1)} \qquad [4.32b]$$

The estimator $\hat{\rho}_a$ is equivalent to $\hat{\tau}_a$ in the following sense: If one of equations 4.30a, 4.30b, 4.32a, 4.32b, or 4.33 is computed for each possible permutation of the ranks in the tied sets, and all resulting values are averaged, that average is equal to the value given by equation 4.32b.

362

Further, the denominator of equation 4.32b can be adjusted to compensate for ties. The denominator of equation 4.32b is effectively reduced by 12U because of tied X ranks and by 12V because of tied Y ranks relative to its value when ties are absent. Substitution of the geometric mean of these adjusted values into the denominator of equation 4.32b in place of $n^3 - n$ yields

$$\hat{\rho}_b = \frac{n(n^2 - 1) - 6\left(\sum_{i=1}^{n} D_i^2 + U + V\right)}{[n(n^2 - 1) - 12U]^{1/2} [n(n^2 - 1) - 12V]^{1/2}} \qquad [4.30b]$$

The estimator $\hat{\rho}_b$ is analogous to $\hat{\tau}_b$. Clearly, $|\hat{\rho}_a| \leq |\hat{\rho}_b|$ and $\hat{\rho}_a \leq \hat{\rho}_s$. All of equations 4.30a, 4.30b, 4.32a, 4.32b, and 4.33 yield the same value for a sample with no ties. When ties are present, equations 4.30a and 4.30b yield one value, 4.32a and 4.32b yield another, and 4.33 yields still a third value.

An example will help to show how the estimators $\hat{\rho}_s$, $\hat{\rho}_a$, and $\hat{\rho}_b$ compare.

Example 3 (continued). When the original data are replaced by ranks, we get

R_i	1	2.5	2.5	5	5	5	7	8
S_i	1.5	4.5	3	1.5	7.5	4.5	6	7.5
$D_i = R_i - S_i$	−.5	−2	−.5	3.5	−2.5	.5	1	.5

Here, $m_1 = 2$, $m_2 = 3$ and $n_1 = n_2 = n_3 = 2$, so $U = [2(2^2 - 1) + 3(3^2 - 1)]/12 = 2.5$ and $V = 3 \times [2(2^2 - 1)]/12 = 1.5$. Since $\sum D_i^2 = 24.5$, equation 4.33 yields $\hat{\rho}_s = 1 - 6(24.5)/(8 \times 63) = 0.7083$, equation 4.32b yields $\hat{\rho}_a = 1 - 6(24.5 + 2.5 + 1.5)/(8 \times 63) = 0.6607$, and equation 4.30b yields

$$\hat{\rho}_b = \frac{8 \times 63 - 6(24.5 + 2.5 + 1.5)}{[(8 \times 63 - 30)(8 \times 63 - 18)]^{1/2}} = 0.6938$$

The considerations dictating the choice between $\hat{\tau}_a$ and $\hat{\tau}_b$ also apply to the choice between $\hat{\rho}_a$ and $\hat{\rho}_b$. If the data represent rankings of items by two judges, then ties represent agreement, and $\hat{\rho}_b$ is appropriate. On the other hand, if one variable represents the ranking of items by an individual and the other represents a *known* objective ordering, $\hat{\rho}_a$ is more suitable. Moreover, in situations in which one of the variables represents time, $\hat{\rho}_a$ may be regarded as a measure of trend.

We have seen that $|\hat{\rho}_a|$ is smallest and $|\hat{\rho}_s|$ tends to be largest in a given sampling situation. But how do the ranges of the three estimators compare? Suppose again for a moment that there are no ties, and suppose also that the Xs are arranged in increasing order so that $R_i = \text{Rank}(X_i) = i$. If all observations are concordant (see the sections on Kendall's τ in this chapter) so that $Y_i < Y_j$ whenever $X_i < X_j$, then $S_i = i$ for all i as well. In this case $D_i = 0$ for each i and $\hat{\rho}_s = 1$. Conversely, if all pairs are discordant, the Ys are in decreasing order, and $S_i = n + 1 - i$. In the latter case,

$$\sum_{i=1}^{n} D_i^2 = \frac{1}{3} n(n^2 - 1)$$

so we can see that $\hat{\rho}_s = -1$. Other assignments of Y ranks lead to values between the extremes just considered, so all three estimators can range from -1 to 1 in the absence of ties.

Now suppose that ties are present. Let q_1 be the number of *distinct* X values in the sample, let q_2 be the number of *distinct* Y values, and let $q = \min\{q_1, q_2\}$. The minimum possible value of $\hat{\rho}_s$ is approximately $2/q^2 - 1$. The maximum possible value of $\hat{\rho}_s$ is 1 when $\Sigma D_i^2 = 0$, but this happens only if the Xs and Ys exhibit identical patterns of ties. The maximum possible vlaue of $\hat{\rho}_a$ is $d/(n^3 - n)$, where d is the denominator of equation 4.30b. This value depends on the observed configuration of ties and is attained by $\hat{\rho}_a$ when $\hat{\rho}_b = 1$.

The estimator $\hat{\rho}_b$ ranges from -1 to 1, inclusive. Since $\hat{\rho}_b$ is a correlation coefficient, its range is unaffected by ties. Consequently, $\hat{\rho}_b$ is frequently the estimator of choice. Once the data have been replaced by ranks, with tied observations being replaced by their average rank, the calculation of $\hat{\rho}_b$ is most easily accomplished by means of equation 4.30a.

Expressions for the moments of $\hat{\rho}_s$, $\hat{\rho}_a$, and ρ_b are actually quite simple in the case of independence. If X and Y are independent, then so are the ranks R_i and S_i. It follows from equation 4.32a that $E(\hat{\rho}_a) = 0$. Moreover, $\hat{\rho}_s$ has mean $E(\hat{\rho}_s) = 0$ and variance

$$\sigma^2(\hat{\rho}_s) = 1/(n - 1) \qquad [4.34]$$

When X and Y are independent. Similar calculations reveal that ρ_b has the same mean and variance as $\hat{\rho}_s$:

$$E(\hat{\rho}_b) = 0 \quad \text{and} \quad \sigma^2(\hat{\rho}_b) = 1/(n - 1) \qquad [4.35]$$

The variance of $\hat{\rho}_a$ is obtained from that of $\hat{\rho}_b$ by noting that the former is a constant multiple of the latter. Consequently,

$$\sigma^2(\hat{\rho}_a) = \frac{[n(n^2 - 1) - 12U]\,[n(n^2 - 1) - 12V]}{n^2(n^2 - 1)^2(n - 1)} \qquad [4.36]$$

Example 3 (continued). For these data, formulas 4.34 to 4.36 yield the values $\sigma^2(\hat{\rho}_s) = \sigma^2(\hat{\rho}_b) = 1/7 = 0.1429$ and

$$\sigma^2(\hat{\rho}_a) = \frac{[8 \times 63 - 12(2.5)]\,[8 \times 63 - 12(1.5)]}{7(8 \times 63)^2} = 0.1296$$

Percentage points of the distribution of $\hat{\rho}_s$ or one of its variants are needed to perform significance tests. Under the hypothesis of independence, the distributions of all three statistics are symmetric about zero, and all are approximately normal for sufficiently large sample sizes. A number of tables of the exact distribution of ρ_s (or ΣD_i^2) are available for small samples. Kendall (1970) tabulates ΣD_i^2 for $n \leqslant 13$. Other tables are given by Owen (1962), Siegel (1956), and Conover (1980). The distributions of $\hat{\rho}_a$ and $\hat{\rho}_b$ are not tabulated because they depend on the observed configuration of ties.

The distributions of equations 4.30a, 4.30b, 4.32a, 4.32b, and 4.33 are rather "jagged," so their normal approximations are not as good as for estimators of τ. This jaggedness is illustrated by Figure 4.2 of Kendall (1970), which shows the frequency distribution of ΣD_i^2 for $n = 8$.

Since $\hat{\rho}_b$ is the product-moment correlation calculated from ranks of the observed data, approximations to the distribution of R are also recommended for $\hat{\rho}_s$ by some authors. One of these approximations stems from the fact that $(n - 2)^{1/2} R/(1 - R^2)^{1/2}$ is distributed approximately as a t random variable with $n - 2$ degrees of freedom for large samples (Hays, 1964; Morrison, 1976) under the hypothesis of independence (see the first section of this chapter). Unless n is *extremely* large, this approximation can be quite inaccurate, especially if the number of ties is significant. It is generally advisable to use the normal approximations based on equations 4.34, 4.35, and 4.36 when exact tables are unavailable.

We now turn to the matter or finding an interpretation for the statistics we have discussed. The Spearman rank correlation coefficient does not estimate an easily defined population parameter. In particular, $\hat{\rho}_s$ and its variants are not good estimators of the population correlation coefficient

ρ. It turns out that the problem of defining a population parameter corresponding to $\hat{\rho}_s$ is closely related to that of determining the distribution of $\hat{\rho}_s$ when X and Y are not independent. Kruskal (1958) has provided the most natural interpretation we have.

Consider three independent observations (X_i, Y_i), (X_j, Y_j), and (X_k, Y_k) of (X, Y). Let π'_c denote the probability that *at least one* pair is concordant with the other two and let π'_d denote the probability that *at least one* pair is discordant with the other two. If (X, Y) has a continuous distribution, then $\pi'_d = 1 - \pi'_c$. Since

$$E(\hat{\rho}_s) = \frac{n-2}{n+1} (\pi'_c - \pi'_d) + \frac{3}{n+1} \tau \qquad [4.37]$$

Kruskal proposes that

$$\rho_s = \pi'_c - \pi'_d$$

be taken as the population analog of $\hat{\rho}_s$. In equation 4.37 τ denotes Kendall's τ, defined by equation 4.16. The parameter ρ_s is the difference between two probabilities: (1) The probability that at least one of three observations is concordant with the other two and (2) the probability that at least one is discordant with the other two. Except when X and Y are independent, $\hat{\rho}_s$ is clearly a biased estimator of ρ_s.

When X and Y are not independent, Hoeffding (1948) has shown that $\hat{\rho}_s$ is approximately normal for large samples. Estimates of the variance of ρ_s are too complicated to present here. The interested reader is referred to Hoeffding's paper (1948: 318-321) for details. The statistics $\hat{\rho}_a$ and ρ_b are also approximately normal for large samples, but results are still more complicated because the exact distributions depend on the observed configuration of ties.

An upper bound on the variance of $\hat{\rho}_s$ can be obtained by means of the inequality

$$\sigma^2(\hat{\rho}_s) \leqslant \frac{3}{n} (1 - \rho_s^2) \qquad [4.38]$$

The right-hand side of equation 4.38 can be approximated by using $\hat{\rho}_s$ to estimate ρ_s. The use of equation 4.38 is conservative in that it produces confidence intervals that are wider than those obtained from actual variance estimates. The difference can be quite large in some cases.

Further references include Hays (1963: 641-647, 651-652). Conover (1980), Kendall (1970), Gibbons (1971: 226-240), Kruskal (1958), and

Hoeffding (1948: esp. 318-321). Hays and Conover give a brief discussion of the properties of $\hat{\rho}_s$ together with several examples. Kendall's treatment of the rank correlation coefficient is most extensive, and Kruskal presents the derivation of ρ_s given here. Gibbons gives a concise derivation of the properties of $\hat{\rho}_s$ and Hoeffding shows that the distributions of $\hat{\rho}_s$ is approximately normal when X and Y are not independent. The last two references are much more mathematically sophisticated than the first four.

5. MEASURES OF ASSOCIATION FOR ORDINAL DATA

Kendall's τ was originally defined for continuous bivariate data, so any version of τ intended for ordinal data must take ties into account. Several versions of τ and three related measures are considered. Except for the way ties are handled, all the measures are quite similar. Notation for this chapter is established in the next section.

Ordinal variables may be inherently discrete, or they may result from categorizing the range of a continuous variable. In either case, the multinomial sampling model is appropriate.

Preliminaries

Suppose that two ordinal variables X and Y are sampled jointly, and that the resulting sample $(X_1, Y_1), \ldots, (X_n, Y_n)$ is classified into an $I \times J$ contingency table. Then p_{ij} is the probability that an arbitrary observation (X_k, Y_k) falls into cell (i, j) of the table; that is, p_{ij} is the probability that X_k falls into (row) category i and Y_k falls into (column) category j. The number of observations that fall into cell (i, j) is denoted by n_{ij}.

From equation 4.15, we know that two pairs of observations must be concordant, discordant, or tied. Further investigation reveals that ties can occur in several ways. Two observations (X_i, Y_i) and (X_j, Y_j) can be tied (1) on X only (i.e., $X_i = X_j$ and $Y_i \neq Y_j$) or (2) on Y only (i.e., $X_i \neq X_j$ and $Y_i = Y_j$), or (3) they can be tied on both X and Y (i.e., $X_i = X_j$ and $Y_i = Y_j$). Observations that are tied only on X fall into the same row of the table, pairs that are tied only on Y fall into the same column, and pairs that are tied on both X and Y fall into the same cell of the table. By the reasoning that led to formula 4.15, we see that

$$\pi_t = \pi_t^X + \pi_t^Y + \pi_t^{XY} \qquad [5.1]$$

where

$$\pi_t^X = P(X_i = X_j \quad \text{and} \quad Y_i \neq Y_j) \qquad [5.2]$$

$$\pi_t^Y = P(X_i \neq X_j \quad \text{and} \quad Y_i = Y_j) \qquad [5.3]$$

and

$$\pi_t^{XY} = P(X_i = X_j \quad \text{and} \quad Y_i = Y_j) \qquad [5.4]$$

From equations 4.15 and 5.1 we see that

$$\pi_c + \pi_d + \pi_t = \pi_c + \pi_d + \pi_t^X + \pi_t^Y + \pi_t^{XY} = 1 \qquad [5.5]$$

How can we express the probabilities in equation 5.5 in terms of the cell probabilities p_{ij}? Further, how can these quantities be estimated from a given sample? Let π_{ij}^c be the probability that a randomly selected observation (X_k, Y_k) is concordant with one *in cell* (i, j), and let π_{ij}^d be the probability that two such members are discordant. In terms of the p_{ij}s, it is easy to see that

$$\pi_{ij}^c = \sum_{i'<i} \sum_{j'<j} p_{i'j'} + \sum_{i'>i} \sum_{j'>j} p_{i'j'} \qquad [5.6]$$

and

$$\pi_{ij}^d = \sum_{i'<i} \sum_{j'>j} p_{i'j'} + \sum_{i'>i} \sum_{j'<j} p_{i'j'} \qquad [5.7]$$

Now, the probability that two randomly selected members of the population are concordant is

$$\pi_c = \sum_{i=1}^{I} \sum_{j=1}^{J} p_{ij} \pi_{ij}^c \qquad [5.8]$$

and the probability that they are discordant is

$$\pi_d = \sum_{i=1}^{I} \sum_{j=1}^{J} p_{ij} \pi_{ij}^d \qquad [5.9]$$

Consider next the terms in equation 5.1. The probabilities that two randomly selected individuals are tied on (1) both X and Y. (2) X alone, and (3) Y alone are:

$$\pi_t^{XY} = \sum_{i=1}^{I} \sum_{j=1}^{J} p_{ij}^2 \qquad [5.10]$$

$$\pi_t^{X} = \sum_{i=1}^{I} p_{i+}^2 - \sum_{i=1}^{I} \sum_{j=1}^{J} p_{ij}^2 \qquad [5.11]$$

and

$$\pi_t^{Y} = \sum_{j=1}^{J} p_{+j}^2 - \sum_{i=1}^{I} \sum_{j=1}^{J} p_{ij}^2 \qquad [5.12]$$

respectively. Substitution of equations 5.10, 5.11, and 5.12 into equation 5.1 reveals that

$$\pi_t = \sum_{i=1}^{I} p_{i+}^2 + \sum_{j=1}^{J} p_{+j}^2 - \sum_{i=1}^{I} \sum_{j=1}^{J} p_{ij}^2 \qquad [5.13]$$

It is also useful to note that

$$\pi_c + \pi_d + \pi_t^{X} = 1 - \pi_t^{Y} - \pi_t^{XY} = 1 - \sum_{j=1}^{J} p_{+j}^2 \qquad [5.14]$$

and

$$\pi_c + \pi_d + \pi_t^{Y} = 1 - \pi_t^{X} - \pi_t^{XY} = 1 - \sum_{i=1}^{I} p_{i+}^2 \qquad [5.15]$$

Finally, we need suitable estimates of equations 5.6 through 5.15. We begin by computing the number[13] of concordant and discordant pairs C and D in the sample $(X_1, Y_1), \ldots, (X_n, Y_n)$.

Observations concordant with one in cell (i, j) are those in cells that lie either "northwest" or "southeast" of that cell. The number of such pairs is

$$C_{ij} = \sum_{i'<j} \sum_{j'<j} n_{i'j'} + \sum_{i'>i} \sum_{j'>j} n_{i'j'} \qquad [5.16]$$

By summing over all cells, we see that

$$2C = \sum_{i=1}^{I} \sum_{j=1}^{J} n_{ij} C_{ij} \qquad [5.17]$$

The factor 2 appears in equation 5.17 because each concordant pair is counted twice in the summation. This repetition can be eliminated by writing

$$C = \sum_{i=1}^{I} \sum_{j=1}^{J} n_{ij} C_{ij}^* \qquad [5.18]$$

where

$$C_{ij}^* = \sum_{i'>i} \sum_{j'>j} n_{i'j'} \qquad [5.19]$$

is the total number of observations "southeast" of cell (i, j). We could as well have taken C_{ij} to be the first term on the right side of equation 5.16. Likewise,

$$2D = \sum_{i=1}^{I} \sum_{j=1}^{J} n_{ij} D_{ij} \qquad [5.20]$$

where

$$D_{ij} = \sum_{i'<i} \sum_{j'>j} n_{i'j'} + \sum_{i'>i} \sum_{j'<j} n_{i'j'} \qquad [5.21]$$

is the number of observations discordant with one in cell (i, j). Note that D_{ij} is the total number of observations in cells "northeast" or "southwest" of cell (i, j). Equivalently,

$$D = \sum_{i=1}^{I} \sum_{j=1}^{J} n_{ij} D_{ij}^* \qquad [5.22]$$

where

$$D_{ij}^* = \sum_{i'<i} \sum_{j'>j} n_{i'j'} \qquad [5.23]$$

is the total number of observations "northeast" of cell (i, j).

Next, we need expressions for the numbers of ties of various types in the sample. An observation in cell (i, j) is tied on both X and Y with all other observations in that cell. Summing over all cells, we obtain

$$2T_{XY} = \sum_{i=1}^{I} \sum_{j=1}^{J} n_{ij}(n_{ij} - 1) = \sum_{i=1}^{I} \sum_{j=1}^{J} n_{ij}^2 - n \qquad [5.24]$$

where T_{XY} is the total number of sample pairs tied on both X and Y.

An observation in cell (i, j) is tied only on X with all other observations in row i not in cell (i, j). Consequently, (twice) the total number of ties involving only X is

$$2T_X = \sum_{i=1}^{I} \sum_{j=1}^{J} n_{ij}(n_{i+} - n_{ij}) = \sum_{i=1}^{I} n_{i+}^2 - \sum_{i=1}^{I} \sum_{j=1}^{J} n_{ij}^2 \qquad [5.25]$$

Likewise,

$$2T_Y = \sum_{j=1}^{J} n_{+j}^2 - \sum_{i=1}^{I} \sum_{j=1}^{J} n_{ij}^2 \qquad [5.26]$$

is twice the total number of ties involving only Y.

Finally, we need analogues to equations 5.14 and 5.15. The total number of pairs in a sample of size n is $\binom{n}{2} = n(n-1)/2$. Thus,

$$2(C + D + T_X + T_Y + T_{XY}) = n(n-1) \qquad [5.27]$$

from which we obtain

$$2(C + D + T_X) = n(n-1) - 2(T_Y + T_{XY}) = n^2 - \sum_{j=1}^{J} n_{+j}^2 \qquad [5.28]$$

and

$$2(C + D + T_Y) = n^2 - \sum_{i=1}^{I} n_{i+}^2 \qquad [5.29]$$

Kendall's τ_b

Kendall originally proposed his measure

$$\tau = \pi_c - \pi_d \qquad [5.30]$$

for continuous variables. The measure in equation 5.30 admits an easy interpretation: If two observations (X_i, Y_i) and (X_j, Y_j) are selected at random from the population, τ is the probability that the observations are concordant (X and Y have like ordering) minus the probability that they are discordant (X and Y have unlike ordering). Two estimators of τ are discussed in Chapter 4:

$$\hat{\tau}_a = (C - D)/\binom{n}{2} = \frac{2(C - D)}{n(n - 1)} \qquad [5.31]$$

and

$$\hat{\tau}_b = \frac{C - D}{\left\{[\binom{n}{2} - U]\,[\binom{n}{2} - V]\right\}^{1/2}}$$

$$= 2(C - D)/\left\{[n(n - 1) - 2U]\,[n(n - 1) - 2V]\right\}^{1/2} \qquad [5.32a]$$

The estimator $\hat{\tau}_b$ is designed to reduce the downward bias exhibited by equation 5.31 in the presence of ties.

Now, $\pi_t = 0$ for continuous populations, while $\pi_t > 0$ in the discrete case. Consequently, the range of τ in the discrete case is restricted relative to its maximum range in the continuous case. Moreover, the range of τ depends on π_t, so τ is not particularly suitable for discrete populations. Likewise, the estimator $\hat{\tau}_a$ is not widely used with discrete data.

On the other hand, the estimator $\hat{\tau}_b$ is widely used in the ordinal case. Moreover, formula 5.32a can be written in simpler form using the notation of contingency tables. The numerator of formula 5.32a is most easily calculated using equations 5.18 and 5.22. Furthermore, expressions for U and V in the denominator of formula 5.32a take a particularly convenient form. Note that the number of tied groups of Xs is I (the number of rows) and the number of tied observations in the ith group is n_{i+}. Thus, equation 4.18 can be written as

$$U = \sum_{i=1}^{I} \binom{n_{i+}}{2} = \frac{1}{2} \sum_{i=1}^{I} n_{i+}(n_{i+} - 1)$$

$$= \frac{1}{2} \left(\sum_{i=1}^{I} n_{i+}^2 - n \right) \qquad [5.33]$$

Likewise, the number of pairs of observations tied on Y is

$$V = \frac{1}{2} \left(\sum_{j=1}^{J} n_{+j}^2 - n \right) \qquad [5.34]$$

Using equations 5.33 and 5.34, the denominator of equation 5.32a can be written as

$$\{[n(n-1) - 2U]\,[n(n-1) - 2V]\}^{1/2}$$

$$= \left[\left(n^2 - \sum_{i=1}^{I} n_{i+}^2\right)\left(n^2 - \sum_{j=1}^{J} n_{+j}^2\right)\right]^{1/2}$$

from which we obtain the formula

$$\hat{\tau}_b = \frac{2(C-D)}{[(n^2 - \sum_i n_{i+}^2)\,(n^2 - \sum_j n_{j+}^2)]^{1/2}} \qquad [5.32b]$$

Finally, from equations 5.28 and 5.29, we get yet another expression for $\hat{\tau}_b$:

$$\hat{\tau}_b = \frac{C-D}{[(C+D+T_X)\,(C+D+T_Y)]^{1/2}} \qquad [5.32c]$$

Note that $C + D + T_X$ is the number of pairs of observations *not* tied on Y, and $C + D + T_Y$ is the number of pairs *not* tied on X: The denominator of equation 5.32c is the geometric mean of these two quantities. Formula 5.32c is the best for comparing the various ordinal measures related to τ, while formula 5.32b is better for computational purposes.

The range of τ is not restricted in the continuous case, so $\hat{\tau}_b$ is the preferred estimator because $\hat{\tau}_a$ tends to underestimate when the data contain ties. In the discrete case, where $\pi_t > 0$, $\hat{\tau}_b$ is not a good estimator of τ; indeed $\hat{\tau}_a$ may actually be better because the range of τ *is* restricted. The estimator $\hat{\tau}_b$ is in fact the maximum likelihood estimator of the quantity

$$\tau_b = \frac{\pi_c - \pi_d}{\left[\left(1 - \sum_{i=1}^{I} p_{i+}^2\right)\left(1 - \sum_{j=1}^{J} p_{+j}^2\right)\right]^{1/2}} \qquad [5.35]$$

under the multinomial sampling model. In view of equations 5.14 and 5.15, $1 - \sum_i p_{i+}^2$ and $1 - \sum_j p_{+j}^2$ are the probabilities, respectively, that randomly selected members of the population are *not* tied on Y (do not fall in the same column) and are *not* tied on X (do not fall in the same row). The denominator of equation 5.35 is the geometric mean of these two probabilities. Unless $p_{i+}^2 = p_{+j}^2 = 0$ for all i and j (that is, unless X and Y are continuous), it is clear that $|\tau_b| < |\tau|$.

Provided not all observations fall in a single cell, τ_b is well defined. For a square table, τ_b ranges from -1 to 1, with $\tau_b = 1$ if all observations fall in the main diagonal and $\tau_b = -1$ when all observations fall in the diagonal running from lower left to upper right.[14] Otherwise, the range of τ_b is still somewhat restricted. In the case of independence, τ_b is zero regardless of whether or not the table is square. Similar statements hold for $\hat{\tau}_b$.

For I = J = 2, equation 5.35 can be written as

$$\tau_b = \frac{P_{11}P_{22} - P_{12}P_{21}}{(P_{1+}P_{+1}P_{2+}P_{+2})^{1/2}}$$

which together with equations 3.60 and 3.1 reveals that the correlation coefficient ρ and the coefficient of mean square contingency ϕ are all of equal magnitude.

Under the multinomial sampling model, $\hat{\tau}_b$ is asymptotically normal with mean $\hat{\tau}_b$ and variance $\sigma_\infty^2(\hat{\tau}_b)$. Let d_1 and d_2 denote the denote the expressions given by equations 5.28 and 5.29, respectively, and let d denote the denominator of equation 5.32. Clearly, $d = (d_1 d_2)^{1/2}$. Now, $\sigma_\infty^2(\hat{\tau}_b)$ can be estimated by means of the following formula:

$$\hat{\sigma}_\infty^2(\hat{\tau}_b) = \frac{1}{n^2} \sum_{i=1}^{I} \sum_{j=1}^{J} n_{ij} z_{ij}^2 - \frac{1}{n} \bar{z}^2 \qquad [5.36]$$

where

$$d^2 z_{ij} = 2nd(C_{ij} - D_{ij}) + n \hat{\tau}_b (n_{i+} d_1 + n_{+j} d_2) \qquad [5.37]$$

and

$$\bar{z} = \frac{1}{n} \sum_{i=1}^{I} \sum_{j=1}^{J} n_{ij} z_{ij}$$

In equation 5.37, C_{ij} and D_{ij} are given by equations 5.16 and 5.21, respectively. If X and Y are independent, $\tau_b = 0$ and equation 5.36 becomes

TABLE 4

Relationship Between Past and Expected Financial Well-Being
Among Voters in Senate Elections

Present Financial	Expected Financial Well-Being (Y)			
Well-Being (X)	Better (1)	Same (2)	Worse (3)	Totals
Better (1)	70	85	15	170
Same (2)	10	134	41	185
Worse (3)	27	60	100	187
Totals	107	279	156	542

SOURCE: Kuklinski and West (1981). Their source: 1978 National Election Study, Center for Political Studies, University of Michigan.

$$\hat{\sigma}_\infty^2(\hat{\tau}_b) = \frac{4}{d^2} \left[\sum_{i=1}^{I} \sum_{j=1}^{J} n_{ij}(C_{ij} - D_{ij})^2 - \frac{4}{n}(C - D)^2 \right] \qquad [5.38]$$

Formula 5.38 should be used to test the hypothesis $\tau_b = 0$, while formula 5.36 should be used to make all other inferences about τ.

Example 4. In a study of economic voting behavior, Kuklinski and West (1981) present the data in Table 4. The data were obtained by asking the following two questions of 542 individuals who voted in 1978 Senate elections: (1) Would you say you are better off, worse off, or about the same financially as you were a year ago? and (2) Do you expect to be better off, worse off, or about the same financially a year from now? One question of interest is how well voters' estimates of past and future financial well-being are correlated.

Values of C_{ij} and D_{ij} for the data in Table 4 are shown in Table 5. From equations 5.17 and 5.20, we obtain 2C = 100,870 and 2D = 27,590. Thus,

$$\hat{\tau}_a = \frac{2(C - D)}{n(n - 1)} = \frac{73,280}{293,222} = 0.250$$

and

$$\hat{\tau}_b = 73,280/[(542^2 - 170^2 - 185^2 - 187^2) \times$$

$$(542^2 - 107^2 - 279^2 - 156^2)]^{1/2}$$

$$= 0.390$$

From equations 5.36 and 5.37 we get $\hat{\sigma}_\infty(\hat{\tau}_b) = (0.0014015)^{1/2} = 0.0374$ as the estimated large-sample standard deviation of $\hat{\tau}_b$. As one would expect, any reasonable confidence interval for $\hat{\tau}_b$ does not contain zero. Had our only interest been in testing the hypothesis $\tau_b = 0$, the value $\hat{\sigma}_\infty(\hat{\tau}_b) = (0.0014872)^{1/2} = 0.0386$ from equation 5.38 should be used in place of the value 0.0374.

The interested reader can verify that $\hat{\kappa} = 0.338$ is the value of Cohen's measure of agreement for these data. Even though past and expected financial well-being are highly correlated, the agreement between them is perhaps not as high as one might expect.

Properties of $\hat{\tau}_b$ for continuous variables are discussed in Chapter 4. Formulas 5.37 and 5.38 are given by Agresti (1976) and by Brown and Benedetti (1977). Additional examples are presented by Hays (1963), Blalock (1972), and Reynolds (1977a). Wilson (1969) has provided a proportional-reduction-in-predictive-error interpretation for τ_b.

Measures Related to Kendall's τ_b

THE KENDALL-STUART τ_c

The measure τ_b and its estimator $\hat{\tau}_b$ cannot attain the extreme values $+1$ or -1 for tables that are not square. Following Kendall, Stuart (1953) proposes an estimator whose range is less restricted. Stuart's estimator is obtained by dividing the numerator of $\hat{\tau}_b$ by its maximum possible value. The maximum value of $2(C - D)$ is attained if all observations fall in an (longest) upper left to lower right diagonal of length $q = \min\{I, J\}$ and all frequencies are equal. In this case, n is a multiple of q, $D = 0$, and we can see from equation 5.17 that 2C has the value

$$2 \left(\frac{n}{q}\right) \left[(q - 1) \; \frac{n}{q} \; + (q - 2) \; \frac{n}{q} \; + \ldots + \; \frac{n}{q}\right] = n^2(q - 1)/q \qquad [5.39]$$

Even if n is not a multiple of q, this maximum (equation 5.39) is nearly attained for large n and (relatively) small q. In view of equation 5.39, Stuart takes

$$\hat{\tau}_c = 2(C - D)/[n^2(q - 1)/q] = \frac{2q(C - D)}{n^2(q - 1)} \qquad [5.40]$$

as an estimator of τ_b. Clearly

TABLE 5
Values of C_{ij} and D_{ij} for Data in Table 4

i \ j	C_{ij} 1	2	3	i \ j	D_{ij} 1	2	3
1	335	141	0	1	0	37	231
2	160	170	155	2	100	42	87
3	0	80	299	3	275	56	0

$$\hat{\tau}_c = \frac{n-1}{n} \frac{q}{q-1} \hat{\tau}_a \qquad\qquad [5.41]$$

and we can see that

$$|\hat{\tau}_a| \leqslant |\hat{\tau}_c| \leqslant |\hat{\tau}_b| \quad \text{for } n \geqslant q. \text{ When } I = J = 2,$$

$$\hat{\tau}_c = \frac{4}{n^2} (n_{11} n_{22} - n_{21} n_{12})$$

which shows that $\hat{\tau}_c$ is a function of the cross-product ratio in fourfold tables. Since $\hat{\tau}_a$ is an unbiased estimator of τ, we have

$$E(\hat{\tau}_c) = \frac{n-1}{n} \frac{q}{q-1} \tau$$

Consequently, $\hat{\tau}_c$ is an asymptotically unbiased estimator of

$$\tau_c = \frac{q}{q-1} \tau$$

a quantity that may bear little relationship to τ_b. Under the multinominal model, $\hat{\tau}_c$ is approximately normal for large n. The estimated variance of τ_c is

$$\hat{\sigma}_\infty^2(\hat{\tau}_c) = \frac{4}{n^4} \left(\frac{q}{q-1}\right)^2 \left[\sum_{i=1}^{I} \sum_{j=1}^{J} n_{ij}(C_{ij} - D_{ij})^2 \right.$$

$$\left. - \frac{4}{n} (C - D)^2 \right] \qquad \qquad [5.42]$$

The coefficient of C − D in equation 5.40 is a constant, so equation 5.42 is also correct under the hypothesis of independence.

It is apparent from equation 5.41 that the difference between $\hat{\tau}_c$ and $\hat{\tau}_a$ increases as q decreases. The dependence of $\hat{\tau}_c$ on the dimensions of the table makes it difficult to interpret, especially if the cageories result from collapsing the range of an underlying continuous variable. Somers (1962b: 809) states that $\hat{\tau}_c$ is "a normed version of a product-moment analogue . . . unlikely to yield a useful interpretation." The value of $\hat{\tau}_a$ decreases as the number of categories decreases and $\hat{\tau}_c$ compensates somewhat. Goodman and Kruskal (1959: 141) argue that such adjustment may be inappropriate since "it could well be the case that a finer cross classification would show that *within* the original cells a complete association did not exist."

Example 4 (continued). From equation 5.41, we see that

$$\hat{\tau}_c = \frac{541}{542} \frac{3}{2} \hat{\tau}_a = 0.374$$

for the data in Table 4. The values of $\hat{\tau}_c$ and $\hat{\tau}_b$ are quite similar in this case.

From equation 5.42, the estimated large-sample standard deviation of $\hat{\tau}_c$ is $\hat{\sigma}_\infty(\hat{\tau}_c) = (0.0013668)^{1/2} = 0.0370$.

The estimator $\hat{\tau}_c$ is discussed by Stuart (1953), Kendall (1970), and Goodman and Kruskal (1954). Goodman and Kruskal give a brief comparison of the behavior of $\hat{\tau}_c$ and $\hat{\gamma}$ (discussed below).

THE GOODMAN-KRUSKAL γ

The Goodman-Kruskal γ is another widely used measure that is closely related to Kendall's τ. This measure is defined by

$$\gamma = \frac{\pi_c - \pi_d}{1 - \pi_t} = \frac{\pi_c - \pi_d}{\pi_c + \pi_d} = \frac{\tau}{\pi_c + \pi_d} \qquad [5.43a]$$

With the aid of equations 5.8, 5.9, and 5.13, γ can be written as

$$\gamma = \frac{\pi_c - \pi_d}{1 - \sum_{i=1}^{I} p_{i+}^2 - \sum_{j=1}^{J} p_{+j}^2 + \sum_{i=1}^{I} \sum_{j=1}^{J} p_{ij}^2}$$

Note that $\gamma = \tau = \tau_b$ if $\tau_t = 0$, while $|\gamma| \geq |\tau_b| \geq |\tau|$ otherwise. Consequently, γ has the same interpretation conditionally that τ has unconditionally: γ is the conditional probability that a pair of observations selected at random from the population are concordant minus the probability that they are discordant, the condition being that the pairs are not tied on either variable.

Unless the population is concentrated in a single row or column of the table, γ is well defined. The measure ranges from -1 to 1, inclusive, assuming the value 1 for a population that lies entirely in an (longest) upper left to lower right diagonal and the value -1 for a population that falls in a lower left to upper right diagonal. If X and Y are independent, $\gamma = 0$, but the converse need not be true.

The maximum likelihood estimator of γ under the multinomial sampling model is

$$\hat{\gamma} = \frac{C - D}{C + D} = \frac{2(C - D)}{n^2 - \sum\limits_{i=1}^{I} n_{i+}^2 - \sum\limits_{j=1}^{J} n_{+j}^2 + \sum\limits_{i=1}^{I} \sum\limits_{j=1}^{J} n_{ij}^2} \qquad [5.44]$$

where C and D are most easily calculated from equations 5.18 and 5.19 and 5.22 and 5.23, respectively. The estimator (equation 5.44) is well defined except when all observations fall in a single row or column of the table. The range of $\hat{\gamma}$ is identical to that of γ. If $\gamma = 1$ (or -1), it follows that $\hat{\gamma} = 1$ (or -1) also. On the other hand, it is possible to have $\hat{\gamma} = 1$ (or -1) even though $\gamma \neq 1$ (or -1). Just as $|\gamma| \geq |\tau_b|$, it is evident from equations 5.44 and 5.32c that $|\hat{\gamma}| \geq |\hat{\tau}_b|$. Finally Yule's Q is identical to the Goodman-Kruskal γ for fourfold tables. Unlike $\hat{\tau}_a$, $\hat{\tau}_b$, and $\hat{\tau}_c$, $\hat{\gamma}$ can achieve its extreme values of $+1$ or -1 in the cases of weak perfect positive or negative correlation.[15]

Under the multinomial sampling model, γ is asymptotically normal with mean $E(\gamma) = \gamma$ and variance

$$\sigma_\infty^2(\hat{\gamma}) = \frac{16}{n(1 - \pi_t)^4} \sum\limits_{i=1}^{I} \sum\limits_{j=1}^{J} p_{ij}[\pi_c \pi_{ij}^d - \pi_d \pi_{ij}^c]^2 \qquad [5.45]$$

where π_{ij}^d and π_{ij}^c are given by equations 5.7 and 5.6. The quantities π_{ij}^d and π_{ij}^c are the probabilities that a randomly selected observation is discordant or concordant, respectively, with a given observation in cell (i, j). Recall from equations 5.8 and 5.9 that π_c and π_d are the probabilities that two pairs of randomly selected observations are concordant or discordant, respectively.

An estimator of equation 5.45 is obtained by replacing π_c, π_d, and so on with their sample analogues:

$$\hat{\sigma}_\infty^2(\hat{\gamma}) = \frac{4}{(C+D)^4} \sum_{i=1}^{I} \sum_{j=1}^{J} n_{ij}(DC_{ij} - CD_{ij})^2 \qquad [5.46]$$

In equation 5.46, C_{ij}, C, D_{ij}, and D are given respectively by equations 5.16, 5.18, 5.21, and 5.22.

Under the hypothesis of independence, γ equals zero. For this case, Brown and Benedetti (1977) give the formula

$$\hat{\sigma}_\infty^2(\hat{\gamma}) = \left[\sum_{i=1}^{I} \sum_{j=1}^{J} n_{ij}(C_{ij} - D_{ij})^2 - \frac{4}{n}(C-D)^2 \right] \bigg/ (C+D)^2 \qquad [5.47]$$

As usual, equation 5.46 should be used for all inferences except testing the hypothesis $\gamma = 0$, in which case equation 5.47 should be used.

When $\pi_t = 0$, equation 5.45 reduces to $16(\pi_{cc} - \pi_c^2)/n$, where π_{cc} is defined as in equation 4.23. Taken together, these results show that $\hat{\tau}_a$ and $\hat{\gamma}$ have the same asymptotic variances. This is as it should be, since $\hat{\gamma}$ and $\hat{\tau}_a$ are equal when $\pi_t = 0$.

Example 4 (continued). For the data in Table 4 we get

$$\hat{\gamma} = \frac{C-D}{C+D} = \frac{50,435 - 13,795}{50,435 + 13,795} = \frac{36,460}{64,230} = 0.570$$

Note that this value is considerably larger than the values of $\hat{\tau}_a$, $\hat{\tau}_b$, and $\hat{\tau}_c$. When the underlying variables are continuous, results of Agresti (1976) indicate that $\hat{\gamma}$ tends to overestimate γ, especially when I and J are small. From equation 5.46, the estimated large-sample standard deviation of $\hat{\gamma}$ is $\hat{\sigma}_\infty(\hat{\gamma}) = (0.0025616)^{1/2} = 0.0506$, while equation 5.47 yields $\hat{\sigma}_\infty(\hat{\gamma}) = (0.0031767)^{1/2} = 0.0564$. From either, it is certainly safe to conclude that $\gamma \neq 0$.

Properties of $\hat{\gamma}$ are given in three papers by Goodman and Kruskal (1954, 1963, 1972) and one by Brown and Benedetti (1977). Formula 5.47 is given by Brown and Benedetti. Together with another form of equation 5.46, Goodman and Kruskal give several numerical examples. Additional numerical examples are given by Hays (1963) and Reynolds (1977a).

SOMERS'S d

The measures proposed by Somers are closely related to τ, but unlike similiar measures, they do not treat X and Y symmetrically. There are actually two measures depending on which variable plays the role of "independent" variable.

Recall that π_t^X is the probability that two randomly selected observations are tied only on X and π_t^{XY} is the probability that they are tied on both X and Y. Then the probability that the two observations are tied on X *without regard to Y* is $\pi_t^X + \pi_t^{XY}$.

Now, Somers's measure $d_{Y \cdot X}$ is defined by

$$d_{Y \cdot X} = \frac{\pi_c - \pi_d}{1 - \pi_t^X - \pi_t^{XY}} \qquad [5.48a]$$

In view of equations 4.15 and 5.1, equation 5.48a can be written as

$$d_{Y \cdot X} = \frac{\pi_c - \pi_d}{\pi_c + \pi_d + \pi_t^Y} \qquad [5.48b]$$

and from equation 5.15, it follows that

$$d_{Y \cdot X} = \frac{\pi_c - \pi_d}{1 - \sum_{i=1}^{I} p_{i+}^2} \qquad [5.48c]$$

The first version of equation 5.48 is easiest to interpret, the second is useful for comparing $d_{Y \cdot X}$ to other measures, and the third is convenient for computational purposes.

From equation 5.48a, it is clear that $d_{Y \cdot X}$ has an interpretation similar to γ. The measure $d_{Y \cdot X}$ is the difference between two conditional probabilities, the conditional probability that two randomly selected observations are concordant minus the conditional probability that they are discordant, the condition in both cases being that the observations do not have the same X value. Let the two observations be (X_i, Y_i) and (X_j, Y_j). Then, in symbols, $d_{Y \cdot X}$ is the difference in the probabilities of the events that $(Y_i - Y_j)(X_i - X_j) > 0$ and $(X_i - Y_j)(X_i - X_j) < 0$, both probabilities being conditional on the event that $X_i \neq X_j$.

When $I = J = 2$, equation 5.48 reduces to

$$d_{Y \cdot X} = \frac{P_{11}P_{22} - P_{21}P_{12}}{P_{1+}P_{2+}} = \frac{P_{11}}{P_{1+}} - \frac{P_{21}}{P_{2+}} \qquad [5.49]$$

From equation 5.49, we see that in a fourfold table, $d_{Y \cdot X}$ is simply the difference between the probability that $Y = 1$, given $X = 1$, and the probability that $Y = 1$, given $X = 2$ (where the levels of X and Y identify the rows and columns of the table).

By interchanging the roles of X and Y, we obtain the measure

$$d_{X \cdot Y} = \frac{\pi_c - \pi_d}{1 - \pi_t^Y - \pi_t^{XY}} = \frac{\pi_c - \pi_d}{\pi_c + \pi_d + \pi_t^X} = \frac{\pi_c - \pi_d}{1 - \sum_{j=1}^{J} p_{+j}^2} \qquad [5.50]$$

In the 2×2 case, equation 5.50 reduces to

$$d_{X \cdot Y} = \frac{P_{11}P_{22} - P_{21}P_{12}}{P_{+1}P_{+2}} = \frac{P_{11}}{P_{+1}} - \frac{P_{12}}{P_{+2}} \qquad [5.51]$$

Interpretations of equation 5.50 and 5.51 are completely analogous to those of 5.48 and 5.49, respectively.

The measure $d_{Y \cdot X}$ is well defined unless the entire population falls into a single row of the table, while $d_{X \cdot Y}$ is well defined if the population does not fall into a single column of the table; both are well defined if the table of population probabilities has nonzero entries in at least two rows and two columns. Both $d_{X \cdot Y}$ and $d_{Y \cdot X}$ are zero when X and Y are independent, although the converse need not hold (except for 2×2 tables) in either case. Both $d_{X \cdot Y}$ and $d_{Y \cdot X}$ can range from -1 to 1. In a square table, $d_{X \cdot Y} = d_{Y \cdot X} = 1$ when the entire population falls in the main diagonal, while both measures equal -1 if the population falls entirely in the diagonal extending from lower left to upper right. It is also possible for $d_{Y \cdot X}$ to assume the extreme values ± 1 in tables that are not square. Provided each column has a single nonzero entry, $|d_{Y \cdot X}|$ can equal 1 even though one or more rows contain multiple nonzero entries. This is so because observations tied on X do not enter into the definition of $d_{Y \cdot X}$. Likewise, $|d_{X \cdot Y}|$ can equal 1 provided each row of the table has a single nonzero entry.

How do $d_{X \cdot Y}$ and $d_{Y \cdot X}$ compare to the other "τ-like" measures? Clearly, $|d_{X \cdot Y}| \leqslant |\gamma|$ and $|d_{Y \cdot X}| \leqslant |\gamma|$. Also, $|d_{X \cdot Y}| \geqslant |e|$ and $|d_{Y \cdot X}| \geqslant |e|$, where e denotes Wilson's e. Further, $\gamma = d_{Y\cdot X}$ and $d_{X\cdot Y} = e$ if $\pi_t^Y = 0$, while $\gamma = d_{X\cdot Y}$ and $d_{Y\cdot X} = e$ when $\pi_t^X = 0$.

It is apparent from equations 5.48c, 5.50, and 5.35 that $d_{X\cdot Y} \times d_{Y\cdot X} = \tau_b^2$. Thus, τ_b is the geometric mean between Somers's two measures. All three measures are equal when $\pi_t^Y = 0$.

Somers (1962b) has shown that $\tau_c \leqslant d_{X\cdot Y}$. Equality holds when $I < J$ and the X-marginal (row) probabilities are all equal. Analogous relationships hold between τ_c and $d_{Y\cdot X}$.

By analogy with the Goodman-Kruskal measures of proportional reduction in predictive error, a symmetric version of somers's d can be defined (Nie et al., 1975: 229):

$$d = \frac{(\pi_c + \pi_d + \pi_t^X)d_{X\cdot Y} + (\pi_c + \pi_d + \pi_t^Y)d_{Y\cdot X}}{(\pi_c + \pi_d + \pi_t^X) + (\pi_c + \pi_d + \pi_t^Y)}$$

$$= \frac{\pi_c - \pi_d}{2 - \sum_{i=1}^{I} p_{i+}^2 + \sum_{j=1}^{J} p_{+j}^2}$$

The measure d is suitable when one of X or Y is arbitrarily selected a priori to play the role of the independent variable; d is well defined when the table of population probabilities has nonzero entries in at least two rows and columns. Clearly, d must be intermediate in value between $d_{X\cdot Y}$ and $d_{Y\cdot X}$.

The maximum likelihood estimator of d_{YX} under the multinomial sampling model is

$$\hat{d}_{Y\cdot X} = \frac{C - D}{C + D + T_Y} \tag{5.52a}$$

where C, D, and T_Y are given respectively by equations 5.18, 5.22, and 5.26. In view of equation 5.29, 5.52a can be written as

$$\hat{d}_{Y\cdot X} = \frac{2(C - D)}{n^2 - \sum_{i=1}^{I} n_{i+}^2} \tag{5.52b}$$

Likewise, the maximum likelihood estimators of $d_{X\cdot Y}$ and d are

$$\hat{d}_{X \cdot Y} = \frac{C - D}{C + D + T_X} = \frac{2(C - D)}{n^2 - \sum\limits_{j=1}^{J} n_{+j}^2}$$

and

$$\hat{d} = \frac{2(C - D)}{n^2 - \frac{1}{2}\left(\sum\limits_{i=1}^{I} n_{i+}^2 + \sum\limits_{j=1}^{J} n_{+j}^2\right)} = \frac{4(C - D)}{2n^2 - \sum\limits_{i=1}^{I} n_{i+}^2 - \sum\limits_{j=1}^{J} n_{+j}^2}$$

Statements about when $\hat{d}_{Y \cdot X}$ and $\hat{d}_{X \cdot Y}$ and d are well defined, about their extreme values, and about their relationships with (estimators of) other measures follow verbatim from those already made about their respective population analogues.

All three estimators have asymptotically normal distributions under the multinomial sampling model. Goodman and Kruskal (1972) give the following expression for the asymptotic variance of $\hat{d}_{Y \cdot X}$:

$$\sigma_\infty^2(\hat{d}_{Y \cdot X}) = \frac{4}{n\delta^2} \sum\limits_{i=1}^{I} \sum\limits_{j=1}^{J} p_{ij}[\nu(1 - p_{i+}) - \delta(\pi_{ij}^c - \pi_{ij}^d)]^2 \qquad [5.53]$$

where

$$\nu = \pi_c - \pi_d \quad \text{and} \quad \delta = 1 - \sum\limits_{i=1}^{I} p_{i+}^2$$

are the numerator and denominator of $d_{Y \cdot X}$. The sample analogue of equation 5.53 serves as an estimator: An algebraically convenient form of the estimator is

$$\hat{\sigma}_\infty^2(\hat{d}_{Y \cdot X}) = \frac{4}{n^4(n + n_{i+})^2} \sum\limits_{i=1}^{I} \sum\limits_{j=1}^{J} n_{ij}[2(C - D)$$

$$- (n + n_{i+})(C_{ij} - D_{ij})]^2 \qquad [5.54]$$

If $d_{Y \cdot X} = 0$, the estimated variance of $\hat{d}_{Y \cdot X}$ becomes

$$\hat{\sigma}^2_\infty(\hat{d}_{Y \cdot X}) = \frac{4\left[\sum\limits_{i=1}^{I} \sum\limits_{j=1}^{J} n_{ij}(C_{ij} - D_{ij})^2 - \frac{4}{n}(C - D)^2\right]}{\left(n^2 - \sum\limits_{i=1}^{I} n_{i+}^2\right)^2} \qquad [5.55]$$

As usual, equation 5.55 should be used to test the hypothesis $d_{Y \cdot X} = 0$, and equation 5.54 should be used otherwise.

Variance formulas for $\hat{d}_{X \cdot Y}$ can be obtained from those for $\hat{d}_{Y \cdot X}$ by symmetry. Corresponding to equations 5.54 and 5.55, we have

$$\hat{\sigma}^2_\infty(\hat{d}_{X \cdot Y}) = \frac{4}{n^4(n + n_{+j})^2} \sum\limits_{i=1}^{I} \sum\limits_{j=1}^{J} n_{ij}[2(C - D)$$

$$- (n + n_{+j})(C_{ij} - D_{ij})]^2$$

and

$$\hat{\sigma}^2_\infty(\hat{d}_{X \cdot Y}) = \frac{4\left[\sum\limits_{i=1}^{I} \sum\limits_{j=1}^{J} n_{ij}(C_{ij} - D_{ij})^2 - \frac{4}{n}(C - D)^2\right]}{\left(n^2 - \sum\limits_{j=1}^{J} n_{+j}^2\right)^2}$$

The method of Example 2 can be used to approximate the variance of $\hat{d}$.

Example 4 (continued). For the data in Table 4, we obtain

$$\hat{d}_{Y \cdot X} = \frac{2(C - D)}{n^2 - \sum\limits_{i=1}^{I} n_{i+}^2} = \frac{2 \times 36{,}640}{542^2 - 170^2 - 185^2 - 187^2}$$

$$= \frac{73{,}280}{195{,}670} = 0.375$$

$$\hat{d}_{X \cdot Y} = \frac{2 \times 36{,}640}{542^2 - 107^2 - 279^2 - 156^2} = \frac{73{,}280}{180{,}138} = 0.407$$

and

$$\hat{d} = \frac{4 \times 36,640}{180,138 + 195,670} = \frac{146,560}{375,808} = 0.390$$

Notice that

$$\hat{d}_{Y \cdot X} \times \hat{d}_{X \cdot Y} = \frac{(73,280)^2}{180,138 \times 195,670} = \hat{\tau}_b^2$$

as indicated earlier. Calculation of the variance estimates (equations 5.54 and 5.55) is left as an exercise for the interested reader.

Somers introduced the asymmetric measures $d_{Y \cdot X}$ and $d_{X \cdot Y}$, and three of his papers (1962a, 1962b, 1968) contain discussions of their properties. A proportional-reduction-in-predictive-error interpretation similar to that for the Goodman-Kruskal τ is given in the 1968 paper. Formula 5.53 is given by Goodman and Kruskal (1972), and additional examples are found in Reynolds (1977a).

WILSON'S e

The last of the measures closely related to τ_b is symmetric. It differs from τ_b and γ in that only pairs of observations tied on both variables are considered irrelevant. Recall that π_t^{XY} is the probability that randomly selected pairs of observations are tied on both X and Y. Whereas γ is defined by ignoring all ties, Wilson's e is defined by ignoring only ties involving both X and Y. Thus

$$e = \frac{\pi_c - \pi_d}{1 - \pi_t^{XY}} = \frac{\pi_c - \pi_d}{\pi_c + \pi_d + \pi_t^X \pi_t^Y} = \frac{\pi_c - \pi_d}{1 - \sum_{i=1}^{I} \sum_{j=1}^{J} p_{ij}^2}$$

Interpretation of e is similar to that of γ and Somers's measures. When two members of the population are selected at random, e is the conditional probability that the pairs are concordant minus the conditional probability that they are discordant, the condition in each case being that the pairs are not tied on both X and Y. Precisely, e is the difference in the probabilities of the event that $(X_i - X_j)(Y_i - Y_j) > 0$ and the event that $(X_i - X_j)(Y_i - Y_j) < 0$, where both probabilities are conditional upon the event that at least one of $(X_i - X_j)$ or $(Y_i - Y_j)$ is not zero.

The measure e is well defined unless the entire population falls in a single cell, and e = 0 when X and Y are independent. It is clear that $|e|$ does not exceed the magnitude of any of the four related measures, τ_b, γ, $d_{Y \cdot X}$ and $d_{X \cdot Y}$. Moreover, e = $d_{X \cdot Y}$ when $\pi_t^Y = 0$ and e = $d_{Y \cdot X}$ when $\pi_t^X = 0$. All five measures are equal when both $\pi_t^X = 0$ and $\pi_t^Y = 0$.

Although e ranges from −1 to 1, it cannot assume the extreme values in its range if either $\pi_t^X > 0$ or $\pi_t^Y > 0$. In particular, the range of e is restricted whenever I ≠ J, since one of π_t^X or π_t^Y is necessarily nonzero in that case. Moreover, the magnitude of e is less than one for (population) tables that exhibit weak perfect correlation. Thus, while d can be regarded as a measure of "weak" association, e is a measure that attains its extreme values only in the case of strict perfect correlation.

By the argument of Somers (1968), Wilson (1974) provides a "proportional-reduction-in-predictive-error" interpretation for e. Wilson further shows that $(e/\tau_b)^2$ is a decreasing function of the probability of pairs tied on one variable but not the other. It can be argued, therefore, that e is more sensitive to the degree to which the population clusters about the diagonal than is τ_b.

The maximum likelihood estimator of e under the multinomial sampling model is

$$\hat{e} = \frac{C - D}{C + D + T_X + T_Y}$$

where C, D, T_X, and T_Y are given, respectively, by equations 5.18, 5.22, 5.25, and 5.26. It is evident from equations 5.24 and 5.27 that

$$\hat{e} = \frac{2(C - D)}{n^2 - \sum_{i=1}^{I} \sum_{j=1}^{J} n_{ij}^2}$$

Statements about the properties of e and its relation to other measures contained in the preceding three paragraphs follow verbatim for e.

Like other closely related measures, $\hat{e}$ is asymptotically normal under the multinomial sampling model. the expected value of $\hat{e}$ is e. A formula for the variance of $\hat{e}$ has not been published. However, an estimate can be obtained from a formula given by Quade (1974: 392). By using only pairs of observations that are "relevant" to its definition, Quade's formula can be used to compute variance estimates for a large number of measures. All pairs that are not tied on both X and Y are relevant for computations involving e. When e = 0, the estimated variance of e becomes

$$\hat{\sigma}^2_{\infty}(\hat{e}) = \frac{4 \sum\limits_{i=1}^{I} \sum\limits_{j=1}^{J} n_{ij}(C_{ij} - D_{ij})^2 - \frac{4}{n}(C - D)^2}{\left(n^2 - \sum\limits_{i=1}^{I} \sum\limits_{j=1}^{J} n_{ij}^2\right)^2}$$ [5.56]

Of course, equation 5.56 is appropriate only for testing the hypothesis $e = 0$.

Example 4 (continued). From Table 4, we see that

$$\sum_{i=1}^{I} \sum_{j=1}^{J} n_{ij}^2 = 70^2 + 85^2 + \ldots + 100^2 = 46,416$$

and, therefore,

$$\hat{e} = \frac{2(C - D)}{n^2 - \sum\limits_{i=1}^{I} \sum\limits_{j=1}^{J} n_{ij}^2} = \frac{73,280}{247,348} = 0.296$$

Notice that $\hat{e}$ is less than each of the other estimators to which it is related.

Wilson's 1974 paper is definitive for the measure e. A supplementary discussion, with examples, is given by Reynolds (1977a).

SUMMARY

It is worthwhile at this point to summarize the relationships among τ and its progeny. Analogous statements hold for the corresponding estimators.

(1) $d_{Y \cdot X} = d_{X \cdot Y} = \tau_b$ if, and only if, $\pi_t^X = \pi_t^Y$

(2) $\gamma = d_{Y \cdot X}$ if, and only if, $\pi_t^Y = 0$

$\gamma = d_{X \cdot Y}$ if, and only if, $\pi_t^X = 0$

(3) $\tau_b = e$ if, and only if, $\pi_t^X = \pi_t^Y = 0$

If (3) holds, then all five of the measures τ_b, γ, $d_{Y \cdot X}$, $d_{X \cdot Y}$, and e are equal. Furthermore,

(4) if $\pi_t^X = \pi_t^Y = \pi_t^{XY} = 0$, than all five of these measures equal τ,

where $\tau = \pi_c - \pi_d$ is the measure originally defined for continuous populations. The sampling theory given in this chapter is inappropriate if (4) holds.

It has already been noted that

$$\tau_b^2 = d_{X \cdot Y} \times d_{Y \cdot X}$$

and it is easy enough to verify that

$$\frac{1}{\gamma} = \frac{1}{d_{X \cdot Y}} + \frac{1}{d_{Y \cdot X}} - \frac{1}{e}$$

Thus, τ_b and γ can easily be determined from $d_{X \cdot Y}$, $d_{Y \cdot X}$, and e. Wilson (1974: 338) argues that these three measures be taken as a "standard set" because each has a reasonable interpretation and because the "asymmetric and strict hypotheses seem to be of greatest substantive interest."

Comments concerning the numerical stability of these estimators in selected sampling situations are given in the next chapter.

Other Measures

Versions of Pearson's product-moment correlation coefficient and Spearman's rank correlation coefficient which are suitable for ordinal data have been published. The product-moment correlation coefficient is calculated from category scores by means of equation 4.9, and the rank correlation coefficient is computed from equation 4.30 using the ranks of category scores. Because these measures are less frequently used than those related to Kendall's tau, their properties are not considered here. The interested reader is referred to Brown and Benedetti (1977) for the correct variance formulas to use with these measures under the multinomial sampling model.

6. CHOOSING AN APPROPRIATE MEASURE

A large number of measures have been discussed in this monograph. With so many measures available, it is not always easy to select a suitable one. Nevertheless, the investigator can reduce the number of alternatives by focusing his or her attention on measures that have properties he or she considers important.

It is desirable to have a measure with a meaningful interpretation. Efforts have been made to give an interpretation for each estimator in terms of some meaningful population parameter or property. It is difficult to interpret measures based on the chi-square statistic and the various measures of the rank correlation coefficient, especially those that result from "norming" some other measure to give it a "nice" range. Generally speaking, the other measures considered have sensible interpretations.

Aside from the question of interpretation, guidelines for selecting an appropriate measure involve the nature and source of the data and the intended use of the measure. One must know whether the data are nominal, ordinal, or continuous in order to choose the correct class of measures. One must know why the measure is being computed in order to select a suitable measure from this class. It matters, for example, whether one is trying to predict, to measure agreement, or to establish association.

The following questions should prove helpful to someone faced with the task of selecting an appropriate measure.

(1) *Are the data nominal?* Measures for nominal data should not depend on category order. Choosing a measure that treats the order of category labels as meaningful when it is not can lead to completely erroneous conclusions.

(2) *Are the data continuous?* The choice in this case depends on what we can assume about the data. If the data are normally distributed, then ρ is the best choice. Otherwise, τ, or even ρ_s, may be a better choice.

The effect of ties should be considered, especially when it comes to choosing among the various measures of Spearman's rank correlation coefficient or Kendall's τ. To some extent, the choice depends on what one is trying to measure: If one is concerned with agreement between two judges, for example, then ρ_b and τ_b are recommended over their counterparts.

(3) *Are the data ordinal?* A good measure for ordinal data should depend on category order because information is lost if the order of the categories is ignored. Information is also lost when the range of a pair of continuous variables is categorized. A "stable" measure is desirable in this case because the loss of information increases as the number of categories decreases. A measure is stable to the extent that its value computed for the cross-classification is similar to that of the "associated measure for ungrouped data computed from the underlying continuous distribution" (Agresti, 1976: 49). Agresti has studied the stability of selected measures, including γ, τ_b, and τ_c, when the underlying bivariate distribution is normal. He concludes that none of the measures is very

stable when the number of categories is small. The Goodman-Kruskal γ is particularly unstable, while τ_b generally fares better than do the other measures. The stability of all measures considered by Agresti improves as ρ decreases.

It is best to avoid using ordinal data to make inferences about an underlying continuous population. If the original data are unavailable, it helps somewhat to assign category labels that are scalar, rather than merely ordinal.

(4) *Is the measure being computed to establish correlation, to measure agreement, or to make predictions, i.e., to establish a cause-effect relationship?* Any measure that treats the two variables symmetrically can be used to measure correlation. Asymmetric measures, such as the Goodman-Kruskal measures or Somers's d, should be used for prediction. If one is interested in how two variables or judges agree, then a suitable measure of agreement should be chosen.

(5) *Is the measure being used to make inferences?* The answer to this question is usually "yes." The ability to make statistical inferences about a measure depends on knowing the sampling distribution of its estimator. Nearly all estimators considered have sampling distributions that are approximately normal for large samples, so the problem becomes one of choosing the correct variance estimate. Under the multinomial model, the correct estimate of variance for testing the hypothesis of independence differs from the estimate to be used for constructing confidence intervals. The nature of the inference dictates the choice.

A study by Brown and Benedetti (1977) emphasizes the importance of using correct variance estimates. The authors have studied the empirical behavior of several measures "in a hypothesis testing situation where the underlying distribution is multinomial" (p. 309) for a variety of hypothetical contingency tables. Three estimates of asymptotic variance are considered: (a) one that is correct when the underlying variables are continuous, (b) one that is correct when the underlying distribution is multinomial, and (c) the modification of (b) that is suitable for testing the hypothesis of independence. The authors conclude that (c) is more reliable than (b) for testing for independence unless sample sizes are large. More important, they conclude that variance estimates computed for continuous populations are not good estimates of their discrete analogues, even for large samples, and therefore should not be used in a multinomial context.

(6) *Is the measure sensitive to marginal totals?* If so, differences between sample marginal probabilities and corresponding population proportions could result in fallacious inferences because the sampling values of the measure may not be representative of its population value. In particular, values of a measure computed from two different samples and/or populations cannot be compared if the measure depends upon marginal totals. Goodman and Kruskal (1954) give an example that shows how inferences can be distorted when tables with different marginal totals are compared. At best, such comparisons can be made only after sample marginals have been "standardized" in some fashion.

Nearly all measures for discrete data are sensitive to changes in marginal totals.

(7) *For what type of association does a measure assume its extreme values?* Some measures assume their extreme values in cases of weak perfect association, others in cases of implicit perfect association, and still others only in the case of strict perfect association. All other things being equal, an investigator should perhaps choose a measure that can assume its extreme values for the type of association that he or she considers most important.

7. CORRELATION AND CAUSATION

It is appropriate to conclude this monograph on a note of caution. When two variables have been shown to be correlated, it is indeed tempting to infer a cause-and-effect relationship between them. Most measures, however, treat the variables symmetrically (the value of the measure remains the same if the roles of the variables are interchanged), and such measures tell us nothing about causality. More sophisticated models are required to establish causality than are needed to merely identify association.

The chi-square statistic in equation 2.2 is symmetric in the sense described, and will be used to illustrate the point being made. Mann et al. (1975) conducted a study to test the theory that smoking causes myocardial infarction (heart attack) in women. In Table 6, a total of 216 patients are classified according to smoking habits (smoker, nonsmoker) and whether or not they had experienced myocardial infarction.

For these data, the statistic X^2 has the value

$$X^2 = \frac{216 \, (14 \cdot 83 - 45 \cdot 74)^2}{59 \cdot 157 \cdot 88 \cdot 128} = 9.73$$

TABLE 6
Classification of 216 Woman Patients According to Incidence
of Myocardial Infarction and Smoking Habits

| | | Myocardial Infarction | | |
		Yes	No	Totals
Smoker	Yes	45	83	128
	No	14	74	88
	Totals	59	157	216

SOURCE: Mann et al. (1975).

It is safe to conclude that the two factors are related, since the probability that $\dot{X}^2$ exceeds 9.73 is less than 0.01 if they are independent.

Showing that a relationship exists between smoking habits and myocardial infarction does not establish cause and effect. On the basis of the analysis presented here, it is equally as valid to conclude that heart attacks cause smoking as vice versa!

The reader interested in cause-effect modeling is referred to Fienberg (1980), Reynolds (1977a, 1977b) or Haberman (1978, 1979) for recent work on the important class of loglinear models.

NOTES

1. Technically, the multinomial distribution is the correct model for sampling with replacement. If sampling is without replacement, the correct model involves the hypergeometric distribution. In practice, differences between the two distributions are negligible if the population is large and the sample small enough relative to the population size. It makes little difference, for example, if a sample of size 25 is selected with or without replacement from the senior class at a large university.

2. Note that two different approximations have been discussed in this section. The binomial distribution can be used to approximate the hypergeometric distribution if the population is large in comparison with the sample size. The normal distribution can be used to approximate the binomial distribution if, in addition, the sample is large.

3. Table 1 exhibits IJ cells defined jointly by the variables X and Y. Here, the IJ cells are the k categories of the previous section, and the variables N_{ij} are the multinomial variables $X_1, \ldots, X_k$.

394

4. Two variables that exhibit this degree of association are said to be *perfectly associated* by some authors (see Reynolds, 1977b: 15-16, for example). In square tables (I = J), where each value of one variable is uniquely associated with a value of the other, the relationship is termed *strict*. When I ≠ J, the relationship is described as *implicit*.

5. The authors' four papers on measures of association, which originally appeared in 1954, 1959, 1963, and 1972, are presented here in book form. References to a specific paper cite the original date of publication.

6. The product multinomial model results when the rows (or columns) of the table are independent samples from two (possibly) different populations. With only two categories per row (or column), the product multinomial model becomes the product binomial model. For example, suppose we are interested in comparing the numbers of male and female faculty members at the various academic ranks. If the male and female faculty members are sampled independently, the product multinomial model is appropriate. This is in contrast to the case in which the entire faculty is sampled as a single population and the same members are then cross-classified according to academic rank and sex.

7. See the next two chapters for definitions of measures that have not previously been discussed.

8. If one cell of a fourfold table is zero, the variables are said to exhibit *weak* perfect association by some authors (see Reynolds, 1977b: 15-16, for example). The two variables are said to exhibit *strict* perfect association if two cells not in the same row or column contain zero. Thus, $|\rho|$ = 1 only if A and B are strictly associated, while $|Q|$ = 1 in both cases.

9. The covariance between two random variables X and Y is defined to be Cov (X, Y) = $\sigma(X, Y) = E[(X - \mu_X) (Y - \mu_Y)]$.

10. When sampling from a bivariate normal population, this hypothesis is equivalent to H_o: X and Y are independent.

11. If an increase in X always corresponds to an increase in Y, or if an increase in X always corresponds to a decrease in Y, then X and Y are monotonically related.

12. For more details, see the discussion of τ_c in the section on Measures Related to Kendall's τ_b. In the terminology of contingency tables, this is the case of strict perfect concordance.

13. It is more convenient to work with counts than with actual sample probabilities.

14. Thus, $|\tau_b|$ = 1 for tables that exhibit strict perfect correlation, while $|\tau| < 1$ in other cases.

15. When π_d = 0, two variables X and Y are said to exhibit *weak perfect positive correlation*. Likewise, they are said to exhibit *weak perfect negative correlation* when π_c = 0. Similar statements can be made for samples, provided π_d and π_c are replaced by D and C, respectively.

REFERENCES

AGRESTI, A. (1976) "The effect of category choice on some ordinal measures of association." Journal of the American Statistical Association 71: 49-55.

ANDERSON, T. W. (1958) An Introduction to Multivariate Statistical Analysis. New York: John Wiley.

BERGESON, A. J. (1977) "Political witch hunts: the sacred and subversive in cross-national perspective." American Sociological Review 42: 220-233.

BISHOP, Y.M.M., S. E. FIENBERG, and P. W. HOLLAND (1975) Discrete Multivariate Analysis: Theory and Practice. Cambridge, MA: MIT Press.

BLALOCK, H. M. (1972) Social Statistics. New York: McGraw-Hill.

BROWN, M. B. [ed.] (1977) BMDP-77: Biomedical Computer Programs, P Series. Berkeley: University of California Press.

——— and J. K. BENEDETTI (1977) "Sampling behavior of tests for correlation in two-way contingency tables." Journal of the American Statistical Association 72: 309-315.

COHEN, J. (1968) "Weighted kappa: nominal scale agreement with provision for scaled disagreement or partial credit." Psychological Bulletin 70: 213-220.

——— (1960) "A coefficient of agreement for nominal scales." Educational and Psychological Measurement 20: 37-46.

COLEMAN, J. S. (1966) "Measuring concordance in attitudes." Baltimore: Johns Hopkins University, Department of Social Relations. (unpublished)

CONOVER, W. J. (1980) Practical Nonparametric Statistics. New York: John Wiley.

CRAMER, H. (1946) Mathematical Methods of Statistics. Princeton, NJ: Princeton University Press.

FIENBERG, S. E. (1980) The Analysis of Cross-Classified Categorical Data. Cambridge, MA: MIT Press.

FISHER, R. A. (1921) "On the 'probable error' of a coefficient of correlation deduced from a small sample." Metron 1, 4: 3-32.

——— (1915) "Frequency distribution of the values of the correlation coefficient in samples from an indefinitely large population." Biometrika 10: 507-521.

FLEISS, J. L. (1971) "Measuring nominal scale agreement among many raters." Psychological Bulletin 76: 378-382.

——— J. COHEN, and B. S. EVERITT (1969) "Large sample standard errors of kappa and weighted kappa." Psychological Bulletin 72: 323-327.

GIBBONS, J. D. (1971) Nonparametric Statistical Inference. New York: McGraw-Hill.

GINI, C. (1912) "Variabilita e mutabilita contributo allo studio delle distribuzioni; relazione statiche," in Studie Economico-Guiridici della R. Universita di Cagliari.

GOODMAN, L. A. and W. H. KRUSKAL (1980) Measures of Association for Cross-Classifications. Springer Series in Statistics, Vol. 1. New York: Springer-Verlag.

——— (1972) "Measures of association for cross-classifications, IV: simplification of asymptotic variances." Journal of the American Statistical Association 67: 415-421.

——— (1963) "Measures of association for cross-classification, III: Approximate sampling theory." Journal of the American Statistical Association 58: 310-364.

——— (1959) "Measures of association for cross-classifications, II: further discussion and references." Journal of the American Statistical Association 54: 123-163.

——— (1954) "Measures of association for cross-classifications. Journal of the American Statistical Association 49: 732-764.

GUTTMAN, L. (1941) "An outline of the statistical theory of prediction," pp. 253-318 in P. Horst et al. (eds.) The Prediction of Personal Adjustment. Bulletin 48. New York: Social Science Research Council.

396

HABERMAN, S. J. (1979) Analysis of Qualitative Data, Vol. II. New York: Academic.
——— (1978) Analysis of Qualitative Data, Vol. I. New York: Academic.
HAYS, W. L. (1963) Statistics for Psychologists. New York: Holt, Rinehart & Winston.
HOEFFDING, W. (1948) "A class of statistics with asymptotically normal distribution."
Annals of Mathematical Statistics 19: 293-325.
KENDALL, M. G. (1970) Rank Correlation Methods. London: Griffin.
——— and A. STUART (1973) The Advanced Theory of Statistics, Vol. II. New York:
Hafner.
KRUSKAL, W. H. (1958) "Ordinal measures of association." Journal of the American
Statistical Association 53: 814-861.
KUKLINSKI, J. H. and D. M. WEST (1981) "Economic expectations and voting behavior
in United States House and Senate elections." American Political Science Review 75:
436-447.
LEIK, R. K. and W. R. GROVE (1971) "Integrated approach to measuring association,"
pp. 279-301 in H. L. Costner (ed.) Sociological Methodology. San Francisco: Jossey-
Bass.
LIGHT, R. J. (1971) "Measures of response agreement for qualitiative data: some generalizations and alternatives." Psychological Bulletin 76: 365-377.
——— (1969) "Analysis of variance for categorical data, with application to agreement and
association." Ph.D. dissertation, Department of Statistics, Harvard University.
——— and B. H. MARGOLIN (1971) "An analysis of variance for categorical data." Journal
of the American Statistical Association 66: 534-544.
MANN, J. I., M. P. VESSEY, M. THOROGOOD, and R. DOLL (1975) "Myocardial in-
farction in young women with special reference to oral contraceptive practice." British
Medical Journal 2: 241-245.
MARGOLIN, B. H. and R. J. LIGHT (1974) "An analysis of variance for categorical data,
II: small sample comparisons with chi-square and other competitors." Journal of the
American Statistical Association 69: 755-764.
MORRISON, D. F. (1976) Multivariate Statistical Methods. New York: McGraw-Hill.
NIE, N. H., C. H. HULL, J. G. JENKINS, K. STEINBRENNER, and D. H. BENT (1975)
Statistical Package for the Social Sciences. New York: McGraw-Hill.
NOETHER, G. E. (1967) Elements of Nonparametric Statistics. New York: John Wiley.
OWEN, D. B. (1962) Handbook of Statistical Tables. Reading, MA: Addison-Wesley.
PEARSON, K. (1948) [1904] "Mathematical contributions to the theory of evolution, XIII.
on the theory of contingency and its relation to association and normal correlation."
Draper's Co. Res. Mem. Biometric. Ser. 1. Reprinted in Karl Pearson's Early Papers.
Cambridge: Cambridge University Press.
PEARSON, K. (1896) "Mathematical contributions to the theory of evolution, III. Regres-
sion, heredity, and panmixia." Philosophical Transcriptions of the Royal Society
A 187: 253-318.
QUADE, D. (1974) "Nonparametric partial correlation," pp. 369-398 in H. M. Blalock, Jr.
(ed.) Measurement in the Social Sciences. Chicago: Aldine-Atherton.
REYNOLDS, H. T. (1977a) The Analysis of Cross-Classifications. New York: Free Press.
——— (1977b) Analysis of Nominal Data. Sage University Papers series on Quantitative
Applications in the Social Sciences, 07-007. Beverly Hills, CA: Sage.
SAKODA, J. M. (1977) "Measures of association for multivariate contingency tables,"
pp. 777-780 in Social Statistics Section Proceedings for the American Statistical Association.

SIEGEL, S. (1956) Nonparametric Statistics for the Behavioral Sciences. New York: McGraw-Hill.

SNEDECOR, G. W. and W. G. COCHRAN (1967) Statistical Methods. Ames: Iowa State University Press.

SOMERS, R. H. (1968) "On the measurement of association." American Sociological Review 33: 291-292.

——— (1962a) "A new asymmetric measure of association for ordinal variables." American Sociological Review 27: 799-811.

——— (1962b) "A similarity between Goodman and Kruskal's tau and Kendall's tau, with a partial interpretation of the latter." Journal of the American Statistical Association 57: 804-812.

STUART, A. (1963) "Calculation of Spearman's rho for ordered two-way classifications." American Statistician 17, 4: 23-24.

——— (1953) "The estimation and comparison of strengths of association in contingency tables." Biometrika 40: 105-110.

SPEARMAN, C. (1904) "The proof and measurement of association between two things." American Journal of Psychology 15: 72-101.

TSCHUPROW, A. A. (1918/1919/1921) "On the mathematical expectation of the moments of frequency distributions." Biometrika 12/13: 140-169, 185-210, 283.

WILSON, T. P. (1974) "Measures of association for bivariate ordinal hypotheses," pp. 327-342 in H. M. Blalock, Jr. (ed.) Measurement in the Social Sciences. Chicago: Aldine-Atherton.

——— (1969) "A proportional-reduction-in-error interpretation for Kendall's tau-b." Social Forces 47: 340-342.

YULE, G. U. (1912) "On the methods of measuring association between two attributes." Journal of the Royal Statistical Society 75: 579-642.

——— (1900) "On the association of attributes in statistics." Philosophical Transcriptions of the Royal Society A194: 257-319.

INDEX

ABOUT THE EDITOR

MICHAEL S. LEWIS-BECK, Professor of Political Science at the University of Iowa, received his Ph.D. from the University of Michigan. Currently, in addition to editing the Sage monograph series *Quantitative Applications in the Social Sciences (QASS)*, he is editor of the *American Journal of Political Science*. He has authored or coauthored numerous books and articles, including *Applied Regression: An Introduction, New Tools for Social Scientists: Advances and Applications in Research Methods, Economics and Elections: The Major Western Democracies*, and *Forecasting Elections*. In addition to his work at the University of Iowa, he has taught quantitative methods courses at the Inter-University Consortium for Political and Social Research (ICPSR) Summer Program at the University of Michigan and The European Consortium for Political Research (ECPR) Summer Program at the University of Essex. Also, he has held visiting appointments at the Catholic University in Lima, Peru and the University of Paris I (Sorbonne) in France.

ABOUT THE AUTHORS

DAVID K. HILDEBRAND is Professor of Statistics at the Wharton School, University of Pennsylvania. He holds a Ph.D. from Carnegie-Mellon University and has authored two texts and several papers, and refereed and reviewed books for many statistics journals, including the *Annals of Mathematical Statistics, Econometrica,* and the *American Statistician.*

JAMES D. LAING, Professor of Decision Sciences at the Wharton School, University of Pennsylvania holds a Ph.D. in political science in formal organizations, coalition behavior, multilateral negotiations, and game theoretic analysis.

ALBERT M. LIEBETRAU is a Senior Research Scientist in the Probabilistic Modeling Group at the Battelle Pacific Northwest Laboratory in Richland, Washington. He holds degrees from the University of Wisconsin and Oregon State University. After receiving his Ph.D. in statistics from the University of Michigan, he joined the faculty of Johns Hopkins University. Since coming to Battelle in 1983, he has concentrated on the development and application of probablistic systems performance models. He has extensive consulting experience, and his publications include articles in the *Journal of Applied Probability,* the *Journal of the Royal Statistical Society (Series B), Communication in Statistics, Geographical Analysis,* and *Water Resources Research.* The statistical methods that he has developed for the treatment of volume calibration and measurement data are internationally recognized. He currently represents the United States as a member of the Probabilistic Systems Assessment Codes Users Group of the OECD Nuclear Energy Agency.

LAWRENCE B. MOHR is Professor of Political Science and Public Policy in the Department of Political Science and the Institute of Public Policy Studies at the University of Michigan. His teaching fields are organization theory, program evaluation, statistics, and the philosophy of social research. He maintains a research and publishing interest in each of these areas.

H. T. REYNOLDS, Professor of Political Science at the University of Delaware, graduated from Dartmouth College and holds a Ph.D. from the University of North Carolina. His research interests are survey research methods and political behavior. He is currently working on a contextual study of American elections.

HOWARD ROSENTHAL, Roger Williams Straus Professor of Social Sciences at Princeton University, holds a Ph.D. in political science from the Massachussetts Institute of Technology. His current interests include statistical models for scaling roll call voting data, and the analysis of balancing political institutions, partisan politics, divided government, and the macroeconomy.

HERBERT F. WEISBERG, Professor of Political Science at the Ohio State University, received his undergraduate education at the University of Minnesota and his Ph.D. from the University of Michigan. He has been coeditor of the *American Journal of Political Science* and is coauthor of *An Introduction to Survey Research and Data Analysis.* He has written numerous journal articles on such diverse topics as congressional roll-call analysis, scaling methods, party identification, and measures of statistical relationship.

* These biographical statements include updated information whenever possible. Otherwise they are as originally published.